Diode, Transistor & FET Circuits Manual

Newnes Circuits Manual Series

Audio IC Circuits Manual R. M. Marston
CMOS Circuits Manual R. M. Marston
Diode, Transistor & FET Circuits Manual R. M. Marston
Electronic Alarm Circuits Manual R. M. Marston
Op-amp Circuits Manual R. M. Marston
Optoelectronics Circuits Manual R. M. Marston
Power Control Circuits Manual R. M. Marston
Timer/Generator Circuits Manual R. M. Marston

Diode, Transistor & FET Circuits Manual

R. M. MARSTON

To Kirsty, Ashley and Brenda, with love.

Newnes
An imprint of Butterworth-Heinemann
Linacre House, Jordan Hill, Oxford OX2 8DP
A division of Reed Educational and Professional Publishing Ltd

A member of the Reed Elsevier plc group

OXFORD BOSTON JOHANNESBURG
MELBOURNE NEW DELHI SINGAPORE

First published 1991
Reprinted 1996

British Library Cataloguing in Publication Data
Marston, R.M.
Diode transistor and FET circuits manual.
– (Newnes circuits manual series)
I. Title II. Series
621.3815

ISBN 0 7506 0228 7

Typeset by Vision Typesetting, Manchester

Printed in Great Britain by St Edmundsbury Press Ltd,
Bury St Edmunds, Suffolk

Contents

Preface		vii
1	Basic diode circuits	1
2	Special diode circuits	29
3	Transistor principles	51
4	Transistor amplifier circuits	65
5	Transistor waveform generators	95
6	Transistor audio amplifiers	121
7	Transistor circuit miscellany	148
8	FET principles	161
9	JFET circuits	176
10	MOSFET and CMOS circuits	190
11	VMOS circuits	206
12	Unijunction transistor circuits	225
Index		243

Preface

This book is, as its title implies, primarily a manual of circuits based on 'discrete' semiconductor components such as diodes, transistors, FETs, and associated devices, and as such it presents a total of over 340 carefully selected and outstandingly useful practical circuits, diagrams, graphs and tables.

The manual is divided into four sections, and a total of twelve chapter headings. The first chapter deals with ordinary diode and rectifier circuits, and the second with special diodes such as zeners, varicaps, and photosensitive and light-emitting types. The second section comprises five chapters (Chapters 3–7) and deals with modern bipolar transistors, and the third comprises four chapters (Chapters 8–11) and deals with major types of field-effect transistor (including the JFET, MOSFET, and VMOS). The final chapter deals with the unijunction transistor (UJT) and some of its thyristor counterparts (such as the PUT, SUS, and SCS).

The book is specifically aimed at the practical design engineer, technician, and experimenter, but will also be of interest to the electronics student and the amateur. It deals with its subject in an easy-to-read, down-to-earth, non-mathematical but very comprehensive manner. Each chapter starts off by explaining the basic principles of its subject and then goes on to present the reader with a wide range of practical circuit designs.

Throughout the volume, great emphasis is placed on practical 'user' information and circuitry, and this book, like all others in the *Circuit Manual* series, abounds with useful circuits and data. All of the semiconductor devices used in the practical circuits are modestly priced and readily available types, with universally recognized type numbers.

R. M. Marston 1991

Preface

[illegible]

1 Basic diode circuits

The solid-state diode is the most fundamental element used in modern electronics, and is available in a variety of forms, including those of signal detector, rectifier, zener 'voltage reference' diode, noise-generator diode, varicap 'variable capacitance' diode, light-sensitive diode (photodiode), and light-emitting diode (LED). This opening chapter looks at the basic characteristics of these devices and shows a variety of ways of using standard diodes and rectifiers.

Basic diode characteristics

The solid-state diode is a two-terminal device that readily passes current in one direction, but blocks it in the other. *Figure* 1.1 shows *a* the conventional symbol and *b* the basic structure of the modern solid-state 'junction' diode; it is formed from a single p–n junction, and the 'p' terminal is known as the *anode* and the 'n' terminal as the *cathode*.

Figure 1.2 illustrates the basic characteristic of the diode. When it is forward biased (with the anode positive relative to the cathode) it acts

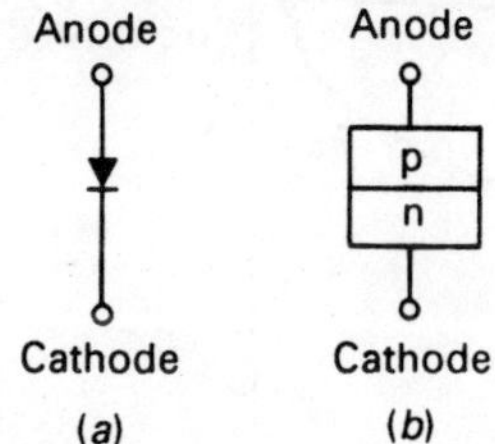

Figure 1.1 *Symbol (a) and structure (b) of solid-state diode*

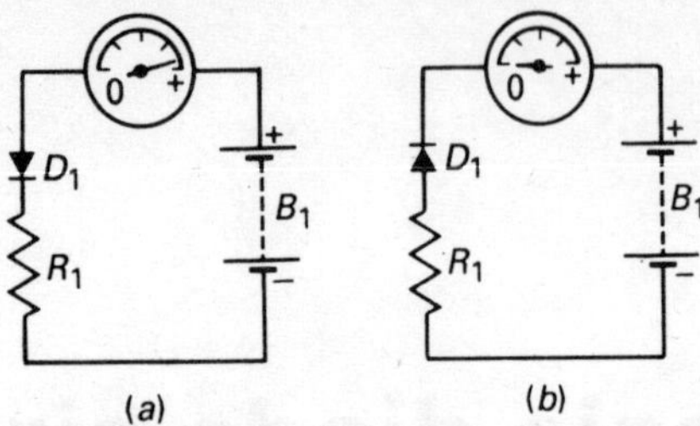

Figure 1.2 *Diode conduction when (a) forward and (b) reverse-biased*

like a low resistance and readily passes current, but when reverse biased (with the anode negative relative to the cathode) it acts like a high resistance and passes near-zero current: this action is implied by the basic diode symbol, which resembles an arrow pointing in the direction of easy current conduction.

Conventional junction diodes are made from either germanium or silicon materials. *Figure* 1.3 compares the basic characteristics of the two types of device when operated at a normal room temperature of 20°C; note the following important points.

(1) A forward-biased junction diode passes little forward current (I_f) until the applied forward voltage (V_f) exceeds a certain 'knee' value (typically 150–200 mV in germanium diodes, 550–

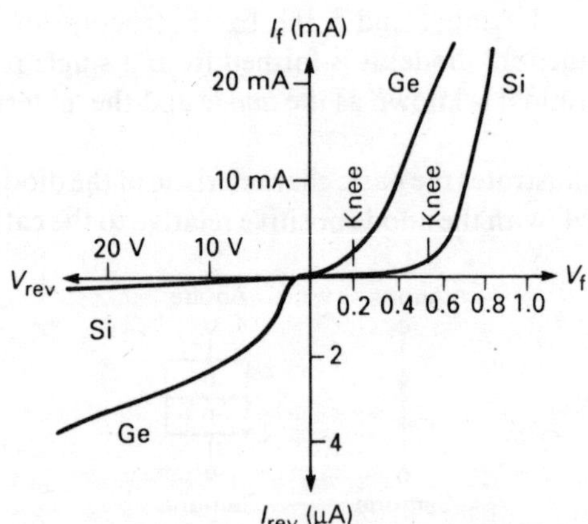

Figure 1.3 *Basic characteristics of germanium (Ge) and silicon (Si) junction diodes (at 20°C)*

600 mV in silicon types). When a diode is operated beyond its knee value, small increases in V_f cause large increases in I_f, e.g. the devices forward dynamic impedance (Z_f) is inversely proportional to applied voltage.

(2) The Z_f of a silicon diode has a typical value (in ohms) of 25/*I*, where *I* is measured in milliamperes; i.e. $Z_f = 25$ ohms at 1 mA, 2.5 ohms at 10 mA, and 0.25 ohms at 100 mA. The Z_f of a germanium diode is greater than that of a silicon type; consequently, its V_f usually exceeds that of a silicon type at I_f values greater than a few tens of milliamperes.

(3) When a diode is reverse-biased by an amount greater than 1 V or so it passes a reverse leakage current (I_r) that is almost directly proportional to the reverse voltage (V_r) value. At normal room temperatures I_r values are measured in microamperes in germanium devices and in nanoamperes in silicon types. I_r is highly temperature dependent, and typically doubles for each 8°C increase in junction temperature.

Because of their low knee voltage values, germanium diodes are used almost exclusively in low-level 'signal detection' applications. The great majority of junction diodes are silicon types, and can be used in many general-purpose applications; diodes that have high reverse voltage and forward current ratings are, by convention, usually called 'rectifiers'.

Special diode characteristics

Ordinary silicon diodes have several special characteristics additional to those already described; the most important of these are illustrated in *Figures* 1.4–1.7.

If a silicon diode is increasingly reverse-biased a point is eventually reached where the reverse current suddenly starts to increase, and any further increase in V_r causes a sharp rise in I_r, as shown in *Figure* 1.4. The voltage at which this action occurs is known as the avalanche or 'zener' value of the device, and is very sharply defined. Some silicon diodes are specially manufactured to exploit the zener effect, and can be used as 'reference voltage' generators; such devices are depicted by the circuit symbol shown in the diagram.

All zener diodes have impedances that inherently fluctuate in a rapid and random manner, and can thus be used as excellent 'white-noise' sources.

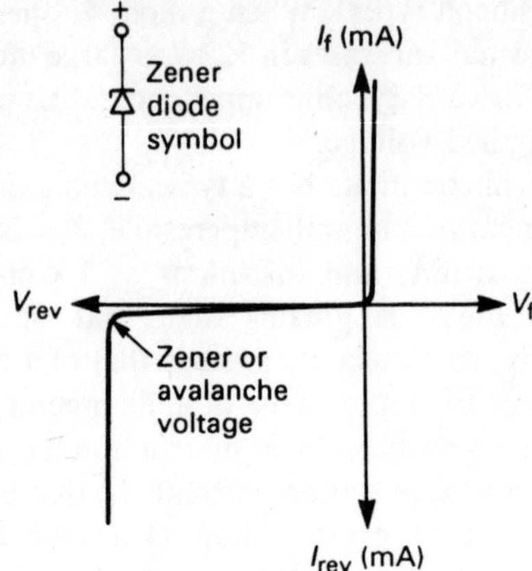

Figure 1.4 *Zener diode symbol and characteristics*

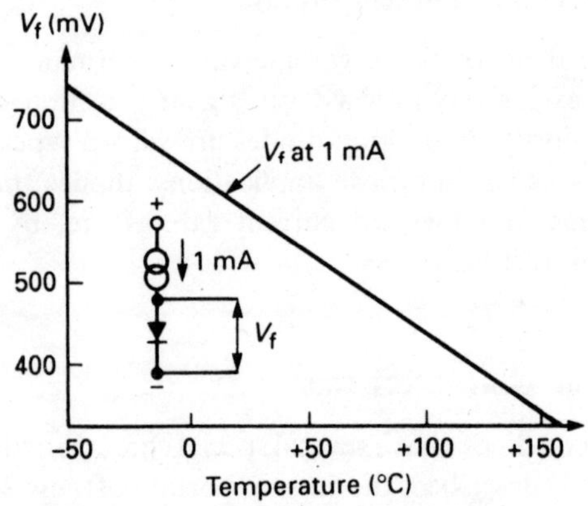

Figure 1.5 *Thermal characteristics of a silicon diode at* $I_f = 1$ *mA*

If a silicon diode is forward-biased via a constant-current generator, its V_f value varies with junction temperature at a rate of −2 mV/°C, as shown in *Figure* 1.5. Thus, if $V_f = 600$ mV at +20°C, it falls to 440 mV at 100°C or rises to 740 mV at −50°C. Silicon diodes can thus be used as temperature-to-voltage converters.

If a silicon diode is reverse-biased from a high-impedance source (as shown in *Figure* 1.6) and its junction capacitance is measured, it will be found to decrease (from perhaps 17 pF at −1 V to maybe 10 pF at −8 V) as the reverse bias is increased. Some silicon diodes

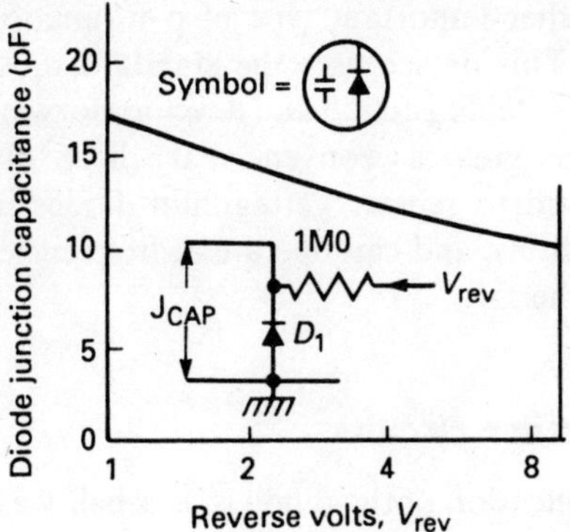

Figure 1.6 *Varactor (varicap) diode symbol and typical characteristics*

are specially manufactured to exploit this 'voltage-variable-capacitor' effect; they are known as 'varicap' or Varactor diodes, and are depicted by the circuit symbol shown in the diagram.

When p–n junctions are reverse-biased their leakage currents and impedances are inherently optosensitive; they act as very high impedances under dark conditions and as low impedances under bright ones. Normal diodes have their junctions shrouded in opaque material to stop this unwanted effect, but some are specially manufactured to exploit it; they are called photodiodes, and use the symbol shown in *Figure* 1.7*a*. Some of these photodiodes are designed to respond to visible light, and some to infra-red (IR) light.

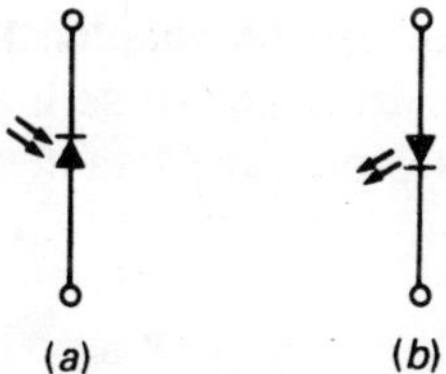

Figure 1.7 *Photodiode (a) and LED (b) symbols*

Another useful type of 'junction diode' device is the LED, or light emitting diode, which is made from an exotic material such as gallium phosphide or gallium arsenide, etc., and which may be designed to emit either red, green, yellow, or infra-red light when suitably forward-biased. These devices use the symbol shown in *Figure* 1.7*b*.

Finally, one other important type of p–n junction device is the Schottky diode. This device uses the standard diode symbol, but offers a very fast switching action and develops forward voltages that are almost half as great as conventional silicon diodes. Schottky diodes can be used to replace germanium diodes in many 'signal detector' applications, and can operate at frequencies up to tens or hundreds of gigahertz.

Half-wave rectifier circuits

The simplest application of the diode is as a half-wave rectifier, and *Figure* 1.8 shows a transformer-driven circuit of this type (with the diode's input voltage (V_{in}) specified in volts r.m.s.), together with relevant output waveforms. Note that if this circuit is used with a purely capacitive load it acts as a peak voltage detector and the output (V_{pk}) equals $1.41 \times V_{in}$, but if used with a purely resistive load it acts as a simple rectifier and gives an r.m.s output of $0.5 \times V_{in}$; if it is used with a resistively loaded capacitive load (as in simple power-supply applications) the output is 'rippled' and has an r.m.s. value somewhere between these two extremes. In capacitively loaded circuits the diode needs a peak reverse-voltage rating of at least $2.82 \times V_{in}$; if purely resistive loading is used, the rating can be reduced to $1.41 \times V_{in}$.

Note that if this circuit is used to power purely resistive loads they will consume only a quarter of maximum power, since power is proportional to the square of applied r.m.s. voltage; very few loads are in fact purely resistive, and *Figures* 1.9–1.11 show how the basic half-wave rectifier circuit can be adapted to give two-level power control of lamps, electric drills, and soldering irons that are operated from the a.c. power lines. Note in each of these circuits that the r.m.s.

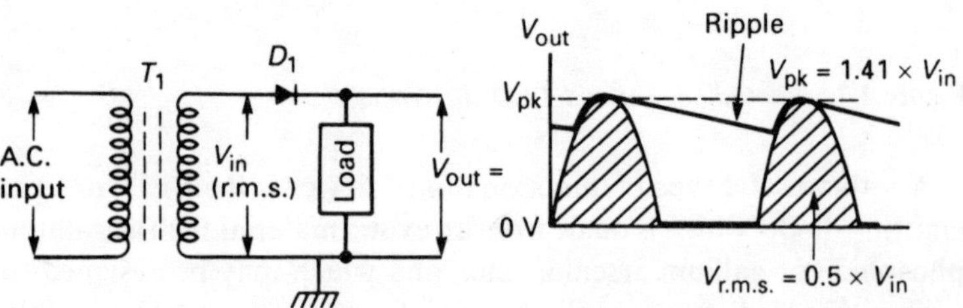

Figure 1.8 *Circuit and waveforms of transformer-driven half-wave rectifier*

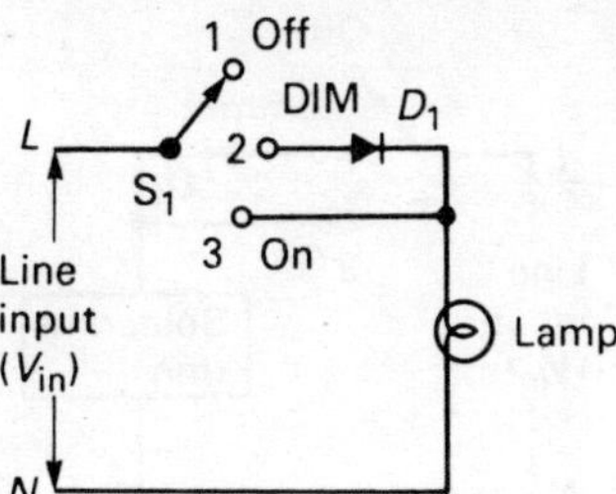

Figure 1.9 *Lamp burns at half brightness in DIM position*

voltage fed to the load equals V_{in} when S_1 is in position 3, or $0.5 \times V_{in}$ when S_1 is in position 2.

The *Figure* 1.9 circuit uses a lamp load, which has a resistance roughly proportional to its filament temperature; when it is operated at half of maximum voltage its resistance is only half of maximum, so the lamp operates at about half of maximum power and thus burns at half-brilliance with S_1 in the DIM position.

The *Figure* 1.10 circuit uses the universal motor of an electric drill (etc.) as its load. Such motors have an inherent self-regulating speed-control capacity, and because of this the motor operates (when lightly loaded) at about 70 per cent of maximum speed when S_1 is in the PART position.

The *Figure* 1.11 circuit uses a soldering iron heating element as its load, and these have a resistance that increases moderately with temperature; thus, when the iron is operated at half voltage its resistance is slightly reduced, the net effect being that the iron operates at about one third of maximum power when S_1 is in the

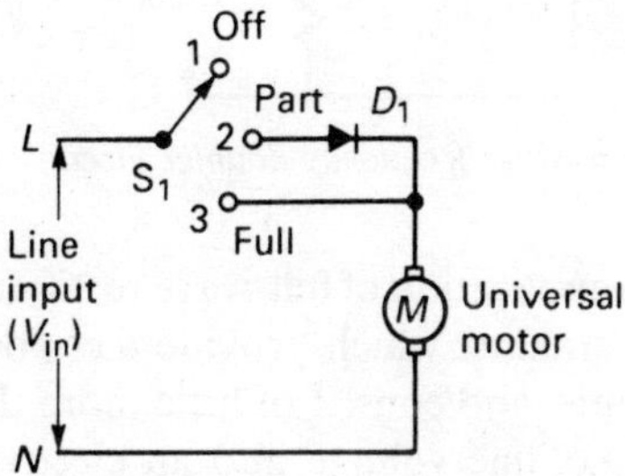

Figure 1.10 *Drill motor runs at 70 per cent of maximum speed in PART position*

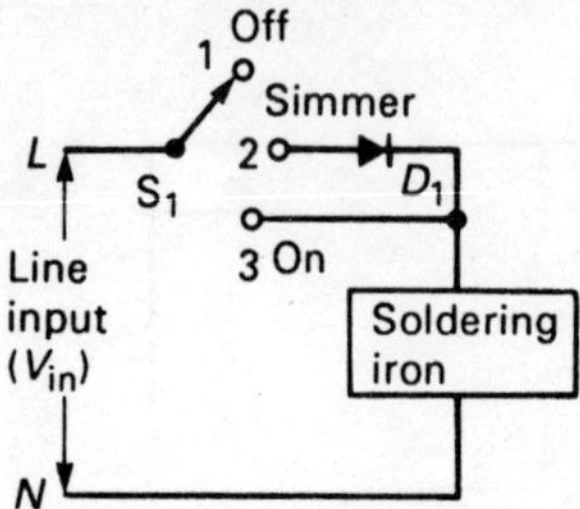

Figure 1.11 *Soldering iron operates at 1/3rd power in SIMMER position*

SIMMER position, thus keeping the iron heated but not to such a degree that its bit deteriorates.

Note that in the *Figure* 1.8–1.11 circuits D_1 can be any type that has a current rating matched to the load requirement and with a peak reverse-voltage rating of at least 1.41 × V_{in}.

Full-wave rectifier circuits

Figure 1.12 shows how four diodes can be connected in the form of a bridge and used to provide full-wave rectification from a single-ended input signal. Note in particular that the output waveform of this circuit has twice the frequency of the input, so this circuit can also be used as a simple frequency doubler.

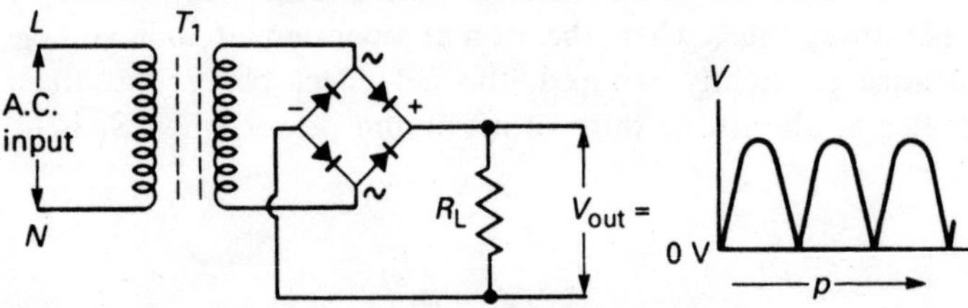

Figure 1.12 *Bridge rectifier/frequency-doubler circuit*

The best-known application of full-wave rectifying techniques is in d.c. power-supply circuits, which provide d.c. power outputs from a.c. power-line inputs, and consist of little more than a transformer that converts the a.c. line voltage into an electrically isolated and more useful a.c. value, and a rectifier–filter combination that converts this new a.c. voltage into smooth d.c. of the desired voltage value.

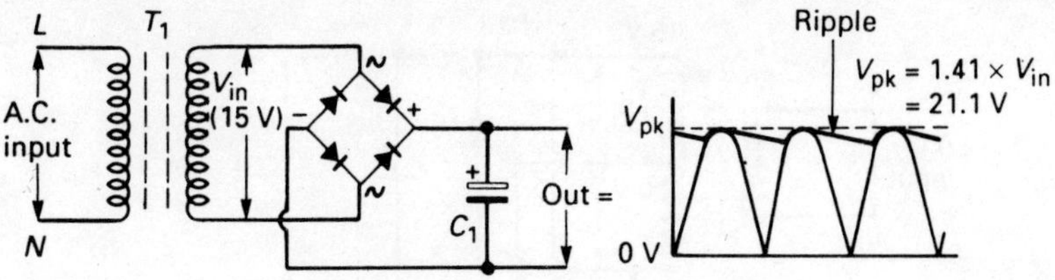

Figure 1.13 *Basic single-ended PSU using bridge rectifier.*

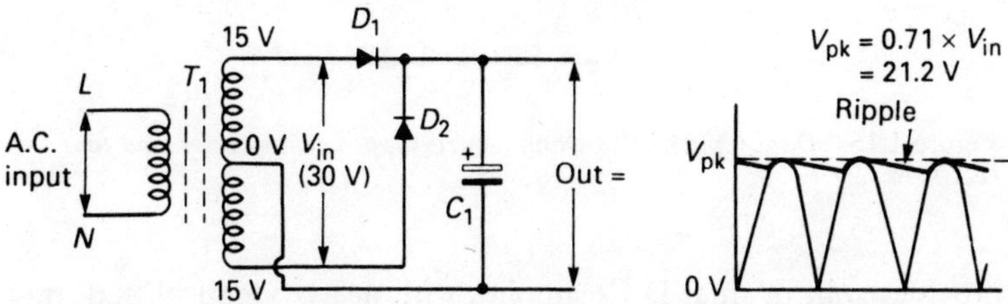

Figure 1.14 *Basic single-ended PSU using centre-tapped transformer*

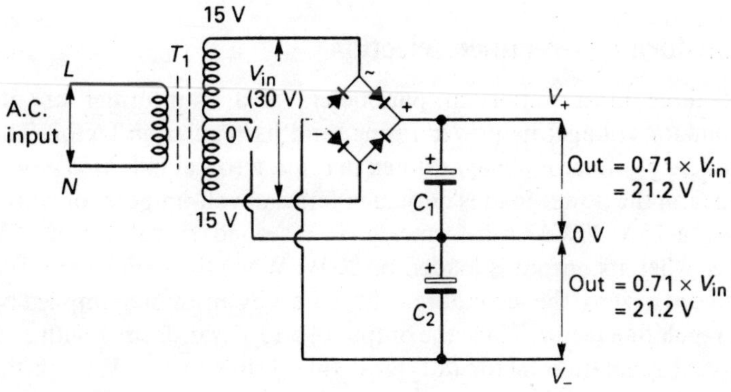

Figure 1.15 *Dual (split) PSU, using centre-tapped transformer and bridge rectifier*

Figures 1.13–1.16 show the four most useful basic power supply circuits. The *Figure* 1.13 circuit provides a D.C. supply from a single-ended transformer and bridge rectifier combination, and gives a performance virtually identical to that of the centre-tapped transformer circuit of *Figure* 1.14. The *Figure* 1.15 and 1.16 circuits each

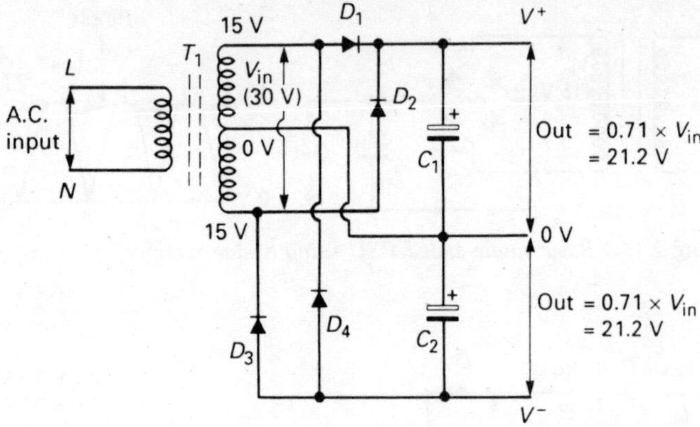

Figure 1.16 *Dual (split) PSU using centre-tapped transformer and four rectifiers*

provides split or dual D.C. supplies with nearly identical performances. The rules for designing these circuits are quite simple, as follows.

Transformer—rectifier selection

The three most important parameters of a transformer are its secondary voltage, its power rating, and its regulation factor. The secondary voltage is always quoted in r.m.s. terms at full rated power load, and the power load is quoted in terms of volt-amperes or watts. Thus, a 15 V 20 VA transformer gives a secondary voltage of 15 V r.m.s. when its output is loaded by 20 W. When the load is removed (reduced to zero) the secondary voltage rises by an amount implied by the **regulation factor**. Thus, the output of a 15 V transformer with a 10 per cent regulation factor (a typical value) rises to 16.5 V when the output is unloaded.

Note here that the r.m.s. output voltage of the transformer secondary is *not* the same as the D.C. output voltage of the complete full-wave rectified power supply which, as shown in *Figure* 1.17, is in fact 1.41 times greater than that of a single-ended transformer, or 0.71 times that of a centre-tapped transformer (ignoring rectifier losses). Thus, a single-ended 15 V r.m.s. transformer with 10 per cent regulation gives an output of about 21 V at full rated load (just under 1 A at 20 VA rating) and 23.1 V at zero load. When rectifier losses are

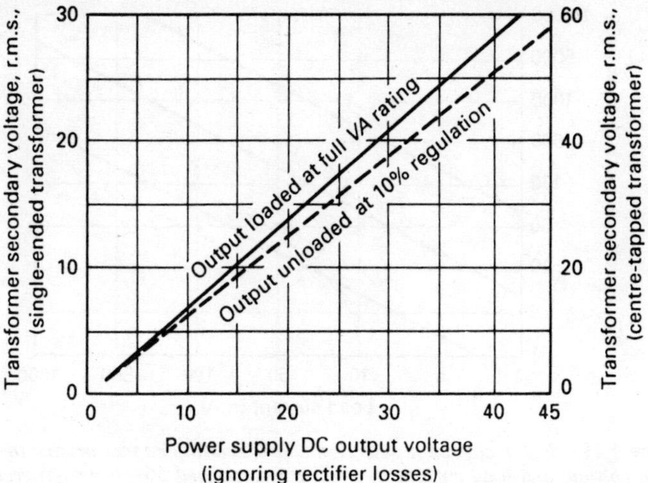

Figure 1.17 *Transformer selection chart. To use, decide on the required loaded D.C. output voltage (say 21 V), then read across to find the corresponding secondary voltage (15 V single-ended or 30 V centre-tapped)*

taken into account the output voltages will be slightly lower than shown in the graph. In the 'two rectifier' circuits of *Figures* 1.14 and 1.16 the losses are about 600 mV, and in the 'bridge' circuits of *Figures* 1.13 and 1.15 they are about 1.2 V. For maximum safety, the rectifiers should have current ratings at least equal to the D.C. output currents.

Thus, the procedure for selecting a transformer for a particular task is quite simple. First, decide the D.C. output voltage and current that is needed; the product of these values gives the minimum VA rating of the transformer. Finally, consult the graph of *Figure* 1.17 to find the transformer secondary r.m.s. voltage that corresponds to the required D.C. voltage.

The filter capacitor

The purpose of the filter capacitor is to convert the full-wave output of the rectifier into a smooth D.C. output voltage; its two most important parameters are its working voltage, which must be greater than the off-load output value of the power supply, and its capacitance value, which determines the amount of ripple that will appear on the D.C. output when current is drawn from the circuit.

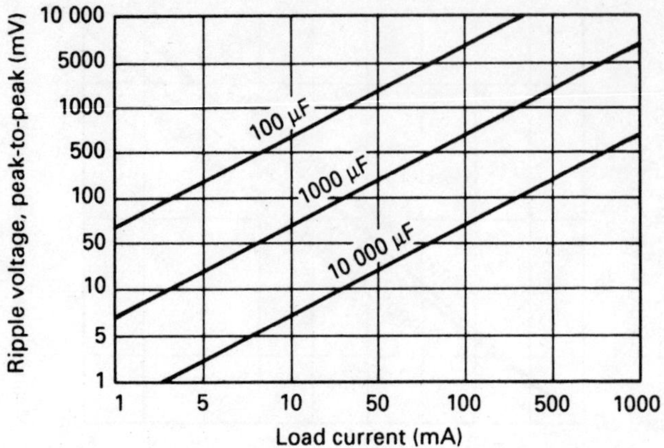

Figure 1.18 *Filter capacitor selection chart, relating capacitor size to ripple voltage and load current in a full-wave rectified 50–60 Hz-powered circuit*

As a rule of thumb, in a full-wave rectified power supply operating from a 50–60 Hz power line, an output load current of 100 mA will cause a ripple waveform of about 700 mV peak-to-peak to be developed on a 1000 μF filter capacitor, the amount of ripple being directly proportional to the load current and inversely proportional to the capacitance value, as shown in the design guide of *Figure* 1.18. In most practical applications, the ripple should be kept below 1.5 V peak-to-peak under full-load conditions. If very low ripple is needed, the basic power supply can be used to feed a three-terminal voltage regulator IC, which can easily reduce the ripple by a factor of 60 dB or so at low cost.

Rectifier ratings

Figure 1.19 summarizes the characteristics of the three basic types of rectifier circuit and gives the minimum peak inverse voltage (PIV) and current ratings of the individual rectifiers. Thus, the full-wave circuit (using a centre-tapped transformer) and the bridge circuit (using a single-ended transformer) each give a typical full-load output voltage of about 1.2E and need diodes with minimum current ratings of 0.5I (where I is the load current value), but the bridge circuit's PIV requirement is only half as great as that of the full-wave circuit.

Circuit	V_{in} (r.m.s.)	No-load output	Full-load output	Rectifier rating	
				PIV	Current
Half wave	E	$1.41 \times E$	E	$2.82 \times E$	I
Full wave	$E + E$	$1.41 \times E$	$1.2 \times E$	$2.82 \times E$	$0.5 \times I$
Bridge	E	$1.41 \times E$	$1.2 \times E$	$1.41 \times E$	$0.5 \times I$

Figure 1.19 *Rectifier circuit characteristics*

Clamping-diode circuits

A clamping-diode circuit is one that takes an input waveform and provides an output that is a faithful replica of its shape but has one edge tightly clamped to the zero-voltage reference point. *Figure* 1.20*a* shows a version which clamps the waveform's negative edge to zero and gives a purely 'positive' output, and *Figure* 1.20*b* shows a version which clamps the positive edge to zero and gives a purely 'negative' output.

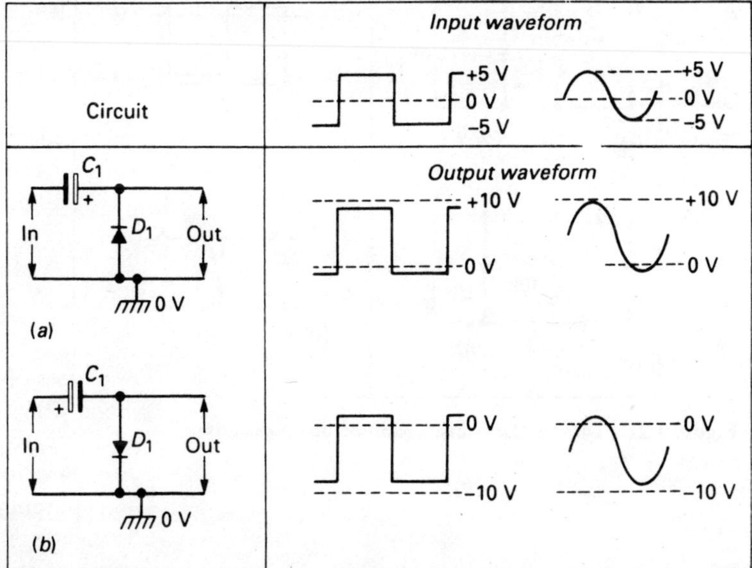

Figure 1.20 *Clamping diode circuits*

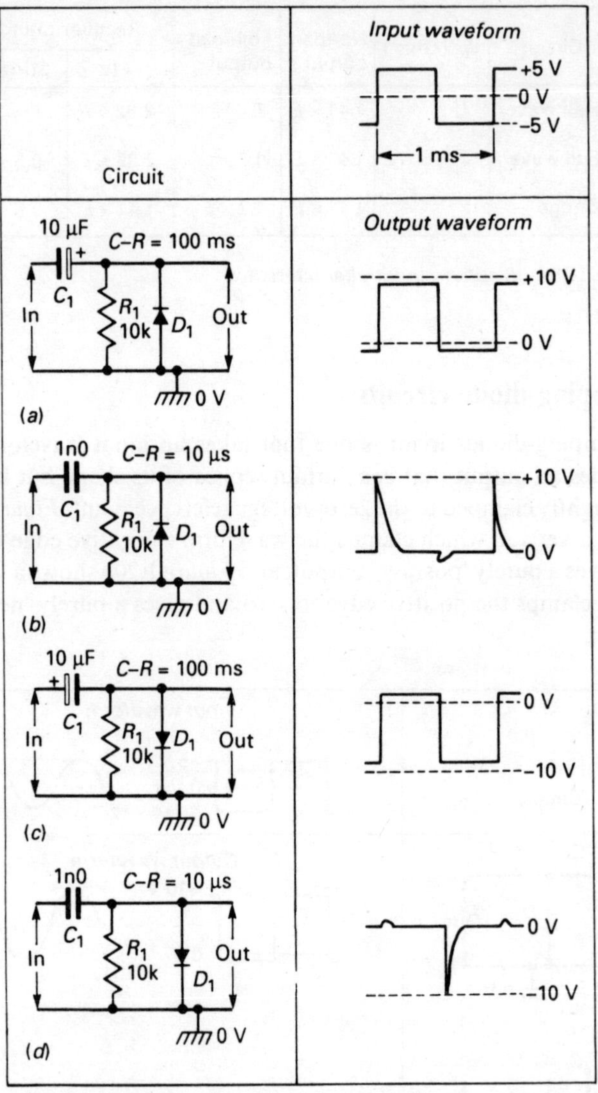

Figure 1.21 *Differentiator/discriminator-diode circuits*

Two important points should be noted about these apparently simple circuits. First, their peak output is (ideally) equal to the peak-to-peak value of the input waveform; thus, if the input swings symmetrically about the zero voltage point (as shown), the peak output value is double that of the input. The second point is that the circuits fall short of the ideal in that the output is in fact clamped to a point that is offset from zero by an amount equal to the diode's V_f value (about 600 mV in silicon types), as illustrated in these and many other diagrams in this chapter.

Figure 1.21 shows what happens to these circuits when a 10k resistor is wired across D_1, and the inputs are fed with a good 1 kHz (=1 ms period) square wave from a low-impedance source. In this case C_1–R_1 form a differentiator network, with a time constant equal to the *C–R* product; if this product is very long (100 ms) relative to the waveform period (1 ms), the circuits act like simple clamping-diode types, as shown in *Figures* 1.21*a* and 1.21*c*. If the *C–R* product is very short (10 μs) relative to the 1 ms waveform period, however, the *C–R* network converts the square wave's rising and falling edges into positive and negative 'spikes' (each with a peak amplitude equal to the peak-to-peak input value) respectively, and D_1 then effectively eliminates (discriminates against) one or other of these spikes, as shown in *Figures* 1.21*b* and 1.21*d*. These last two are thus useful in detecting the leading or trailing edges of square or pulse waveforms, etc., and are generally known as differentiator/discriminator diode circuits.

In an ordinary clamping circuit the diode clamps one edge of the waveform to the zero-voltage reference point. The basic circuit can however, be used to clamp the waveform edge to a reference voltage other than zero by simply tying the 'low' side of the diode to a suitable bias voltage; such circuits are known as biased clamping-diode types, and a variety of these (with very long *C–R* products) are shown in *Figure* 1.22.

Figure 1.22*a* shows a biased clamping-diode circuit using a +2 V clamping point and a 'negative output' diode (as in *Figure* 1.20*b*), so that (ideally) the output swings from +2 to −8 V when fed from a 10 V peak-to-peak input. Note that if the diode is reversed (as in *Figure* 1.20*a*) and a +5 V bias point is used, the output will swing between +5 and +15 V.

Figures 1.22*b–d* show circuits using pairs of clamping diodes. Obviously, a waveform can not be clamped to two different voltages at the same time, so in these circuits one diode acts effectively as a

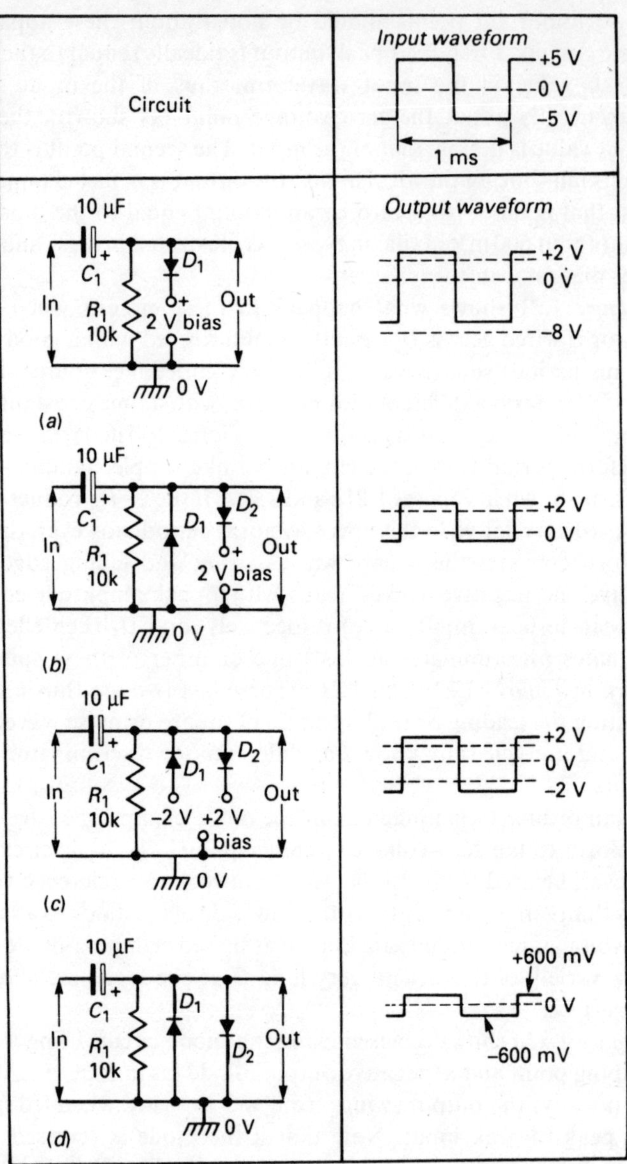

Figure 1.22 *Biased clamping diode circuits*

clamp and the other as a waveform clipper. The matter of precise diode task designation is purely academic; thus, in *Figure* 1.22*b*, it does not matter if D_1 is regarded as a 0 V clamp and D_2 as a +2 V clipper, or if D_2 is regarded as a +2 V clamp and D_1 as a 0 V clipper; the net effect is the same – the output is effectively clipped at 0 and +2 V. Similarly, the *Figure* 1.22*c* circuit (which uses −2 V and +2 V reference points) is effectively clipped at −2 V and +2 V. Finally, *Figure* 1.22*d* uses a pair of zero-voltage reference points and ideally gives zero output, but, because of the 'offsetting' effects of the D_1 and D_2 V_f voltages (about 600 mV each), in fact gives output clipping at +600 mV and −600 mV.

Diode 'rectifier' circuits

Figure 1.23 shows four different ways of using a single diode as a half-wave rectifier; in all cases it is assumed that the input comes from a low-impedance source, the output feeds a high impedance, and the output waveform is 'idealized' (it ignores the effects of diode offset). Thus, the *Figure* 1.23*a* and *d* circuits give positive outputs only, and *Figures* 1.23*b* and *c* give negative outputs only. Note, however, that the 1.23*a* and *b* circuits have low output impedances (roughly equal to the input signal source impedance), but that the 1.23*c* and *d* designs have high output impedances (roughly equal to the R_1 value).

Figure 1.24 shows how the *Figure* 1.23*c* and 1.23*d* circuits can be combined to make a very useful signal 'limiter' which can accept a variety of inputs and gives an output that is amplitude-limited at ±600 mV via D_1 and D_2. It can be used as a triangle-to-sine waveform converter by adjusting RV_1 to give gentle clipping of the triangle peaks (generated sine-wave distortion is typically about 2 per cent), or can be used as an audio signal noise limiter by adjusting RV_1 to give clipping of the worst of the noise bursts, as shown.

Figure 1.25 shows how the *Figure* 1.23*a*/*b* circuits can be modified to give outputs that are above or below a selected 'bias' or reference level. Thus, *Figure* 1.25*a* produces outputs of only +2 V or greater, *Figure* 1.25*c* gives outputs of +2 V or less, 1.25*c* of −2 V or greater, and 1.25*d* of −2 V or less. In all cases, the output load impedance is assumed to be small relative to the R_1 value.

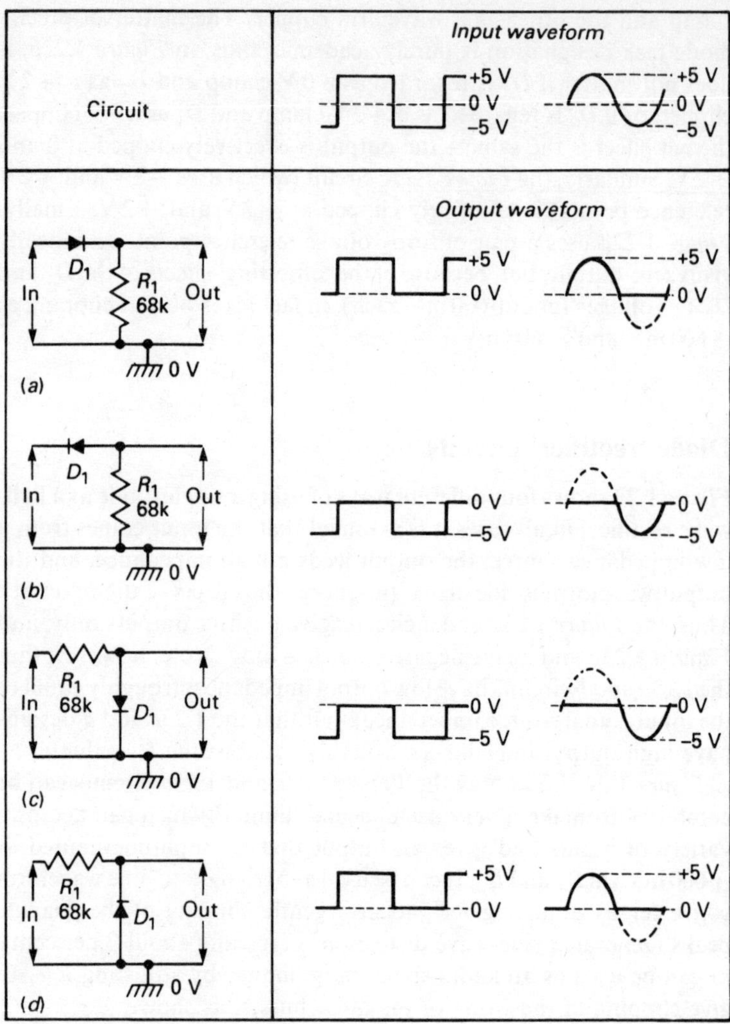

Figure 1.23 *Single-diode 'rectifier' circuits*

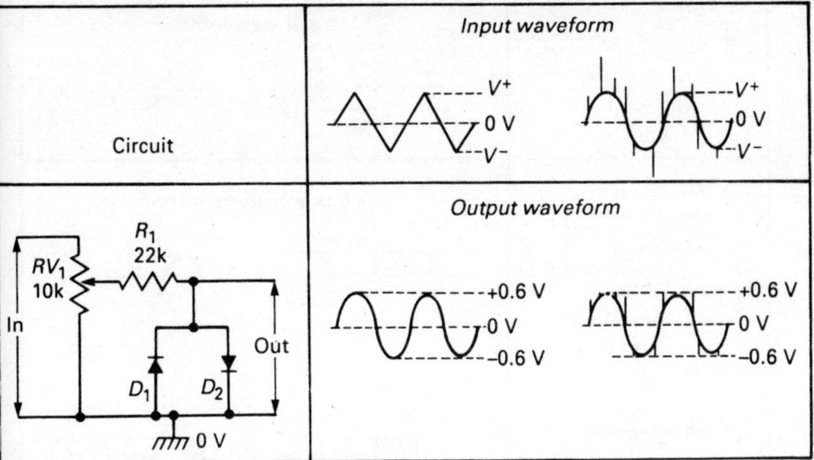

Figure 1.24 *Two-diode 'limiter' circuits*

Voltage multiplier circuits

Figures 1.26–28 show various ways of connecting diodes and capacitors to make effective A.C. 'voltage multiplier' circuits that give a D.C. output equal to some multiple of the *peak* voltage value of an A.C. input signal. Although these circuits look rather complicated, their operation is in fact quite simple. Thus, the 'voltage doubler' circuit of *Figure* 1.26 in fact consists of a simple C_1–D_1 clamping diode network (like *Figure* 1.20*a*), which gives an A.C. output with a peak value equal to the peak-to-peak value of the input, followed by a peak voltage detector (D_2–C_2) that gives a D.C. output equal to the peak values of D_2's input voltage. *Figure* 1.26*a* shows the conventional diagram of this circuit, and *Figure* 1.26*b* shows it redrawn as a 'standard' voltage-doubler section.

Figure 1.27 shows a voltage tripler circuit, which gives a D.C. output equal to three times the *peak* voltage value of a symmetrical A.C. input signal. In this case (as can be seen from *Figure* 1.27*a*) D_3–C_3 act as a peak voltage detector that generates +5 V on the D_3–C_3 junction, and C_1–D_1–D_2–C_2 act as a voltage doubler section (identical to *Figure* 1.26) that generates a 'voltage doubled' output on top of this +5 V potential, thus giving a final 'tripled' output of

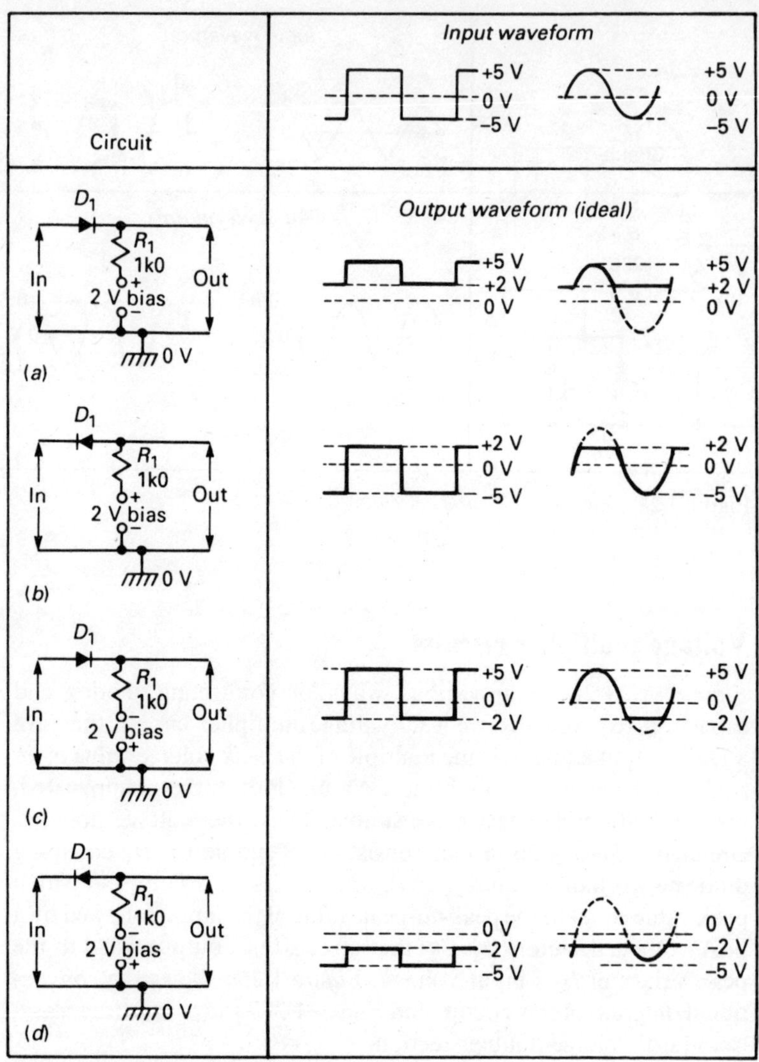

Figure 1.25 *Biased single-diode 'rectifier' circuits*

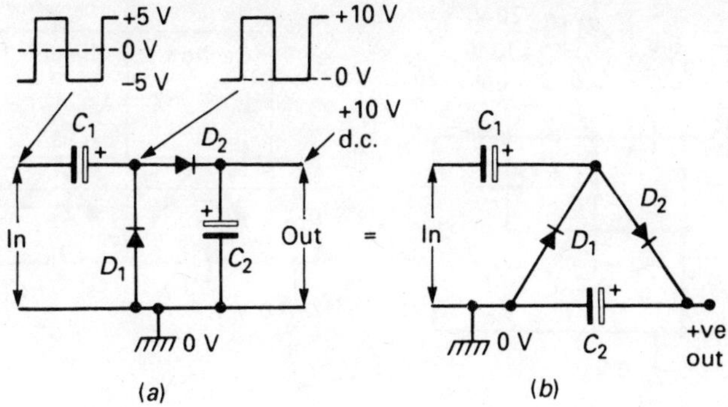

Figure 1.26 *Voltage-doubler circuit*

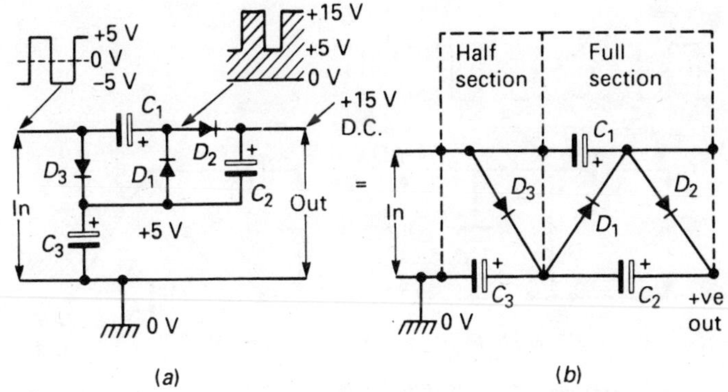

Figure 1.27 *Voltage-tripler circuit*

+15 V. Thus, this circuit in fact consists of a D_3–C_3 'half section' plus a full C_1–D_1–D_2–C_2 'doubler' section, as shown in *Figure* 1.27*b*.

Figure 1.28 shows a voltage quadrupler circuit, which gives a D.C. output equal to four times the *peak* voltage value of a symmetrical A.C. input signal. In this case C_1–D_1–D_2–C_2 act as a voltage-doubler section that generates +10 V on the D_2–C_2 junction, and C_3–D_3–D_4–C_4 act as another voltage-doubler section that generates another +10 V between the D_2–C_2 junction and the D_4–C_4 junction, to give a final +20 V of output between the D_4–C_4 junction and ground.

Note from *Figures* 1.27*b* and 1.28*b* that any desired amount of voltage multiplication can be obtained by wiring appropriate numbers of full and half 'multiplier' sections in series. Thus, seven times

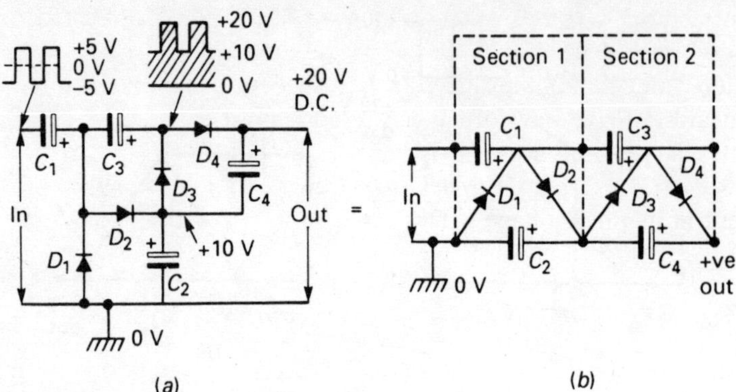

Figure 1.28 *Voltage-quadrupler circuit*

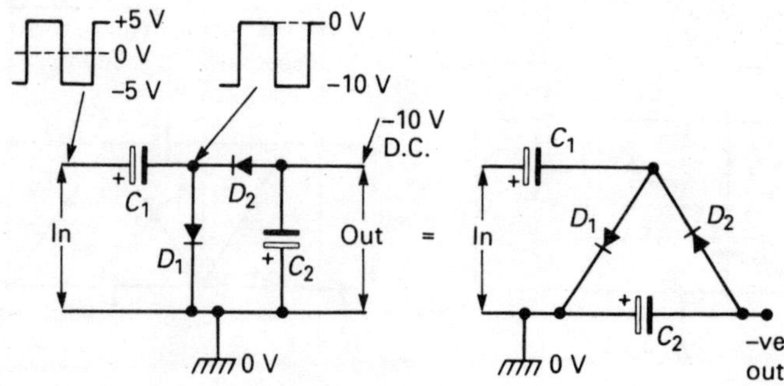

Figure 1.29 *Negative voltage-doubler circuit*

multiplication can be obtained by wiring three full sections in series with a single 'half' input section. In all cases, all multiplier diodes and capacitors need minimum ratings of twice the peak input voltage value.

The *Figure* 1.26–1.28 circuits are all designed to give positive output voltages; they can be made to give negative output voltages by simply reversing the polarities of all multiplier diodes and capacitors, as in the negative voltage doubler of *Figure* 1.29.

The diode pump circuit

In the basic voltage doubler of *Figure* 1.26, C_1 and C_2 have equal values, and C_2 charges to the full 'doubled' value within a few cycles of initial input signal connection. If, however, C_1 is made small relative to C_2, each new input cycle makes the C_2 charge increase by a small 'step' value that diminishes with each successive cycle, so that a non-linear 'staircase' waveform is generated across C_2 as it moves towards full charge; such a circuit is known as a 'diode-pump', and takes $2 \times C_1/(C_1 + C_2)$ input cycles to charge C_2 to approximately 75 per cent of its final voltage value.

Damping diode circuits

When the operating current of an inductive device such as a transformer, coil, or electric motor, etc., is suddenly interrupted, the inductor intrinsically generates a substantial switch-off back-e.m.f., which may damage associated electronic or electromechanical devices. This danger can be eliminated by wiring a damping diode across the inductor, as in the relay circuit of *Figure* 1.30. Here, D_1 stops the $RLA–SW_1$ junction from swinging more than 600 mV above the positive supply. Alternatively, D_2 (shown dotted) can be used to prevent the junction from swinging more than 600 mV below the negative supply rail.

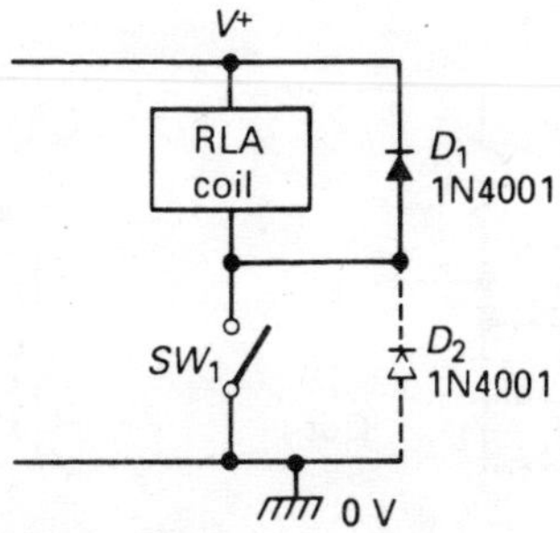

Figure 1.30 *Damping diode circuit limits relay coil back-e.m.f.s to safe values*

Single-diode 'damping' protection is adequate for most practical applications. In critical applications in which SW_1 is replaced by a transistor or other solid-state switch, perfect protection can be obtained by using both diodes to make a two-diode damper that stops back-e.m.f.s from going more than 600 mV above the positive or below the negative supply-rail lines.

Diode gate circuits

Figure 1.31 shows how a few diodes and a resistor can be used to make an OR gate that gives a high (logic-1) output when any one of its inputs is high, and also shows the truth table of the circuit when it is wired in the two-input mode. The circuit can be given any desired number of inputs by simply adding extra diodes, as shown dotted by D_3 and D_x.

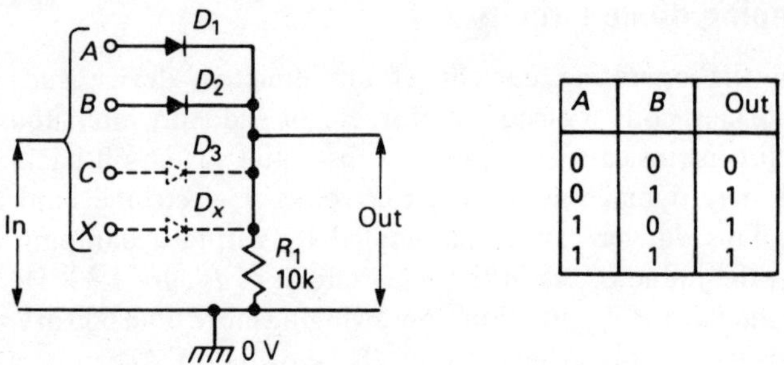

A	B	Out
0	0	0
0	1	1
1	0	1
1	1	1

Figure 1.31 *Diode OR gate circuit, with two-input truth table*

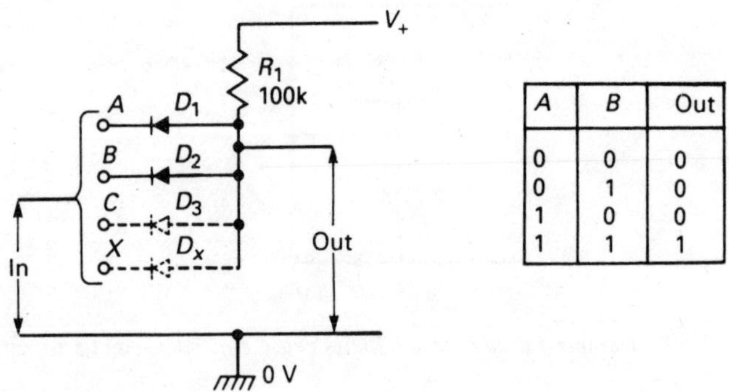

A	B	Out
0	0	0
0	1	0
1	0	0
1	1	1

Figure 1.32 *Diode AND gate circuit, with two-input truth table*

Figure 1.32 shows an AND version of the diode gate, which gives a high output only when all inputs are high, and also shows its truth table when used in the two-input mode. The circuit can be given any desired number of diode inputs.

Miscellaneous diode circuits

Figures 1.33–38 show a variety of useful diode circuits. The *Figure* 1.33 design protects a polarity-sensitive load (an electronic circuit, etc.) against damage from an incorrectly applied battery voltage. If the battery is correctly connected it feeds the load via D_1 but is blocked from the alarm buzzer via D_2; if it is wrongly connected, D_1 blocks the load's current and D_2 enables the alarm buzzer.

The *Figure* 1.34 circuit gives polarity protection to the load via the bridge-connected D_1-to-D_4 set of rectifiers, which ensure correct load polarity irrespective of the polarity of the supply battery.

Figure 1.35 shows how to make a high-value non-polarized capacitor from a pair of electrolytic types and two diodes; each diode effectively shorts out its capacitor if connected to the 'wrong' polarity. The circuit has an effective capacitance equal to the C_1 or C_2 value.

Figure 1.36 shows how a pair of silicon diodes can be used to protect a moving-coil current meter against overload damage. Such meters can withstand 2–3 times full-scale deflection (f.s.d.) without damage, and in this circuit R_x must be chosen so that about 300 mV is developed across the diodes at f.s.d.; under this condition the diodes

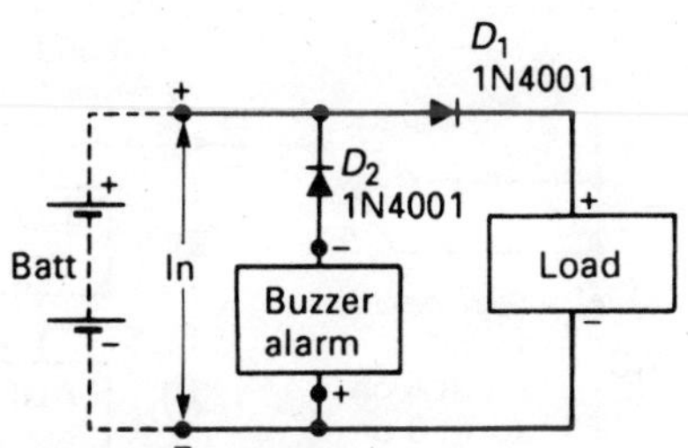

Figure 1.33 *Polarity protection circuit*

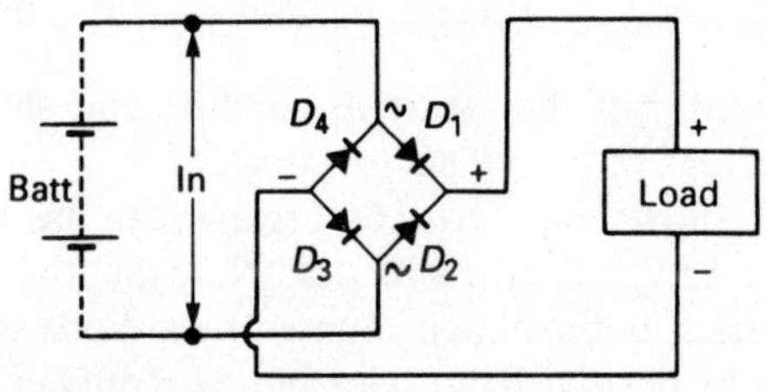

Figure 1.34 *Alternative polarity protection circuit*

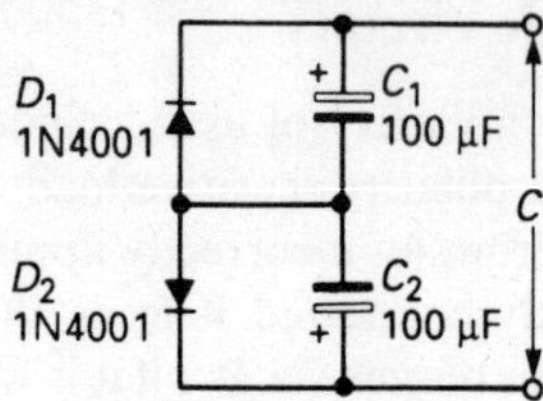

Figure 1.35 *Making a high-value (100 μF) non-polarized capacitor*

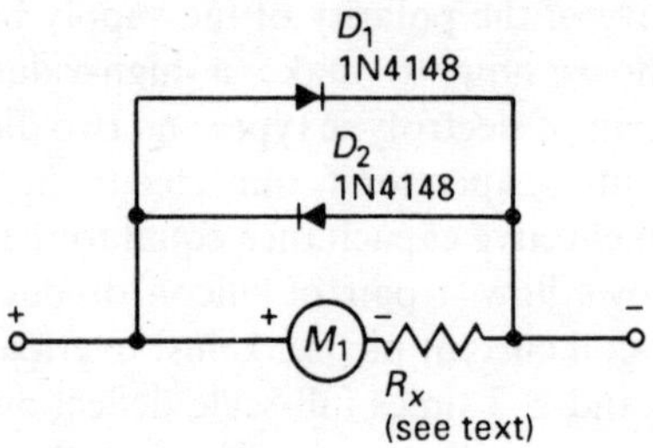

Figure 1.36 *D.c.-meter overload protection*

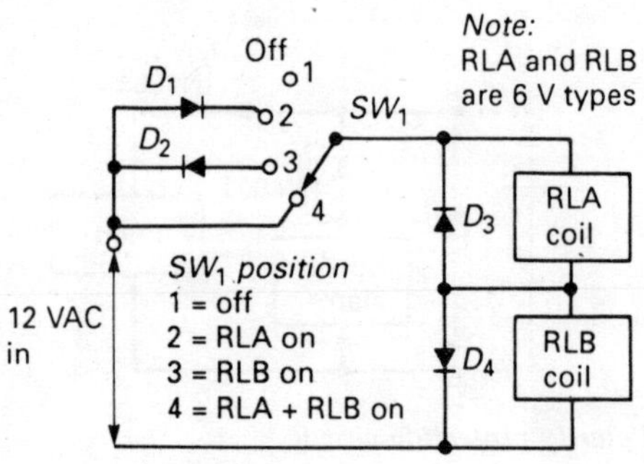

Figure 1.37 *Dual relay control*

pass zero current, but they start to conduct and shunt the meter current at readings of twice f.s.d. or greater.

Figure 1.37 shows how two 6 V relays can be independently controlled via a 12 V A.C. two-wire link. Note that the two relay coils are wired in series, but are each shunted by a diode so that *RLA* is turned on only by positive half-cycles and *RLB* only by negative half-cycles. Thus, when SW_1 is set to position 1, zero power is fed to the

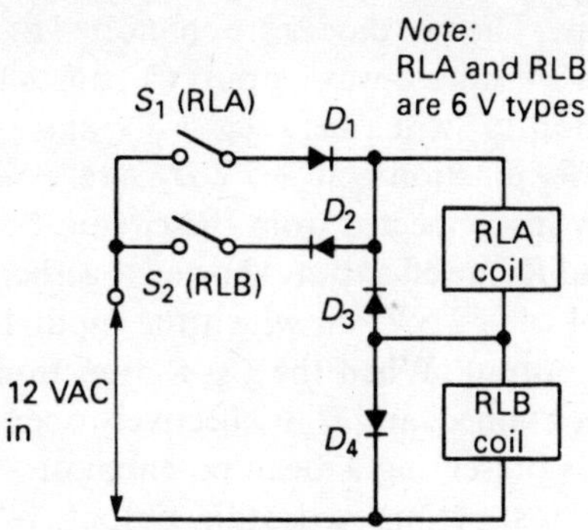

Figure 1.38 *Alternative dual relay control*

relays, and they are both off; in position 2 only positive half-waves are fed to the relays, so *RLA* turns on; in position 3 only negative half-waves are fed to the relays, so *RLB* turns on; finally, in position 4 full-wave a.c. is fed to the relays, and *RLA* and *RLB* both turn on.

Figure 1.38 shows a modified version of the above circuit, in which each relay can be independently controlled via its own on/off switch. The circuit operates in the same basic way as described above.

A 'scope trace doubler

Figure 1.39 shows how a pair of diodes can be used as the basis of a simple but very effective oscilloscope trace doubler, which allows two individual signals to be simultaneously displayed on the screen of a

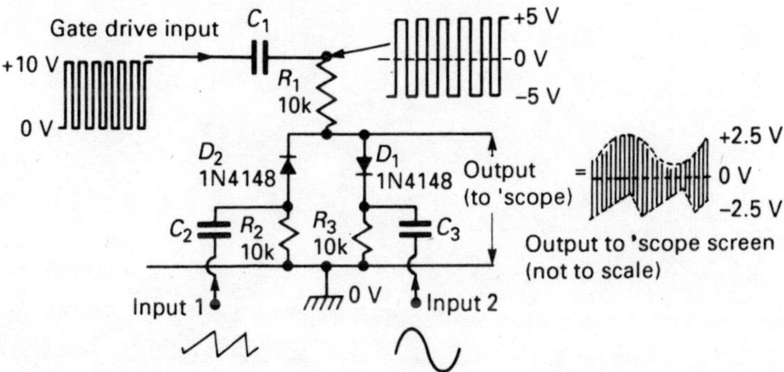

Figure 1.39 *Diode gate circuit used as a 'scope trace doubler*

single-beam 'scope. The two diodes are connected as simple gates that are driven via a 10 V square-wave input; C_1 causes the gate signal at the C_1–R_1 junction to switch between +5 V and −5 V.

When the C_1–R_1 junction is at +5 V D_2 is reverse-biased and R_2–C_2 are effectively disconnected from the circuit, but D_1 is forward-biased and R_1 and R_3 are effectively shorted together, thus presenting a mean potential of +2.5 V, on which the input-1 signal is superimposed, at the output. When the C_1–R_1 junction is at −5 V the reverse action is obtained, and D_1 is effectively open circuit and D_2 is short circuit, thus presenting a mean potential of −2.5 V, on which the input-2 signal is superimposed, at the output. When this complex output signal is fed to the input of a single beam 'scope, the vertical switching transitions disappear, and the tube displays input-1 vertically displaced above input-2; the trace separation can be varied by altering the amplitude of the square-wave gate-drive signal.

The gate-drive square-wave frequency can either be made high relative to that of the 'scope's time base, or can be exactly half the time-base frequency (via a binary divider); in the latter case, the 'scope displays the input-1 and input-2 signals on alternate sweeps.

2 Special diode circuits

Chapter 1 of this volume looked at the basic characteristics of the junction diode and associated devices (zeners, varicaps, photodiodes, LEDs, etc.), and then showed a whole range of practical applications of ordinary diodes and rectifiers. The present chapter continues the theme by looking at practical applications of the 'associated' devices mentioned above. It starts off by looking at zener diode circuits.

Zener diode circuits

If a silicon diode is increasingly reverse biased a point is eventually reached where its reverse current suddenly starts to increase, and any further increase in V_r causes a sharp rise in I_r. The voltage at which this action occurs is known as the avalanche or 'zener' value of the device, and is very sharply defined. Zener junction diodes are specially manufactured to exploit this effect, and are of great value as 'reference voltage' generators.

Figure 2.1 shows how a zener diode can be used to generate a fixed voltage by passing a modest current through it from the supply line via limiting resistor R_1. The zener output voltage is not greatly influenced by sensible variations in the zener current value (caused by variations in supply voltage or R_1 value, etc), and the output thus acts as a stable reference voltage. The R_1 value is found from the formula

$$R_1 = (V_{in} - V_z)/I_z.$$

In most applications, I_z should be set at about 5 mA.

Figure 2.2 shows how the above circuit can be modified to act as a simple voltage regulator that can supply output currents of a few tens

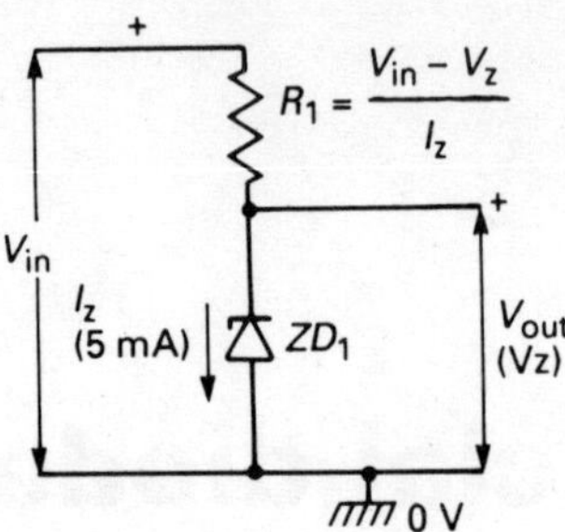

Figure 2.1 *Basic zener voltage reference circuit*

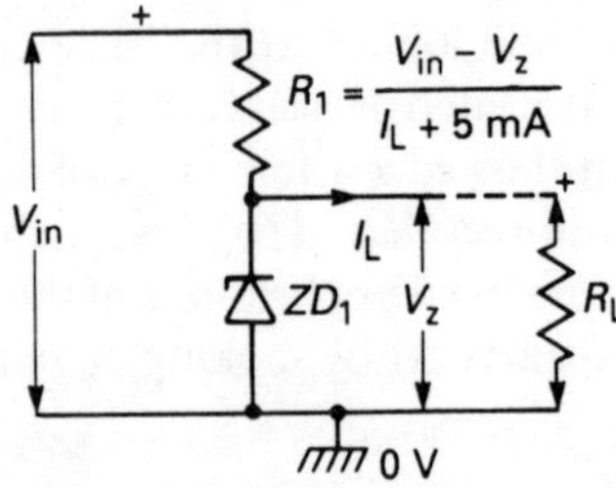

Figure 2.2 *Basic zener voltage regulator circuit*

of milliamperes to an external load. Here, the R_1 value is selected so that it passes the maximum desired output current plus 5 mA. Thus, when the specified maximum output load current is being drawn the zener passes only 5 mA, but when zero load current is drawn the zener passes all of the R_1 current and thus dissipates maximum power. Note that the zener's power rating must not be exceeded under this 'no load' condition.

Practical zener diodes are readily available in a variety of voltage values (ranging in steps from 2.7 V to about 100 V) and power ratings (typically 500 mW, 1.3 W, 5 W, and 20 W), and usually have a basic voltage tolerance within ± 5 per cent of their specified value. Other important parameters of a zener diode are its temperature coefficient (indicating the effects of thermal variations on output voltage) and its dynamic impedance (indicating the effects of zener current variations on output voltage). *Figure* 2.3 shows the typical parameter values of 500 mW zeners with standard voltages in the 2.7–16 V range.

Vz (volts)	Temp. coeff. (mV/°C)	Dynamic impedance (ohms)	Vz (volts)	Temp. coeff. (mV/°C)	Dynamic impedance (ohms)
2.7	−1.8	120	6.8	+2.7	15
3.0	−1.8	120	7.5	+3.7	15
3.3	−1.8	110	8.2	+4.5	20
3.6	−1.8	105	9.1	+6.0	25
3.9	−1.4	100	10.0	+7.0	25
4.3	−1.0	90	11	+8.0	35
4.7	+0.3	85	12	+9.0	35
5.1	+1.0	75	13	+10.5	35
5.6	+1.5	55	15	+12.5	40
6.2	+2.0	27	16	+14.0	40

Figure 2.3 *Typical parameter values of 500 mW, 2.7–16 V zener diodes*

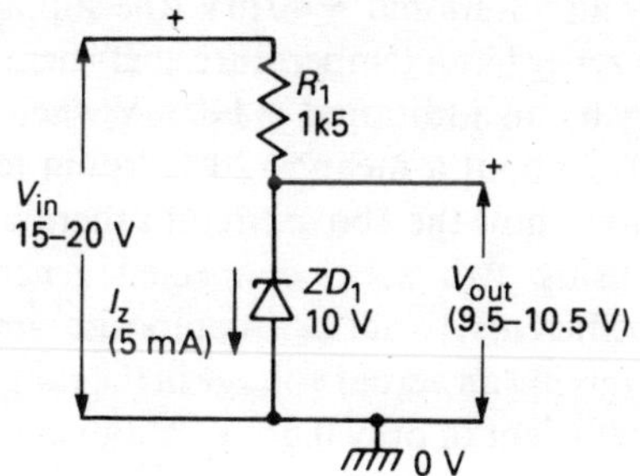

Supply rejection = ± 40 mV
Temp. rejection (20°C ± 20°C) = ±140 mV

Figure 2.4 *Simple 10 V zener reference circuit*

Figures 2.4–7 show some practical variations of the zener voltage reference circuit, with performance details based on the parameters listed in *Figure* 2.3.

Figure 2.4 shows a basic 10 V reference circuit, using a single zener diode and powered from a 15–20 V input. R_1 is given a value of 1k5, to set the zener current at 5 mA at a 'mean' supply value of 17.5 V. The zener has a 5 per cent tolerance, so the actual output voltage will be between 9.5 and 10.5 V. Variations in supply voltage (between 15 and 20 V) cause the zener current to vary by ±1.6 mA and, since the 10 V

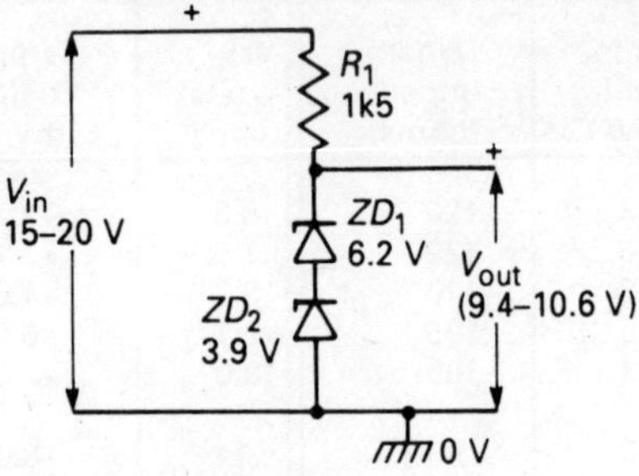

Figure 2.5 *Thermally compensated 10 V zener reference circuit*

zener has a dynamic impedance of 25 ohms, makes the zener output voltage vary by an additional ±40 mV (the supply rejection factor). Also, since this zener has a temperature coefficient of +7 mV/°C, the output will vary by an additional ±140 mV when the temperature is varied by ±20°C about a mean +20°C 'room temperature' value.

Figure 2.5 shows how the above circuit's thermal regulation can be improved by using two series-connected zeners, with opposing temperature coefficients, to act as a 'composite' zener with a nominal value of 10.1 V (giving an actual voltage in the range 9.4–10.6 V) and a temperature coefficient of only 0.6 mV/°C (giving a variation of only

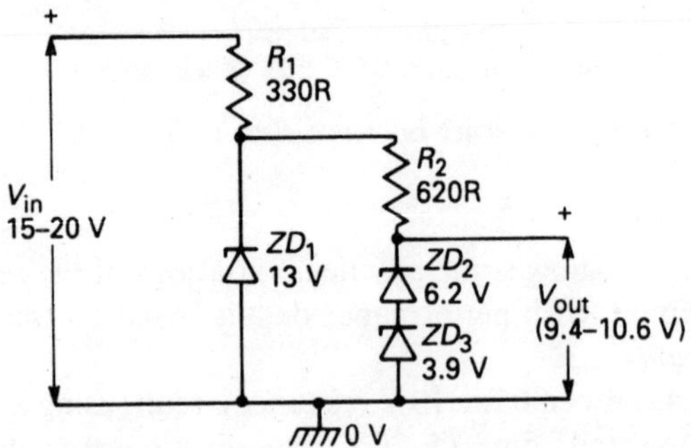

Figure 2.6 *Thermally compensated 10 V zener reference, with pre-regulator stage*

± 12 mV over the $+20°C \pm 20°C$ range). Note, however, that this 'zener' has a dynamic impedance of 127 ohms, and thus gives a supply rejection factor of ± 203 mV.

Figure 2.6 shows how the regulation of the above circuit can be improved by fitting it with a pre-regulating zener stage (ZD_1), which holds the R_1–R_2 junction within ± 265 mV of a nominal 13 V value over the full span of supply-voltage variations, thus giving a final supply rejection factor of ± 53 mV and a thermal rejection factor of ± 12 mV over the full temperature range. Note that R_2's value is chosen to give a '10 V zener' current of about 5 mA, and that R_1's value is chosen so that it will supply a current greater than this when V_{in} is at 15 V, so that ZD_1 does not cut off under this condition.

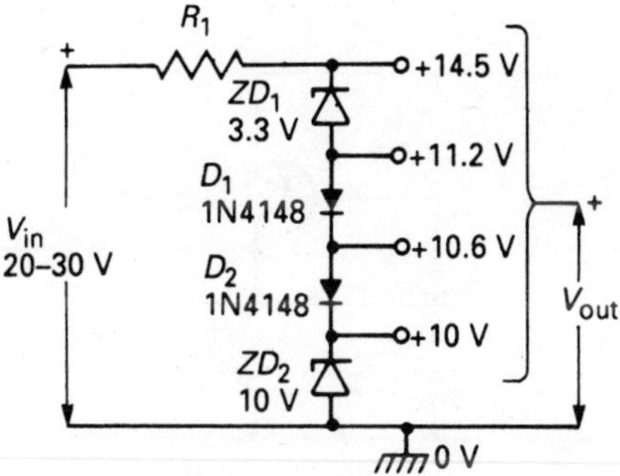

Figure 2.7 *Zeners and ordinary silicon diodes can be combined to give 'odd-ball' reference voltage values*

Finally, *Figure* 2.7 shows how zeners and ordinary silicon diodes can be wired in series to give 'odd-ball' reference voltage values. Each silicon diode 'drops' about 600 mV at a forward current of 5 mA, and has a temperature coefficient of -2 mV/°C. The supply (V_{in}) voltage must be much greater than the largest output reference voltage (14.5 V).

Regulator current boosting

The simple voltage regulator circuit of *Figure* 2.2 can be used to supply output load currents up to a maximum of a few tens of milliamperes. Greater output currents can easily be obtained by wiring a current-boosting emitter-follower buffer or 'series pass' stage

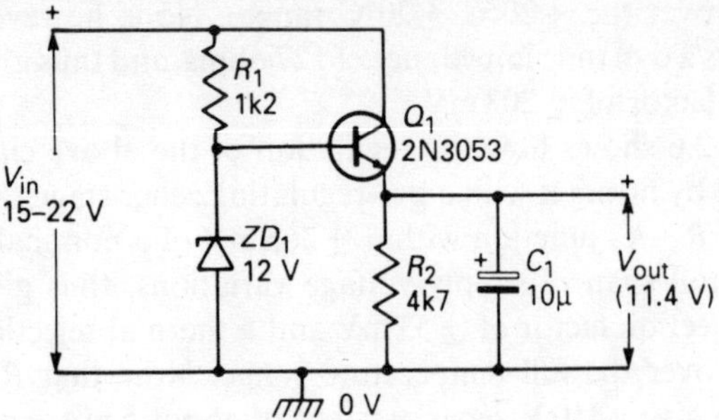

Figure 2.8 *Zener voltage regulator with current-boosting series-pass output stage; nominal output voltage is 11.4 V*

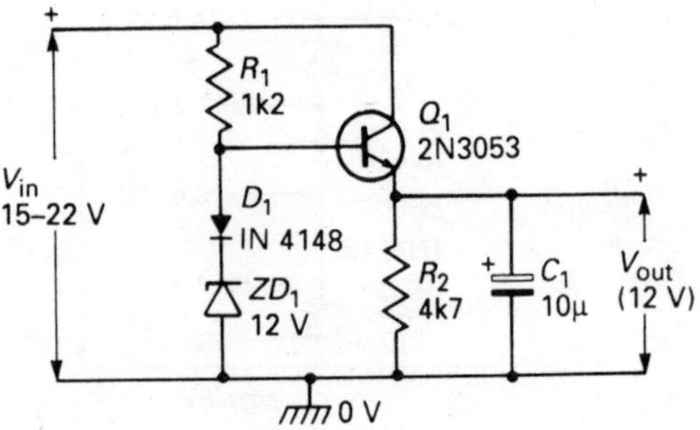

Figure 2.9 *This modified series-pass circuit gives an output of 12 V*

between the zener output and the load, as shown in *Figure* 2.8. This simple circuit reduces the zener current loading variations by a factor of about 100 (i.e. the current gain of Q_1). Note, however, that the output voltage is about 600 mV (equal to Q_1's base–emitter volt drop) less than the zener voltage. This latter snag can be overcome either by wiring a silicon diode in series with the zener diode (to boost Q_1's input voltage by 600 mV), as shown in *Figure* 2.9, or by wiring Q_1 into the feedback loop of a precision op-amp voltage follower stage, as shown in *Figure* 2.10.

Note that the output load current of each of the above three circuits is limited to about 100 mA by the power rating of Q_1; higher currents can be obtained by replacing Q_1 with a power Darlington transistor.

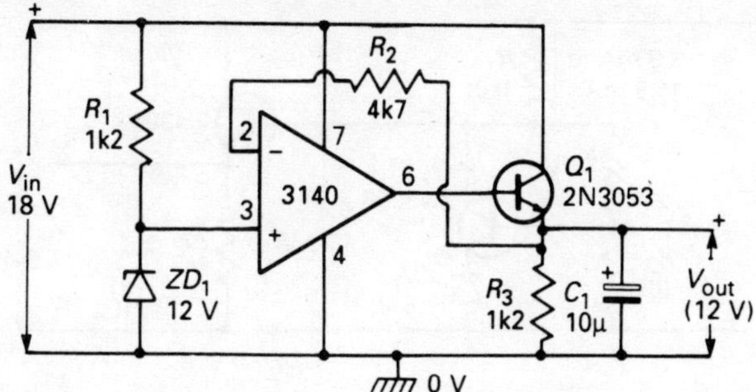

Figure 2.10 *12 V regulator incorporating an op-amp in its series-pass network*

Variable voltage circuits

Figures 2.11–13 show various ways of generating zener-derived variable reference or regulator voltages. In *Figure* 2.11 circuit Q_1 is wired as a modified common-emitter amplifier, and gives an output of $(1+[RV_1/R_2])$ times Q_1's base-to-ground voltage, which equals the sum of Q_1's base–emitter junction voltage (600 mV) and the ZD_1 voltage (6.2 V), i.e. 6.8 V total. The output of this circuit is thus variable from 6.8 to 13.6 V via RV_1. Note, however, that Q_1's base–emitter junction has a $-2\,\text{mV}/^\circ\text{C}$ temperature coefficient and ZD_1

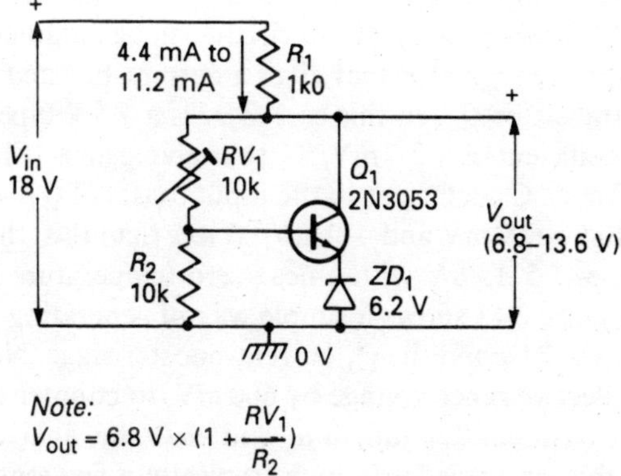

Figure 2.11 *Variable zener voltage reference, with near-zero temperature coefficient*

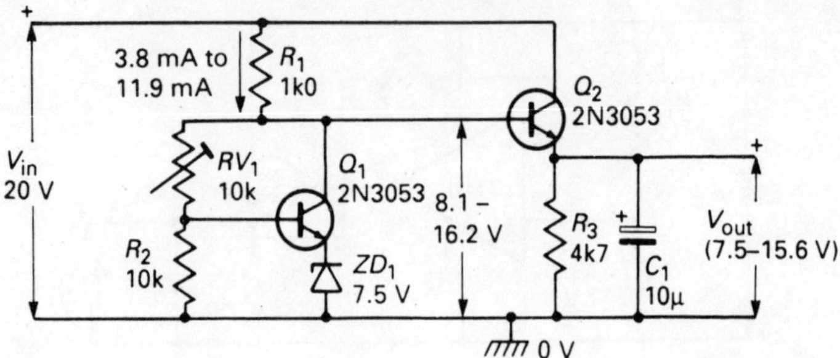

Figure 2.12 *Variable voltage regulator, with near-zero temperature coefficient*

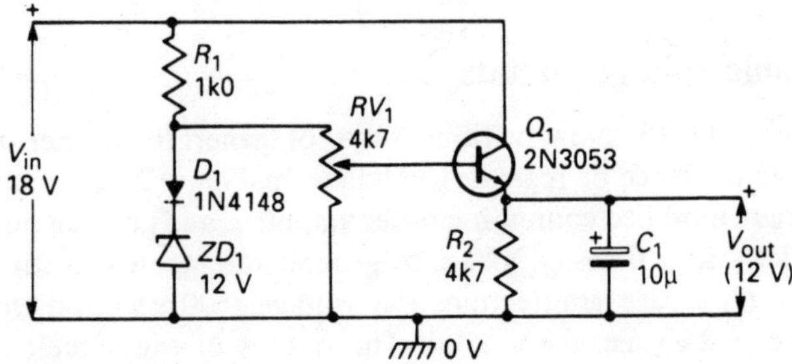

Figure 2.13 *Wide-range (0–12 V) voltage reference/regulator circuit*

has a +2 mV/°C one, and that they thus cancel each other and give a final near-zero temperature coefficient at the circuit's output.

Figure 2.12 shows how the above circuit can be modified for use as a variable voltage regulator that gives a current-boosted output via series-pass transistor Q_2. In this case ZD_1 is a 7.5 V type and has a temperate coefficient of +3.7 mV/°C, thus giving an 8.1–16.2 voltage with a +1.7 mV/°C coefficient to the input (base) of Q_2, which gives an output that is 600 mV and −2 mV/°C less than this, thus giving a final output of 7.5–15.6 V with a near-zero temperature coefficient.

Finally, *Figure* 2.13 shows a simple way of generating a stable 0–12 V output via RV_1 and the Q_1 current-booster stage. Note that D_1 boosts the effective zener voltage by 600 mV, to counter the 600 mV loss of Q_1's base–emitter junction, and that the final output impedance of this circuit is fairly high (typically a few tens of ohms), being roughly equal to the output impedance of RV_1 slider divided by the current gain of Q_1.

Miscellaneous zener circuits

To complete this look at the zener diode, *Figures* 2.14–18 show a miscellaneous collection of useful application circuits.

Figure 2.14 shows how a 6.8 V zener can be used as a voltage dropper to enable a 1000 μF, 6 V electrolytic capacitor to be used with a 12 V D.C. supply. The zener must have a large enough power ($V \times I$) rating to handle C_1's ripple currents; a 5 W rating is adequate for most purposes.

Figure 2.15 shows how a 5.6 V zener can be used as a voltage dropper to enable a 6 V relay to be used with a 12 V D.C. supply. This circuit also helps improve the relay's effective on/off ratio. Suppose the basic relay normally turns on at 5 V and off at 2.5 V, thus giving a 2:1 on/off ratio; in this circuit it will turn on at 10.6 V and off at 8.1 V, thus giving a 1.3:1 on/off ratio.

Figure 2.16 shows how a resistor and zener diode can be used as a half-wave limiter in an A.C. circuit. The positive halves of the

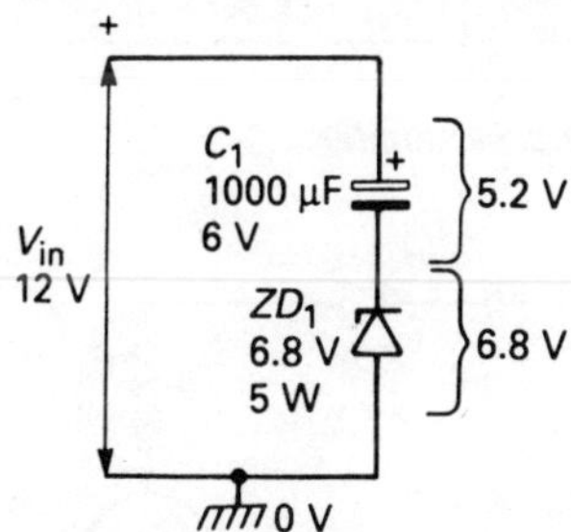

Figure 2.14 *Zener voltage dropper used with electrolytic capacitor*

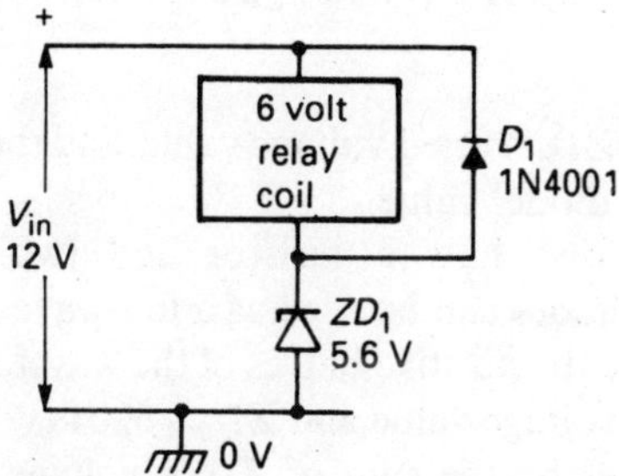

Figure 2.15 *Zener voltage dropper used with relay coil*

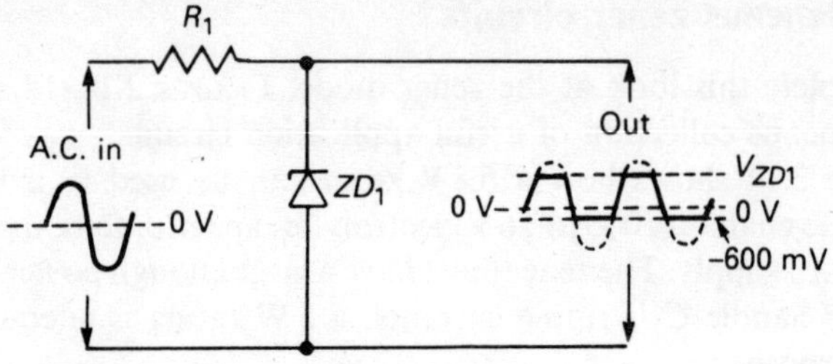

Figure 2.16 *Half-wave zener limiter*

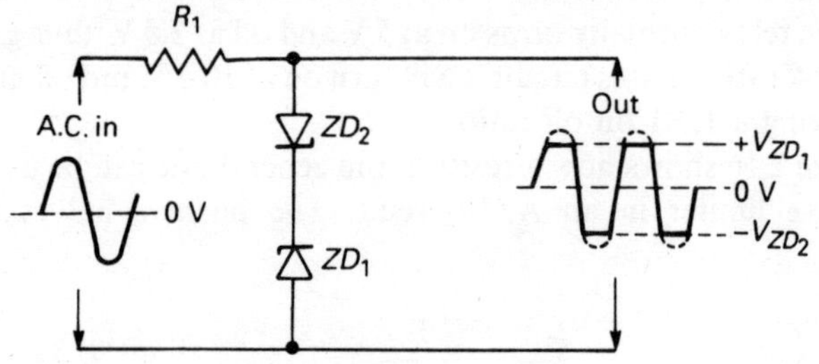

Figure 2.17 *Full-wave zener limiter*

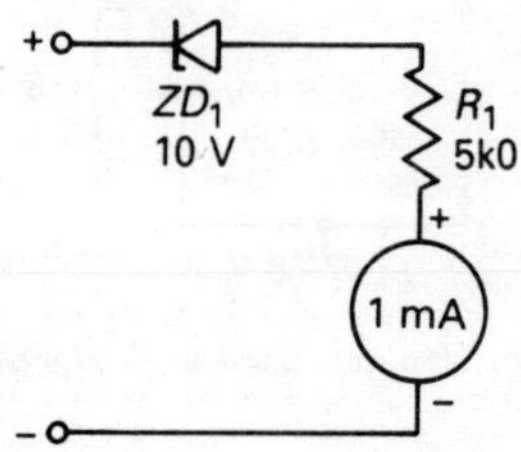

Figure 2.18 *Suppressed-zero (10–15 V) meter*

waveform limit at ZD_1's rated voltage value, and the negative ones its 600 mV 'junction diode' value.

Figure 2.17 shows how a resistor and two inversely series-connected zener diodes can be used as a full-wave limiter in an A.C. circuit. In this case the positive halves of the waveform are limited by the sum of ZD_1's voltage value and ZD_2's 600 mV 'diode' value, and the negative halves by the sum of ZD_2's voltage value and ZD_1's 600 mV 'diode' value.

Finally, *Figure* 2.18 shows how a zener, a multiplier resistor (R_1) and a 1 mA f.s.d. moving-coil meter can be used to make a suppressed-zero meter, which in this case spans the range 10–15 V. The zener sets the minimum voltage reading of the meter (10 V), and R_1 is given a value of 1000 ohms/V to set its span (5 V) and thus its f.s.d. value (15 V).

LED basic circuits

A light-emitting diode (LED) is a special type of junction diode that emits a fairly narrow bandwidth of visible (usually red, orange, yellow or green) or invisible (infra-red) light when stimulated by a forward electric current. LEDs have typical power-to-light energy-conversion efficiencies some ten to fifty times greater than a simple tungsten lamp and have very fast response times (about 0.1 μs, compared with tens or hundreds of milliseconds for a tungsten lamp), and are thus widely used as 'visual' indicators and as moving-light displays; a variety of basic LED circuits are shown in the present chapter.

A significant voltage (about 2 V) is developed across a LED when it is passing a forward current, and *Figure* 2.19 shows the typical forward voltages of different coloured standard LEDs at forward currents of 20 mA. If a LED is reverse-biased it avalanches or 'zeners' at a fairly low voltage value, as shown in *Figure* 2.20; most practical LEDs have maximum reverse voltage ratings in the range 3–5 V.

In use, a LED must be wired in series with a current-limiting device such as a resistor; *Figure* 2.21 shows how to work out the *R* value needed to give a particular current from a particular supply voltage. In practice, *R* can be connected to either the anode or the cathode of the LED. The LED brightness is proportional to the LED current; most LEDs will operate safely up to absolute maximum currents of 30–40 mA.

A LED can be used as an indicator in an A.C. circuit by wiring it in inverse parallel with a normal diode, as shown in *Figure* 2.22, to

Colour	Red	Orange	Yellow	Green
V_f (typical)	1V8	2V0	2V1	2V2

Figure 2.19 *Typical forward voltages of standard LEDs at $I_f = 20\,mA$*

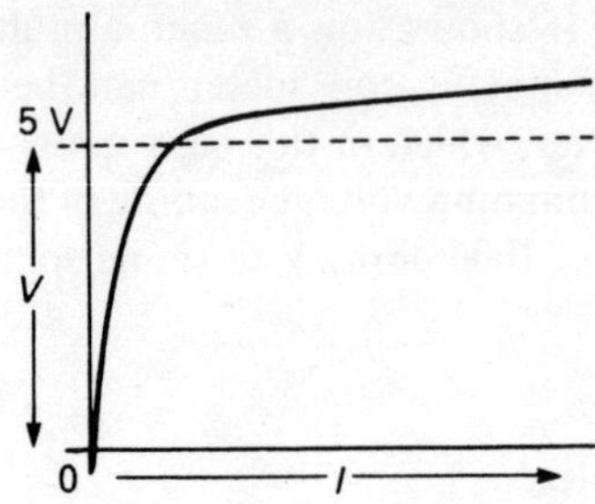

Figure 2.20 *A reverse-biased LED acts like a zener diode*

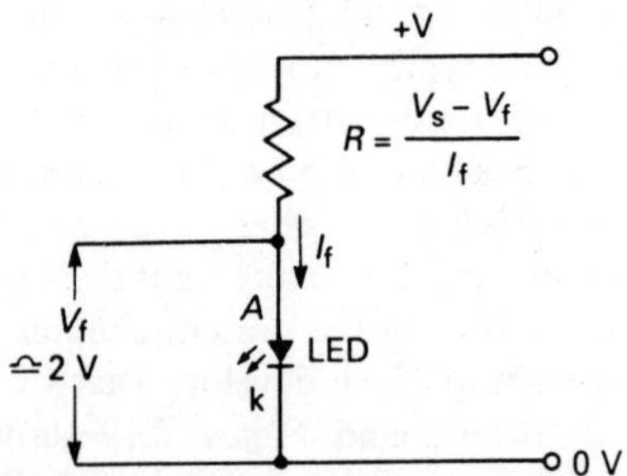

Figure 2.21 *Method of finding the* R *value for a given* V_s *and* I_f

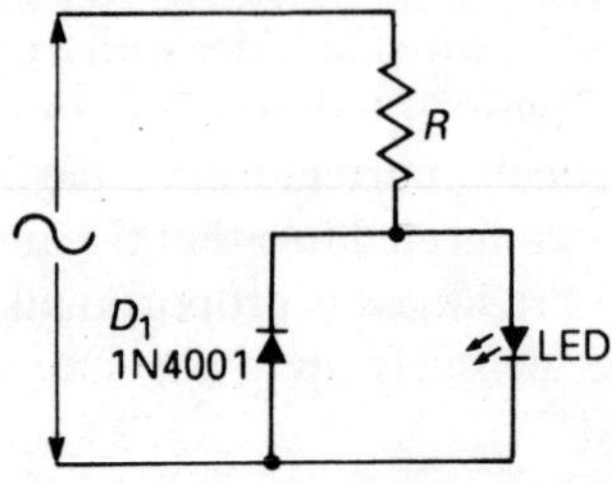

Figure 2.22 *Using a LED as an indicator in a low-voltage A.C. circuit*

prevent the LED being reverse biased; for a given brightness, the *R* value should be halved relative to that of the D.C. circuit. Note that if this circuit is used with high-value A.C. supplies, *R* may need a fairly high power rating; thus, if used with a 250 V supply it will need a minimum rating of 2.5 W at a mean LED current of 10 mA. This snag can be overcome by replacing *R* with a current-limiting series

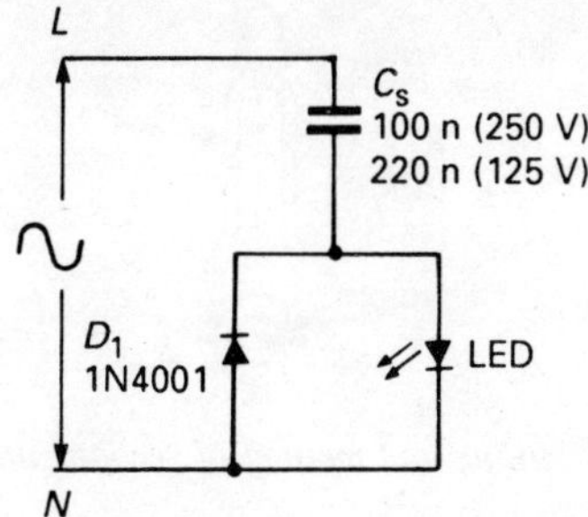

Figure 2.23 *Using a LED as an indicator in an A.C. power line circuit*

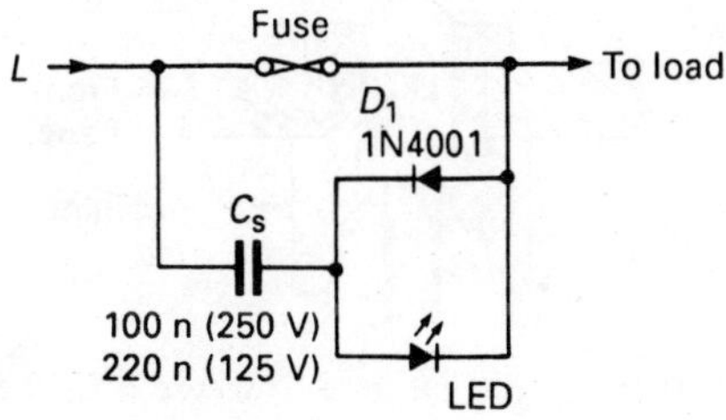

Figure 2.24 *A.C. power line 'fuse blown' indicator*

capacitor, as shown in *Figure* 2.23. Here, the C_s impedance limits the LED current to the desired value, but C_s dissipates near-zero power, since its current and voltage are 90° out of phase. C_s values of 100 nF and 220 nF are usually adequate on 250 V and 125 V 50–60 Hz A.C. lines respectively.

The basic *Figure* 2.23 circuit can be used as a 'blown fuse' indicator by wiring it as shown in *Figure* 2.24. Normally, the circuit is shorted out by the fuse, but becomes enabled when the fuse is 'blown'; under this condition the load current is limited by the C_s value.

Practical usage notes

The first practical problem that will be met when using a LED is that of identifying its polarity. Most LEDs have their cathodes identified by a notch or flat on the package, or by a short lead, as indicated in the 'outline' diagram of *Figure* 2.25. This practice is not universal, however, so the only sure way to identify a LED is to test it in the basic

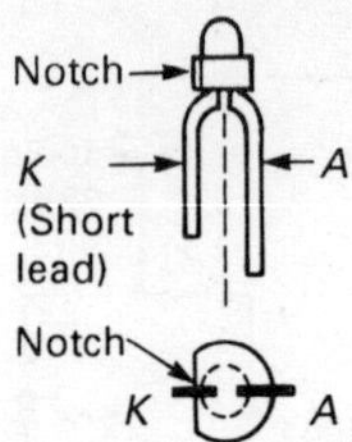

Figure 2.25 *Typical outline and method of recognizing the polarity of a LED*

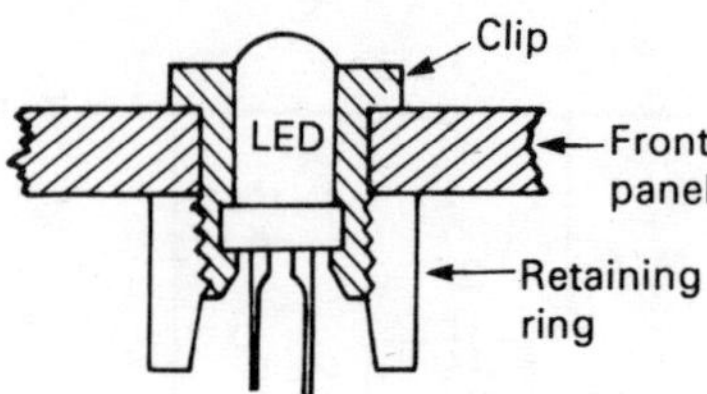

Figure 2.26 *CLIP and RING kit used to secure a LED to a front panel*

basic *Figure* 2.21 circuit: try the LED both ways round: when it glows, the cathode is the most negative of the two terminals; always test an LED before soldering it into circuit.

Special mounting kits, comprising a plastic clip and ring, are available for fixing LEDs into PC boards and front panels, etc. *Figure* 2.26 illustrates the functioning of such a kit.

Most LEDs come in the form of a 'single LED' package of the type shown in *Figure* 2.25. Multi-LED packages are also available, however. The best known of these are the seven-segment displays, comprising seven (or eight) LEDs packaged in a form suitable for displaying alphanumeric characters. So-called 'bar-graph' displays, comprising 10–30 linearly mounted LEDs in a single package, are also available.

Most LEDs provide only a single output colour. A few specialist devices do however provide 'multi-colour' outputs. These are actually two-LED devices, and *Figure* 2.27 shows one such device that comprises a pair of LEDs connected in inverse parallel, so that the colour green is emitted when the device is biased in one direction, and

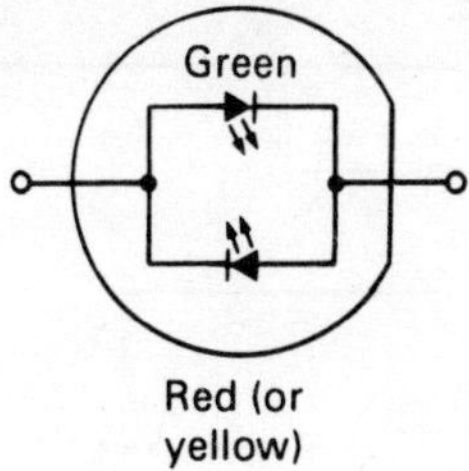

Figure 2.27 *'Bi-colour' LED actually houses two LEDs connected in inverse parallel*

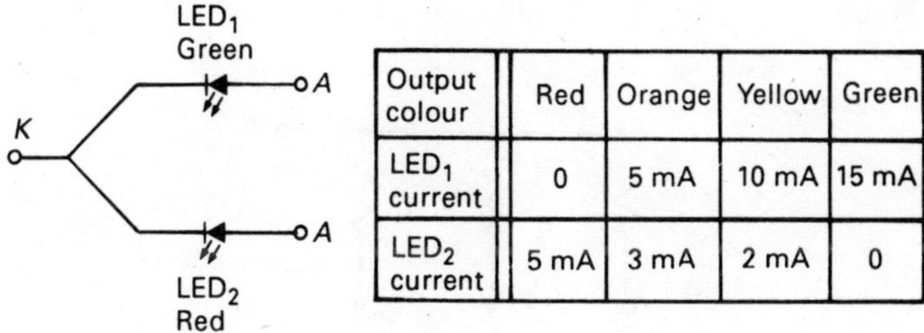

Output colour	Red	Orange	Yellow	Green
LED_1 current	0	5 mA	10 mA	15 mA
LED_2 current	5 mA	3 mA	2 mA	0

Figure 2.28 *'Multicolour' LED, giving four colours from two junctions*

red (or yellow) is emitted when it is biased in the reverse direction. This device is useful for giving polarity indication or null detection.

Another type of 'multicolour' LED is shown in *Figure* 2.28. This comprises a green and a red LED mounted in a three-pin common-cathode package. This device can generate green or red colours by turning on only one LED at a time, or can generate orange and yellow ones by turning on the two LEDs in the ratios shown in the table.

A very important practical point concerns the use of 'second grade' or 'out-of-spec' devices advertised as 'bargain packs'. These devices often have forward volt drops in the range 3–10 V, and may thus be quite useless in many practical applications. *Always* test these devices before use.

Multi-LED circuits

Several LEDs can be driven from a single power source by wiring the LEDs in series as shown in *Figure* 2.29. Note that the supply voltage

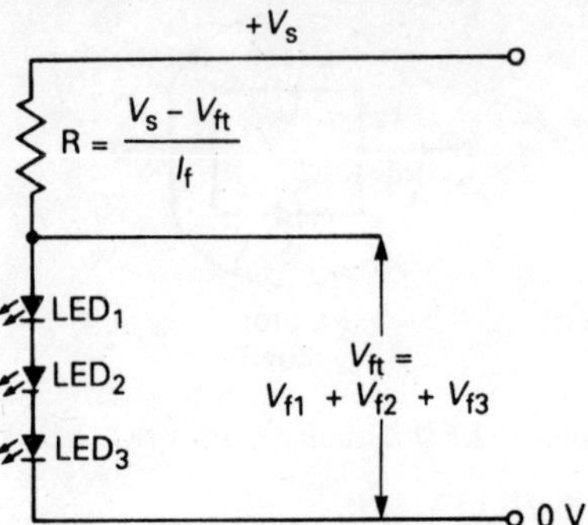

Figure 2.29 *LEDs wired in series and driven via a single current-limiting resistor*

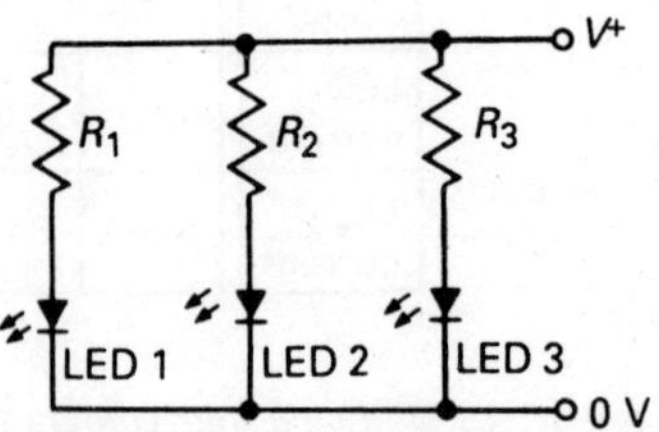

Figure 2.30 *This circuit can drive a large number of LEDs, but at the expense of high current*

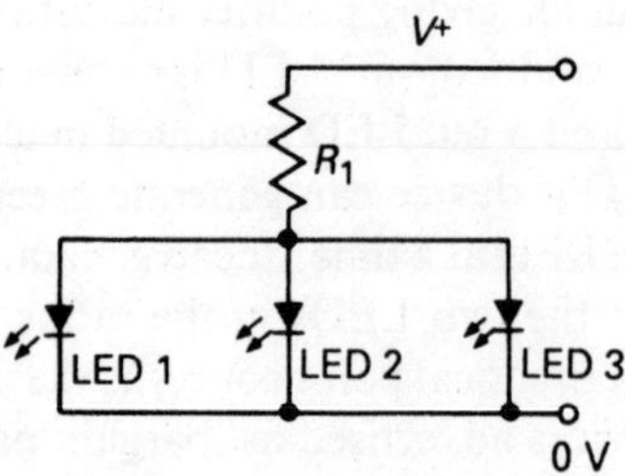

Figure 2.31 *This LED-driving circuit will not work. One LED will hog all the current*

must be significantly greater than the sum of the individual LED forward voltages. This circuit thus draws minimal total current, but is limited in the number of LEDs that it can drive. A number of these circuits can, however, be wired in parallel, so that almost any number of LEDs can be driven from a single source.

Another way of powering several LEDs is to simply wire a number of the *Figure* 2.21 circuits in parallel, as shown in *Figure* 2.30. Note, however, that this is very wasteful of current (which is equal to the sum of the individual LED currents).

Figure 2.31 shows a 'what *not* to do' circuit. This design will not work correctly because inevitable differences in LED forward voltage characteristics will usually cause one LED to 'hog' most of the available current, leaving little or none for the remaining LEDs.

LED-control circuits

The three most widely used types of visible-output LED-control circuits are (ignoring those used for alphanumeric LED control) those used for LED 'flashing', for LED 'sequencing', and for LED 'dot' or 'bar' analogue-value indication.

'Flasher' circuits turn a LED repeatedly on and off, to give an eye-catching display action; they may control a single LED or may control two LEDs in such a way that one turns on as the other turns off and vice versa. 'Sequencer' circuits drive a chain of LEDs in such a way that each LED in the chain is switched on and off in a time-controlled sequence, so that a ripple of light seems to run along the chain. Finally, analogue-value indicator circuits drive a chain of linearly spaced LEDs in such a way that the length of chain that is illuminated is proportional to the analogue value of a voltage applied to the input of the driver circuit, e.g. so that the circuit acts like an analogue voltmeter.

Simple LED-flasher circuits

One of the simplest types of LED display circuit is the LED flasher, in which a single LED repeatedly switches alternately on and off, usually at a rate of one or two flashes per second. A two-LED flasher is a simple modification of this circuit, but is arranged so that one LED switches on when the other switches off, and vice versa. To complete this look at simple LED circuits, *Figures* 2.32 and 2.33 show practical examples of two-LED flasher circuits (readers looking for more complex LED display circuits will find stacks of them in the author's *Optoelectronics Circuits Manual*, available from Butterworth-Heinemann Ltd.)

Figure 2.32 shows the practical circuit of a two-transistor two-LED

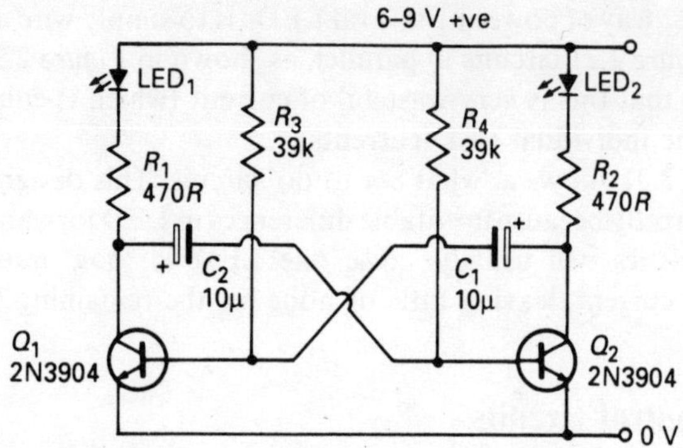

Figure 2.32 *Transistor two-LED flasher circuit operates at 1 flash per second*

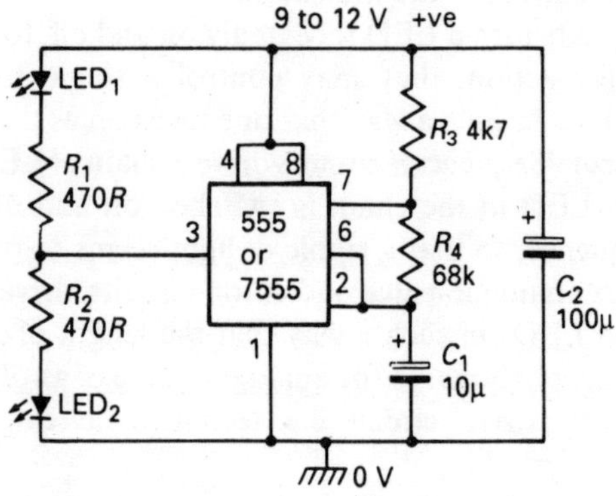

Figure 2.33 *IC two-LED flasher circuit operates at about 1 flash per second*

flasher, which can be converted to single-LED operation by simply replacing the unwanted LED with a short circuit. Here, Q_1 and Q_2 are wired as a 1 cycle-per-second astable multivibrator, with switching rates controlled via C_1–R_3 and C_2–R_4.

Finally, *Figure* 2.33 shows an IC version of the two-LED flasher. This design is based on the faithful old 555 timer chip or its more modern CMOS counterpart, the 7555. The IC is wired in the astable mode, with its time constant determined by C_1 and R_4. The action is such that output pin-3 of the IC alternately switches between the ground and the positive supply voltage levels, alternately shorting out or disabling one or other of the two LEDs. The circuit can be converted to single-LED operation by omitting the unwanted LED and its associated current-limiting resistor.

Photodiodes

When p–n silicon junctions are reverse-biased their leakage currents and impedances are inherently photosensitive; they act as very high impedances under dark conditions and as low impedances under bright ones. Normal diodes have their junctions shrouded in opaque material to stop this unwanted effect, but photodiodes are specially manufactured to exploit it, and have their junctions encased in translucent material. Some photodiodes are designed to respond to visible light, and some to infra-red (IR) light. In use, the photodiode is simply reverse-biased and the output voltage is taken from across a series-connected load resistor, which may be connected between the diode and ground, as in *Figure* 2.34*a*, or between the diode and the positive supply line, as in *Figure* 2.34*b*.

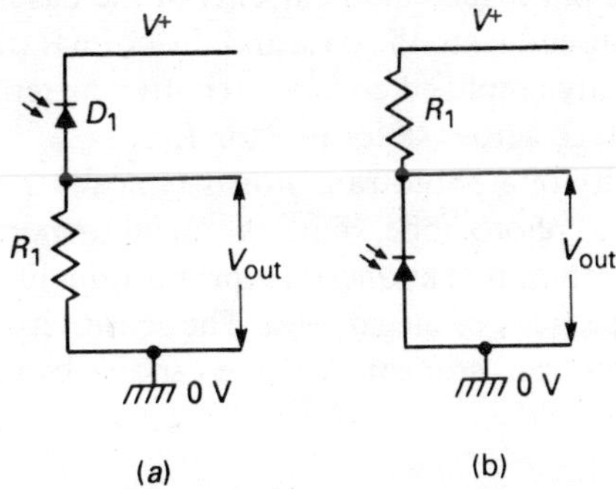

Figure 2.34 *Alternative ways of using a photodiode*

Photodiodes have a far lower light sensitivity than cadmium sulphide LDRs, but give a far quicker response to changes in light level. Generally, LDRs are ideal for use in slow-acting direct-coupled 'light-level' sensing applications, while photodiodes are ideal for use in fast-acting a.c.-coupled 'signalling' applications. Typical photodiode applications include IR remote-control circuits, IR 'beam' switches and alarm circuits, and photographic 'flash' slave circuits, etc.

Phototransistors

Ordinary silicon transistors are made from an n–p–n (or p–n–p) sandwich, and thus inherently contain a pair of photosensitive junctions. Not surprisingly, they are also available in phototransistor form, and use the standard symbol of *Figure* 2.35.

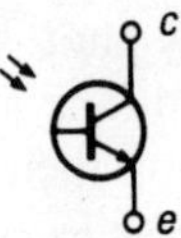

Figure 2.35 *Phototransistor symbol*

Figure 2.36 shows three different basic ways of using a phototransistor. In each case the base–collector junction of the transistor is effectively reverse-biased and thus acts as a photodiode. In *Figure* 2.36*a* the transistor base is grounded, and the device acts as a simple photodiode. In *Figures* 2.36*b* and 2.36*c* the base terminal is open circuit and the photogenerated currents of the base–collector junction thus feed directly into the base and, by normal transistor action, generate a greatly amplified collector–emitter current that produces an output voltage across series resistor R_1.

The sensitivity of a phototransistor is typically 100 times greater than that of a photodiode, but its useful maximum operating frequency (a few hundred kilohertz) is proportionally lower than that of a photodiode (tens of megahertz). The sensitivity (and operating speed) of a phototransistor can be made variable by wiring a variable

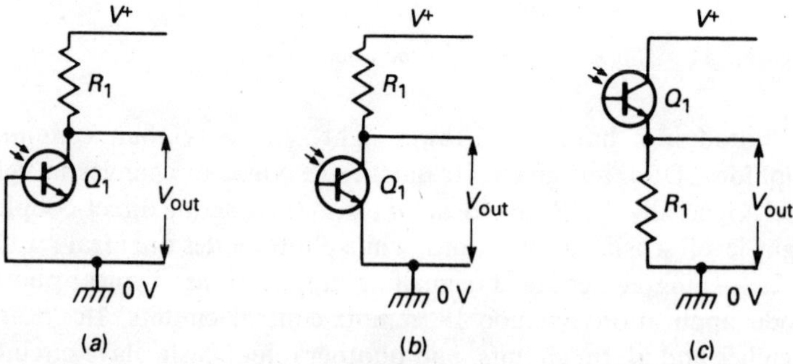

Figure 2.36 *Alternative ways of using a phototransistor*

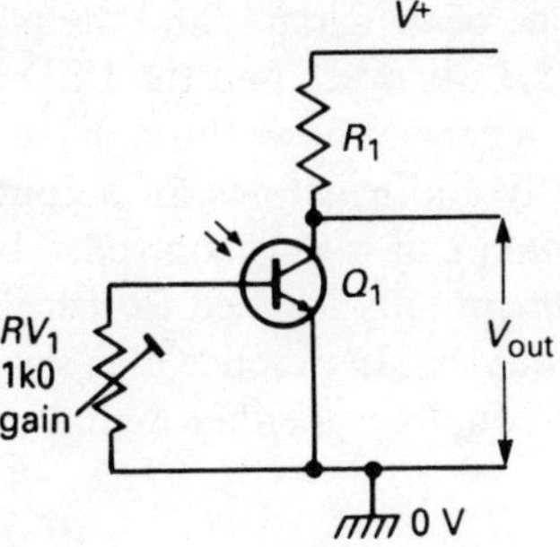

Figure 2.37 *Variable-sensitivity phototransistor circuit*

resistor between the base and emitter, as shown in *Figure* 2.37; with RV_1 open circuit, phototransistor operation is obtained; with RV_1 short circuit, photodiode operation occurs.

Note in the *Figure* 2.34–37 'opto' circuits that, in practice, the R_1 'load' value is usually chosen on a compromise basis, since the circuit voltage gain increases but the useful operating bandwidth decreases as the R_1 value is increased. Also, the R_1 value must, in many applications, be chosen to bring the photosensitive device into its linear operating region.

Optocouplers

An optocoupler is a device housing an LED (usually an IR type) and a matching phototransistor (or photodiode); the two devices are closely optically coupled and mounted in a light-excluding housing. *Figure* 2.38 shows a basic optocoupler 'usage' circuit. The LED is

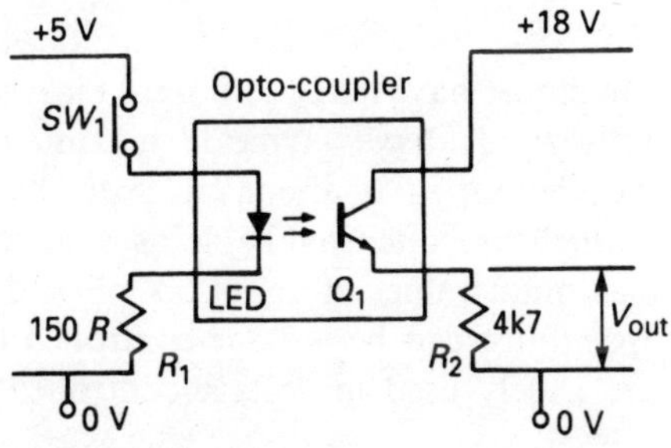

Figure 2.38 *Basic optocoupling circuit*

used as the input side of the circuit, and the phototransistor as the output. Normally, SW_1 is open, and the LED and Q_1 are thus off. When SW_1 is closed a current flows through the LED via R_1, and Q_1 is turned on optically and generates an output voltage across R_2. Note that the output circuit is thus controlled by the input one, but that the two circuits are fully isolated electrically (this is the major benefit of the optocoupler). In practice, this simple circuit can easily be modified to give coupling of either digital or analogue signals.

Varicap diode circuits

Finally, to complete this look at special diode circuits, *Figure* 2.39 shows a basic varicap diode usage circuit. The diode is reverse-biased via R_1 and a stable external control voltage (usually variable from zero to about 10 V), and the varicap is coupled to an external circuit via blocking capacitor C_1. The varicap capacitance is maximum at zero bias, and decreases as bias is increased.

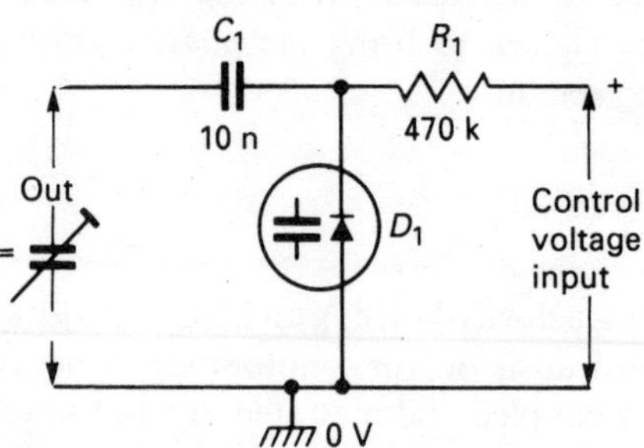

Figure 2.39 *Basic varicap diode usage circuit*

Ordinary silicon diodes have maximum (zero bias) capacitances of a few picofarads and have typical maximum-to-minimum capacitance ratios (Cap ratios) of about 2:1. Specially manufactured varicap diodes (which are often available as a matched pair) are available with maximum values of about 500 pF and Cap ratios of 20:1 (i.e. the capacitance can be voltage-controlled from 25 pF to 500 pF). They are widely used in voltage-controlled tuning applications, etc.

3 Transistor principles

The bipolar transistor is one of the most important elements used in modern electronics, and forms the basis of most linear and digital integrated circuits (ICs) and operational amplifiers (op-amps), etc. In its discrete form it can function as either a digital switch or as a linear amplifier, and is available in many low-, medium-, and high-power forms.

This chapter looks at bipolar transistor characteristics, and presents a round-up of basic application configurations; Chapters 4–7 take detailed looks at many practical linear and digital application circuits.

Bipolar transistor basics

A bipolar transistor is a three-terminal (base, emitter, and collector) current-amplifying device, in which a small input current can be used to control the magnitude of a much larger output current. The term 'bipolar' indicates that the device is made from semiconductor materials in which conduction relies on both positive and negative (majority and minority) charge carriers.

A practical transistor is, in essence, made from a three-layer sandwich of n-type and p-type semiconductor materials, with the *base* terminal connected to the central layer, and the *collector* and *emitter* terminals connected to the outer layers. Thus, the device may use an n–p–n construction sandwich, as shown in *Figure* 3.1*a*, in which event it is known as an npn transistor and uses the standard symbol of *Figure* 3.1*b*, or it may use a p–n–p structure, as shown in *Figure* 3.2*a*, in which event it is known as a pnp transitor and uses the standard symbol of *Figure* 3.2*b*.

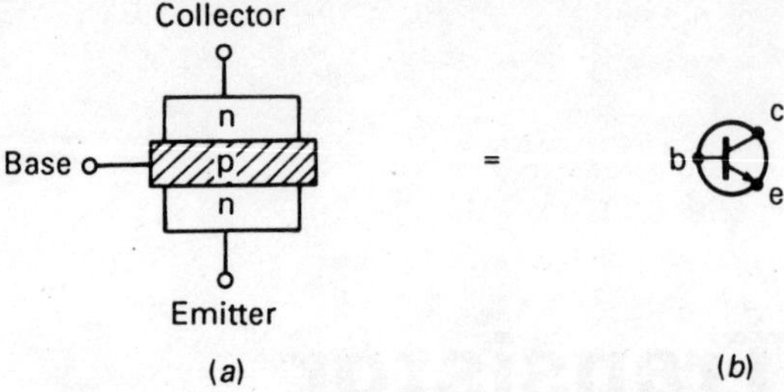

Figure 3.1 *Basic construction (a) and symbol (b) of npn transistor*

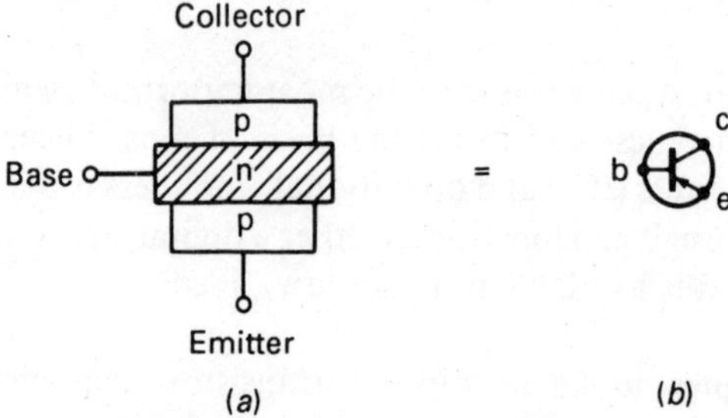

Figure 3.2 *Basic construction (a) and symbol (b) of pnp transistor*

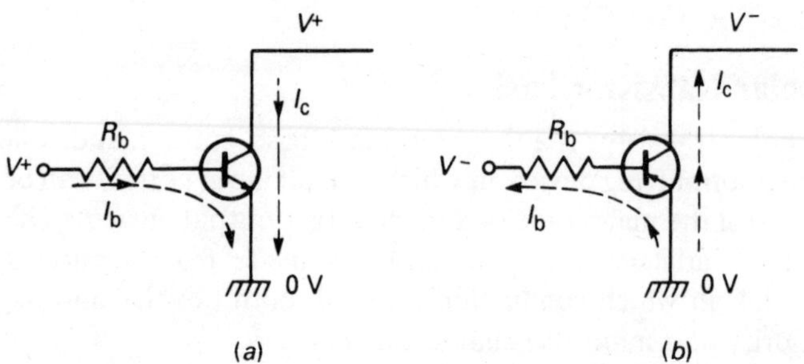

Figure 3.3 *Polarity connections to (a) npn and (b) pnp transistors*

In use, npn and pnp transistors each need a power supply of the appropriate polarity, as shown in *Figure* 3.3. An npn device must have a supply that makes the collector positive to the emitter; its 'output', or main-terminal signal current, flows from collector to emitter and has its amplitude controlled by an input current that flows from base to emitter via an external current-limiting resistor

(R_b) and a positive bias voltage. A pnp transistor must have a negative supply; the main-terminal current flows from emitter to collector, and is controlled by an emitter–base input current that flows to a negative bias voltage.

A wide variety of bipolar transistor types is available. *Figure* 3.4 lists the basic characteristics of two typical general-purpose low-power types, the 2N3904 (npn) and the 2N3906 (pnp), which are each housed in a TO-92 plastic case. Note from this list that $V_{CEO(max)}$ is the maximum voltage that may be applied between the collector and emitter when the base is open-circuit, and $V_{CBO(max)}$ is the maximum voltage that may be applied between the collector and base when the emitter is open-circuit. $I_{c(max)}$ is the maximum *mean* current that can be allowed to flow through the collector terminal of the device, and $P_{T(max)}$ is the maximum *mean* power that the device can dissipate, without the use of an external heat sink, at normal room temperature.

One of the most important parameters of the transistor is its forward current transfer ratio, or h_{fe}; this is the current-gain or output/input current ratio of the device (typically 100–300 in the two devices listed). Finally, the f_T figure indicates the available gain/bandwidth product frequency of the device, i.e., if the transistor is used in a voltage feedback configuration that provides a voltage gain of × 100, the bandwidth will be 100th of the f_T figure, but if the voltage gain is reduced to × 10 the bandwidth will increase to $f_T/10$, etc.

Parameter	2N3904	2N3906
Transistor type	npn	pnp
I_C (max)	200 mA	−200 mA
$V_{CEO\ (max)}$	40 V	−40 V
$V_{CBO\ (max)}$	60 V	−40 V
$P_{T\ (max)}$	310 mW	310 mW
h_{fe} (= a.c. beta)	100–300	100–300
f_T (typ) = gain/bandwidth product	300 MHz	250 MHz

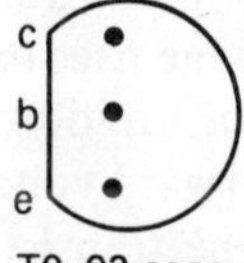

Figure 3.4 *General characteristics and outlines of the 2N3904 and 2N3906 low-power transistors*

Transistor characteristics

To get the maximum value from a transistor, the user needs an understanding of both the static and the dynamic characteristics of the device. By 'static' characteristics we mean the way the device appears, between individual terminals, under d.c. conditions or when looked at with an analogue ohmmeter.

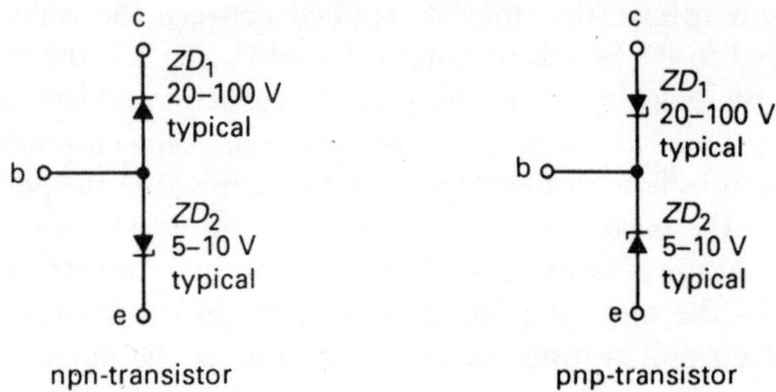

Figure 3.5 *Static equivalent circuits of npn and pnp transistors*

Figure 3.5 shows the static equivalent circuits of npn and pnp transistors. Each device is equal to a pair of reverse-connected zener diodes wired in series between the collector and emitter terminals, with the base terminal wired to their 'common' point. This equivalent circuit can in fact be inferred from the transistor's basic construction (shown in *Figures* 3.1 and 3.2). A diode is inherently formed at each n–p or p–n semiconductor junction, and when sufficiently reverse biased it inevitably reaches an avalanche point, and thus acts as a zener diode. In most low-power transistors the base–emitter junction has a typical zener value in the range 5–10 V, while the base–collector junction has a typical zener value in the range 20–100 V.

Thus, the transistor's base–emitter junction acts like an ordinary diode when forward-biased and as a zener when reverse-biased. If the transistor is a silicon type its forward-biased junction passes near-zero current until the bias voltage rises to about 600 mV, but beyond this value the current increases rapidly. When forward biased by a fixed current, the junction's forward voltage has a thermal coefficient of about −2 mV/°C. When the transistor is used with the emitter open-circuit, the base–collector junction acts like that just described, except for a greater zener value. If the transistor is used with its base

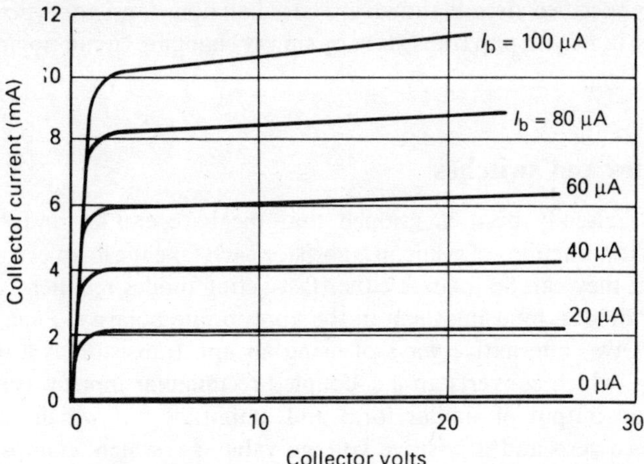

Figure 3.6 *Typical transfer characteristics of low-power npn transistor with* h_{fe} *value of 100 nominal*

open-circuit, the collector–emitter path acts like a zener diode wired in series with an ordinary diode.

The transistor's dynamic characteristics can be understood with the aid of *Figure* 3.6, which shows the typical forward transconductance characteristics of a low-power npn silicon transistor with a nominal h_{fe} value of 100. Thus, when the base current (I_b) is zero, the transistor passes only a very small collector leakage current. When the collector voltage is greater than a few hundred millivolts the collector current value is almost directly proportional to base current, and is little influenced by the collector voltage value. The device can thus be used as a constant-current generator by feeding a fixed bias current into the base, or can be used as an excellent linear amplifier by superimposing the input signal on a nominal input current (as shown later in this chapter).

Practical applications

The transistor can be used in a vast range of useful applications, and in a broad range of different basic circuit configurations. The remainder of this chapter presents a brief summary of the most important of these basic configurations. Unless otherwise mentioned, all the specified circuits shown are based on npn transistor types, but can be used with pnp transistors by simply changing circuit polarities, etc.

Diodes and switches

It has already been mentioned that the base–emitter and base–collector junctions of a silicon transistor each take the form of a zener diode; they can be used as either fast-acting diodes/rectifiers, or as zener diodes, by using them in the appropriate polarity. *Figure* 3.7 shows two alternative ways of using an npn transistor as a diode clamp, which converts an a.c.-coupled rectangular input waveform into an output of similar form and amplitude but which swings between zero and a positive voltage value, i.e. which 'clamps' the output signal to the zero-volts reference point. In practice, it is best to use the base–collector diode in this type of application, as its zener value is higher than that of the base–emitter junction.

Figure 3.8 shows how an npn transistor can be used as a zener diode

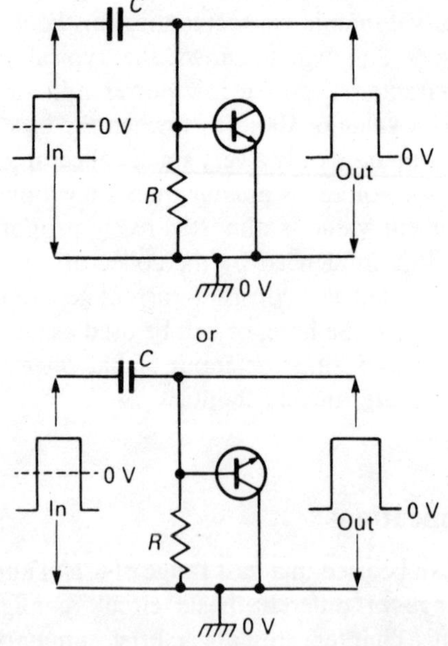

Figure 3.7 *Clamping diode circuit, using npn transistor as diode*

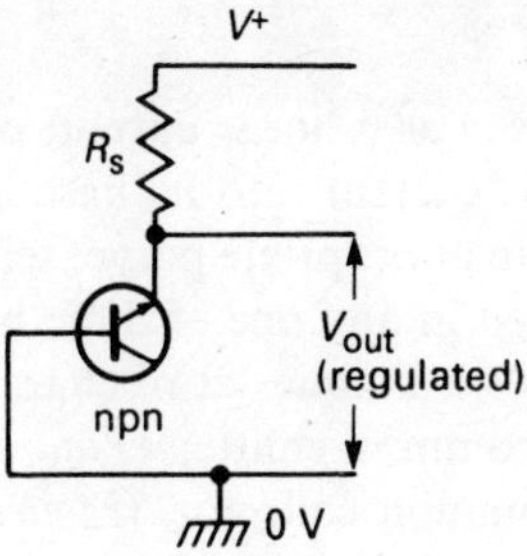

Figure 3.8 *A transistor used as a zener diode*

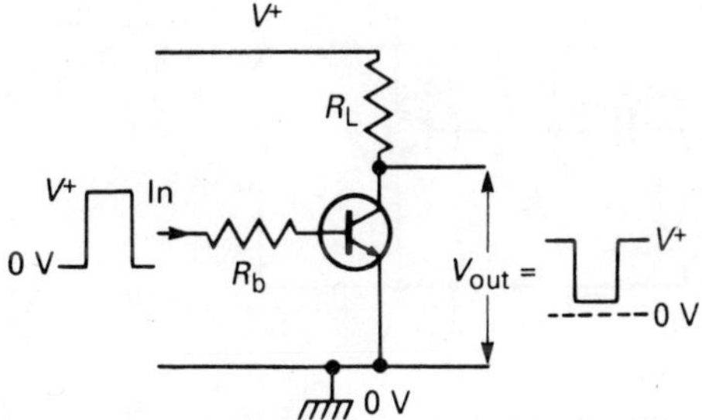

Figure 3.9 *Transistor switch or digital inverter*

that converts an unregulated supply voltage into a fixed-value regulated output with a typical value in the range 5–10 V, depending on the invididual transistor. Only the base–emitter junction is suitable for use in this application.

Figure 3.9 shows a transistor used as a simple electronic switch or digital inverter. Its base is driven (via R_b) by a digital input that is at either zero volts or at a significant positive value, and load R_L is connected between the collector and the positive supply rail. When the input voltage is zero the transistor switch is cut off, so zero current flows through the load, and the full supply voltage is available between collector and emitter. When the input is high the transistor switch is driven fully on, so maximum current flows in the load and near-zero volts (usually a few hundred millivolts) is developed between collector and emitter. The output voltage is an inverted form of the input signal.

Linear amplifiers

A transistor can be used as a linear current or voltage amplifier by feeding a suitable bias current into its base and then applying the input signal between an appropriate pair of terminals. The transistor can in this case be used in any one of three basic operating modes, each of which provides a unique set of characteristics. These three modes are known as 'common-emitter' (*Figure* 3.10), 'common-base' (*Figure* 3.11), and 'common-collector' (*Figure* 3.12).

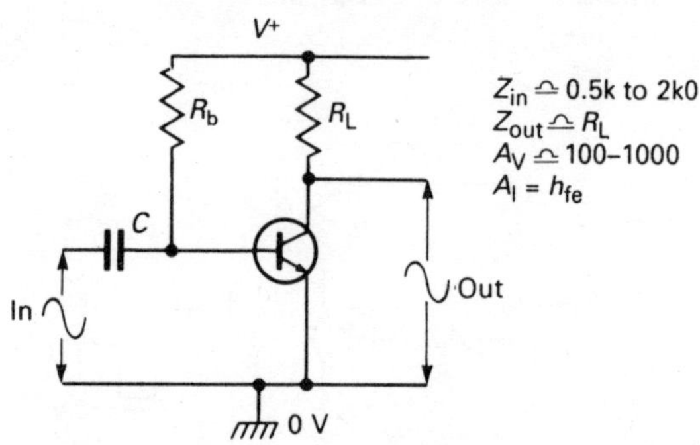

Figure 3.10 *Common-emitter linear amplifier*

In the common-emitter circuit of *Figure* 3.10, load resistor R_L is wired between the collector and positive supply line, and a bias current is fed into the base via R_b, whose value is chosen to set the collector at a quiescent half-supply voltage value (to provide maximum undistorted output signal swings). The input signal is applied between base and emitter via C, and the output signal (which is phase-inverted relative to the input) is taken between the collector and emitter. This circuit gives a medium-value input impedance and a fairly high overall voltage gain.

In the common-base circuit of *Figure* 3.11 the base is biased via R_b and is a.c.-decoupled (or a.c.-grounded) via C_b. The input signal is effectively applied between the emitter and base via C_1, and the amplified but non-inverted output signal is effectively taken from between the collector and base. This circuit features good voltage gain, near-unity current gain, and a very low input impedance.

In the common-collector circuit of *Figure* 3.12 the collector is shorted to the positive supply rail and is thus effectively at ground

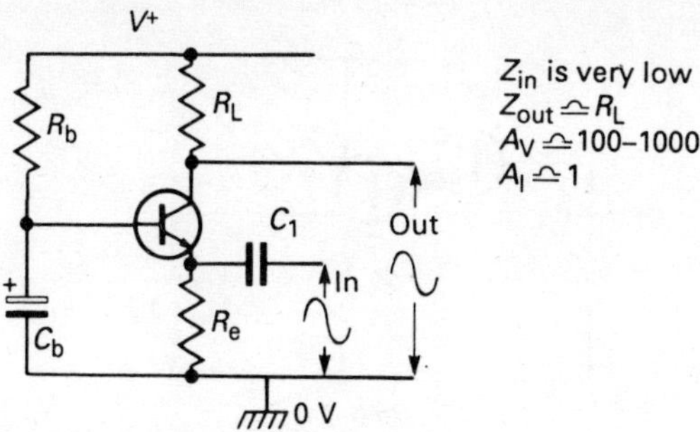

Figure 3.11 *Common-base linear amplifier*

impedance level. The input signal is applied between base and ground ('collector'), and the non-inverted output is taken from between emitter and ground ('collector'). This circuit gives near-unity overall voltage gain, so the output 'follows' (but is about 600 mV less than) the input signal; the circuit is thus known as a d.c.-voltage follower, or as an 'emitter' follower.

A major feature of the emitter follower circuit is its very high input impedance, this being equal to the product of the R_L and h_{fe} values. An ultra-high input impedance can be obtained by replacing the single transistor of *Figure* 3.12 with a pair of transistors connected in the Darlington or Super-Alpha mode, as in *Figure* 3.13. Here, the emitter current of the input transistor feeds directly into the base of the output transistor, and the pair act like a single transistor with an overall h_{fe} value equal to the product of the two individual h_{fe} values,

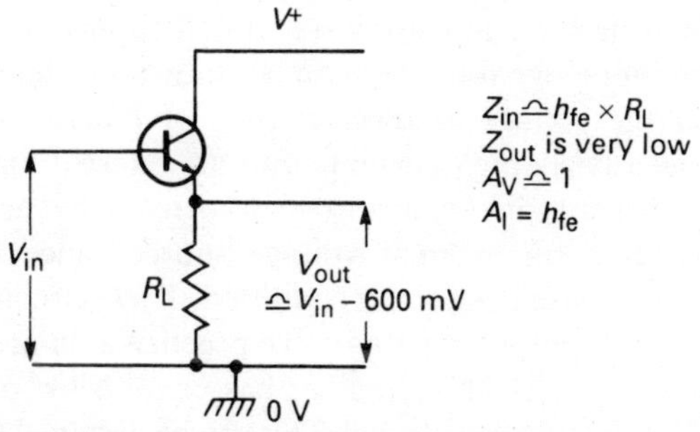

Figure 3.12 *D.c. common-collector linear amplifier or voltage follower*

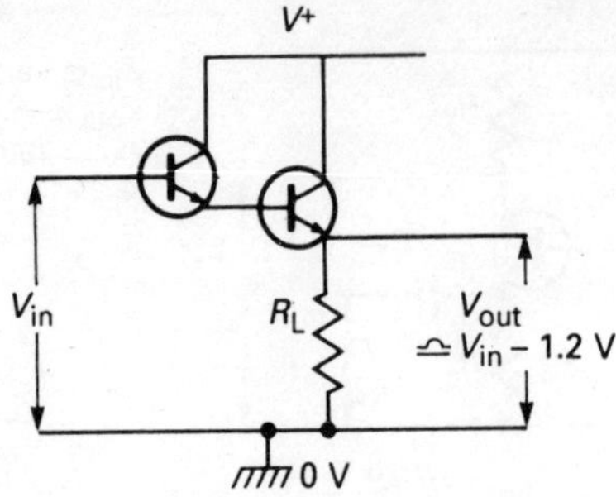

Figure 3.13 *Darlington or Super-Alpha d.c. emitter follower*

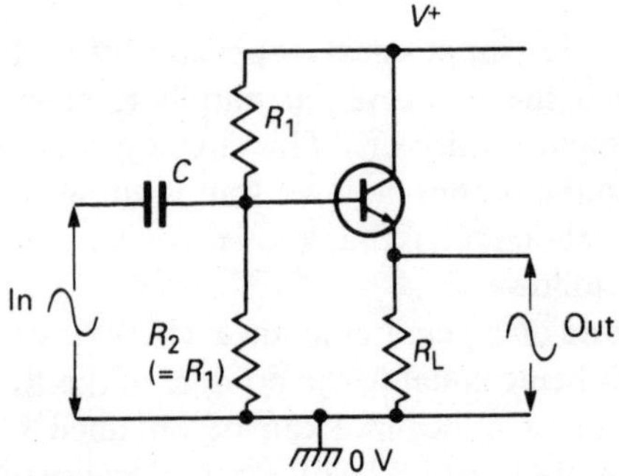

Figure 3.14 *A.c. common-collector amplifier or voltage follower*

i.e. if each transistor has an h_{fe} value of 100, the pair act like a single transistor with an h_{fe} of 10 000.

The *Figure* 3.12 voltage follower circuit can be modified for a.c. use by simply biasing the transistor base to half-supply volts and a.c.-coupling the input signal to the base, as shown in *Figure* 3.14.

Note that the voltage follower circuits of *Figures* 3.12–14 can 'source' or feed fairly high currents into an external load via their emitters, but can not 'sink' or absorb high currents that are applied to the emitters from an external voltage source, since the emitter becomes reverse-biased under this condition. These circuits thus have only a 'unilateral' output capability. In practice a 'bilateral' output characteristic (in which the amplifier has equal 'sink' and 'source' output capabilities) is often needed. This can be obtained by using the complementary emitter follower circuit of *Figure* 3.15, in which the

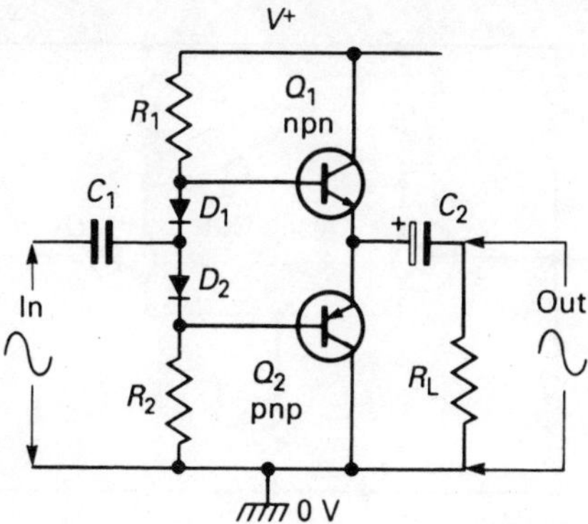

Figure 3.15 *Complementary or 'bilateral' a.c. emitter follower circuit*

series-connected npn–pnp pair of transistors are biased (via the R_1–D_1–D_2–R_2 network) to pass a small quiescent current. In use, Q_1 can provide large source currents, and Q_2 can absorb large sink currents.

Phase splitters

Transistor linear amplifiers can be made to act as active filters or as oscillators, etc., by connecting suitable feedback networks between their inputs and outputs. Another useful linear amplifier application is that of a phase splitter, which provides a pair of anti-phase output signals from a single input signal. *Figures* 3.16 and 3.17 show circuits of this type.

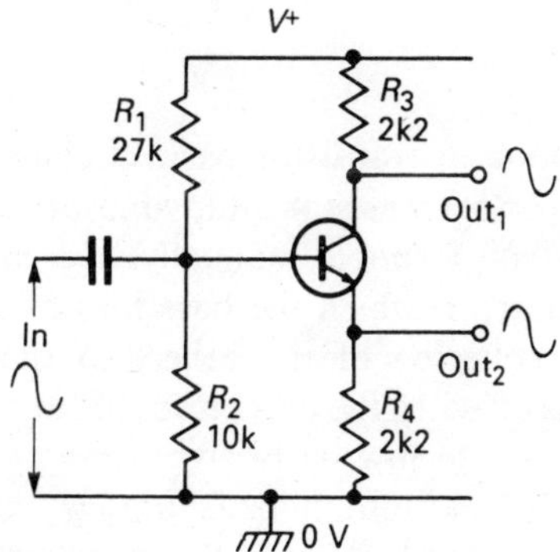

Figure 3.16 *Phase splitter*

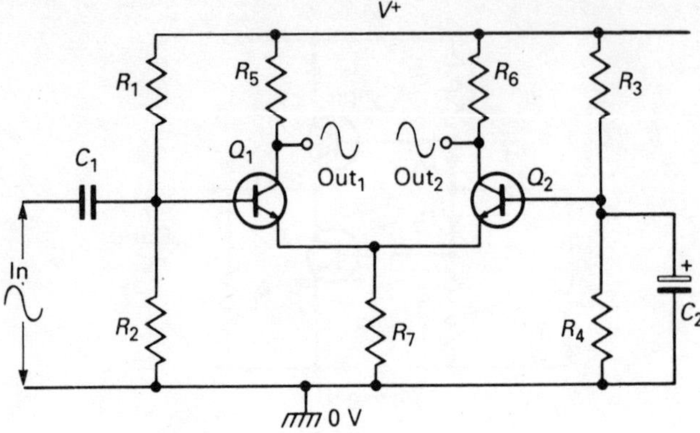

Figure 3.17 *Long-tailed pair phase splitter*

In the *Figure* 3.16 circuit the transistor is wired as a common-emitter amplifier with virtually 100 per cent negative feedback applied via emitter resistor R_4, which has the same value as collector resistor R_3. A unity-gain inverted signal is thus available at Out_1, and a unity-gain non-inverted signal appears at Out_2.

The *Figure* 3.17 phase splitter circuit is known as a long-tailed pair, since the two transistors share a common emitter-feedback resistor (R_7). The basic circuit action is such that a rising signal on Q_1 base causes the R_7 voltage to rise and thus reduce the Q_2 bias voltage, and vice versa, thus causing anti-phase output signals to be generated on Q_1 and Q_2 collectors.

Multivibrators

To complete this look at transistor basic circuits, *Figures* 3.18–21 show four basic types of transistor multivibrator circuit. The *Figure* 3.18 design is that of a simple manually triggered cross-coupled bistable multivibrator, in which the base bias of each transistor is derived from the collector of the other, so that one transistor automatically turns off when the other turns on, and vice versa. Thus, the output can be driven low by briefly turning Q_2 off via S_2; the circuit automatically locks into this state until Q_1 is turned off via S_1, at which point the output locks into the high state, and so on.

Figure 3.19 shows a monostable multivibrator or one-shot pulse

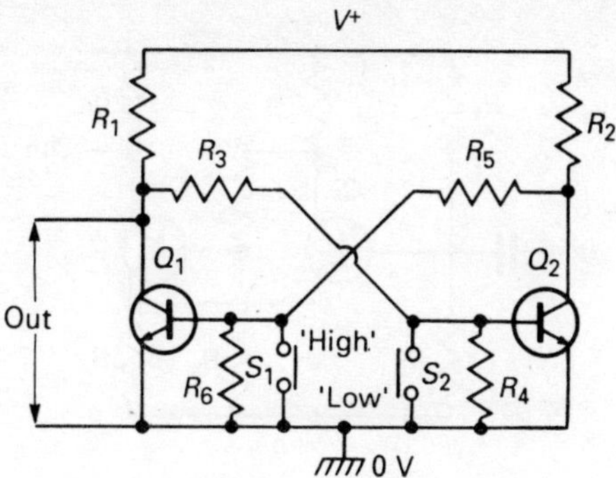

Figure 3.18 *Manually triggered bistable multivibrator*

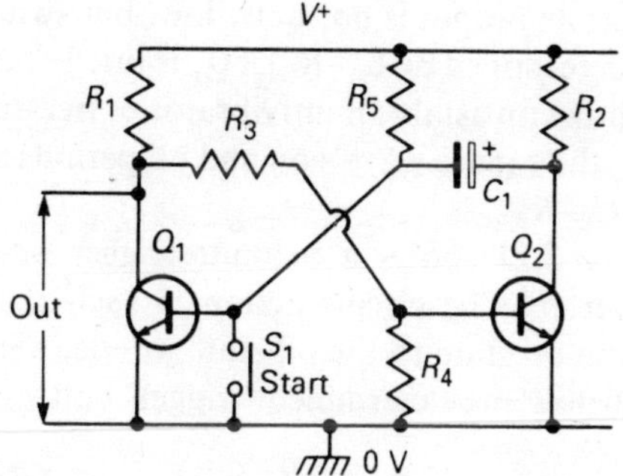

Figure 3.19 *Manually triggered monostable multivibrator*

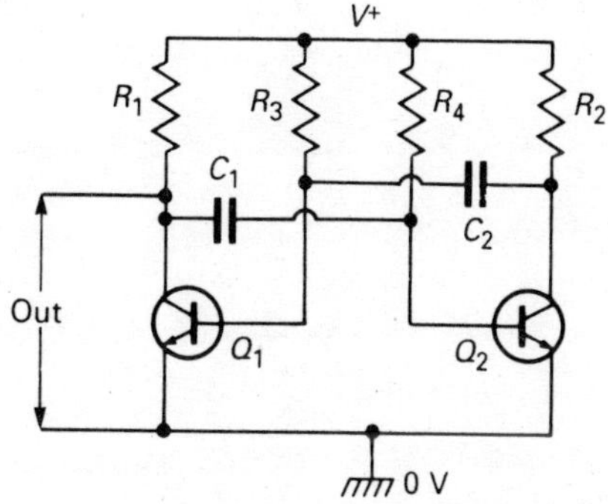

Figure 3.20 *Astable multivibrator or free-running square-wave generator*

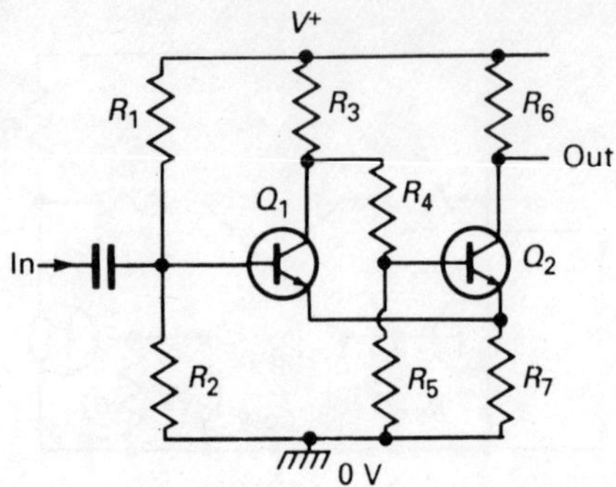

Figure 3.21 *Schmitt trigger or sine-to-square waveform converter*

generator circuit; its output is normally low, but switches high for a pre-set period (determined by C_1–R_5) if Q_1 is briefly turned off via S_1.

Figure 3.20 shows an astable multivibrator or free-running square-wave generator; the square wave's on and off periods are determined by C_1–R_4 and C_2–R_3.

Finally, *Figure* 3.21 shows a Schmitt trigger or sine-to-square waveform converter. The circuit action is such that Q_2 switches abruptly from the on state to the off state, or vice versa, as Q_1 base goes above or below pre-determined 'trigger' voltage levels.

4 Transistor amplifier circuits

Chapter 3 gave the reader an introductory outline of bipolar transistor characteristics, and gave a round-up of popular application configurations. This present chapter looks at practical ways of using the transistor in the three basic amplifier configurations, which are shown in *Figure* 4.1 and have their performances summarized in *Figure* 4.2. Note that the common-collector amplifier gives near-unity overall voltage gain and has a high input impedance, while the common-emitter and common-base amplifiers both give high values of voltage gain but have medium to low values of input impedance.

This chapter is divided into three major sections, each presenting a variety of circuits based on one of the three basic amplifier configurations. It starts off by dealing with common-collector amplifier circuits.

Common-collector amplifier circuits

The common-collector amplifier (also known as the grounded-collector amplifier or emitter follower or voltage follower) can be used in a wide variety of digital and analogue amplifier applications. This section starts off by looking at 'digital' circuits.

Digital amplifiers

Figure 4.3 shows a simple npn common-collector digital amplifier or emitter follower, in which the input signal is either low (at zero volts) or high (at a substantial positive value that is not greater than the supply rail voltage). When the input is low transistor Q_1 is fully cut off, and the output is at zero volts. When the input is high Q_1 is on and current I_L flows in load resistor R_L, thus generating an output voltage

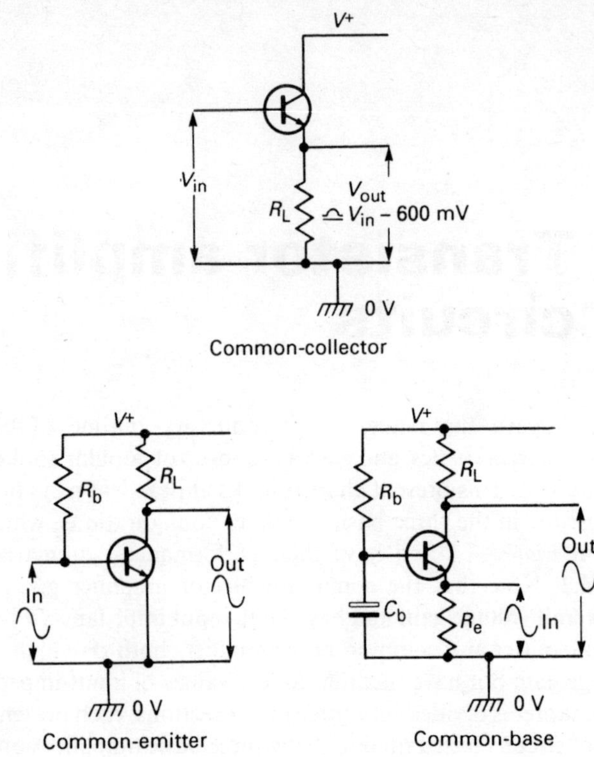

Figure 4.1 *The three basic transistor configurations*

	Common collector	Common emitter	Common base
Z_{in}	High(≏ $h_{fe} \times R_L$)	Medium (≏1k0)	Low (≏40*R*)
Z_{out}	Very low	≏ R_L	≏ R_L
A_V	≏1	High	High
A_I	≏ h_{fe}	≏ h_{fe}	≏1
Cut-off frequency	Medium	Low	High
Voltage phase shift	Zero	180°	Zero

Figure 4.2 *Comparative performances of the three basic configurations*

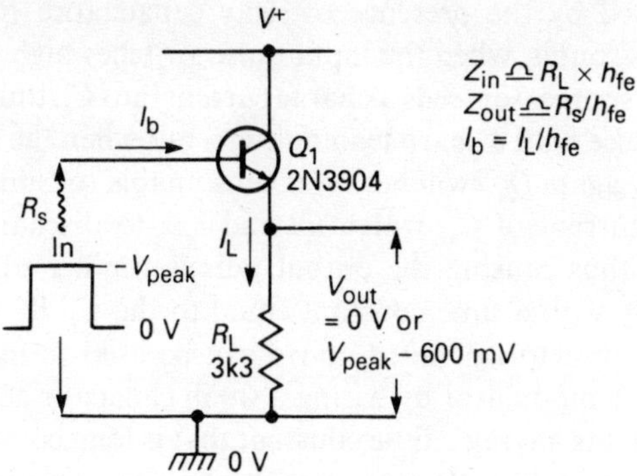

Figure 4.3 *Common-collector digital amplifier*

across R_L: intrinsic negative feedback causes this output voltage to take up a value that is one base–emitter junction volt-drop (about 600 mV) below the input voltage value. Thus, the output voltage 'follows' (but is 600 mV less than) the input voltage.

Note that this circuit's input (base) current equals the I_L value divided by the transistor's h_{fe} value (nominally 200 in the 2N3904) and that the circuit's input impedance equals the R_L value multiplied by h_{fe}, i.e., nominally 660k in the example shown. The circuit's output impedance equals the input signal source impedance (R_s) value divided by h_{fe}. Thus, the *Figure* 4.3 circuit has a high input impedance, a low output impedance, and provides unity voltage gain, and acts essentially as a unity-gain 'buffer' circuit.

If this buffer circuit is fed with sharp input pulses it may be found that its output has a deteriorated trailing edge, as shown in *Figure* 4.4.

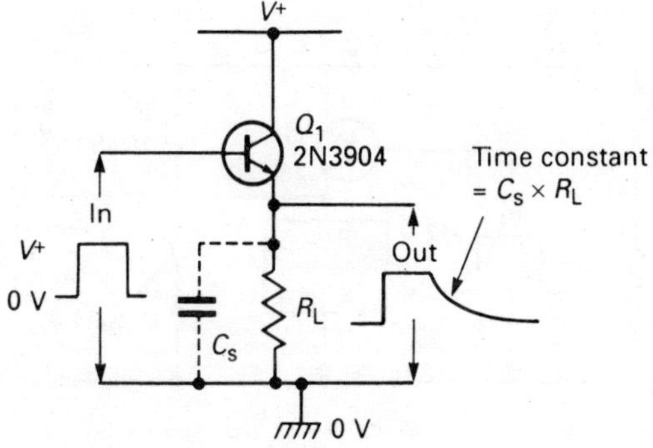

Figure 4.4 *Effect of* C_s *on the output pulses*

This is caused by the presence of stray capacitance (C_s) between emitter and ground; when the input pulse switches high Q_1 turns on and rapidly 'sources' or feeds a charge current into C_s, thus producing an output pulse with a sharp leading edge, but when the input signal switches low again Q_1 switches off is thus unable to 'sink' or absorb the charge current of C_s, which instead has to discharge via load resistor R_L, thus causing the output pulse's trailing edge to decay exponentially with a time constant equal to the C_s–R_L product.

The basic principle detailed above can be used to make an AM radio signal demodulator by wiring a small capacitor across R_L, the two components having a time constant that is long compared to the carrier wavetime but short compared to the modulation signal wavetime.

Relay drivers

The basic switching circuit of *Figure* 4.3 can be used to drive a wide variety of resistive loads, including filament lamps and LED–resistor combinations, etc., without modification, but if used to drive inductive loads such as transformers, coils, or loud speakers, etc., it must be fitted with a diode protection network to limit inductive switch-off back-e.m.f's to a safe value. One very useful type of inductor-driving circuit is the relay driver, and a number of examples of this are shown in *Figures* 4.5–9.

The npn relay driver of *Figure* 4.5 can be used in either the latching or non-latching modes, and enables the relay to be activated either via a digital input or via an electromechanical switch (SW_1); the relay turns on when the input signal is fully positive or SW_1 is closed, and turns off when the input signal is zero or SW_1 is open. Relay contacts

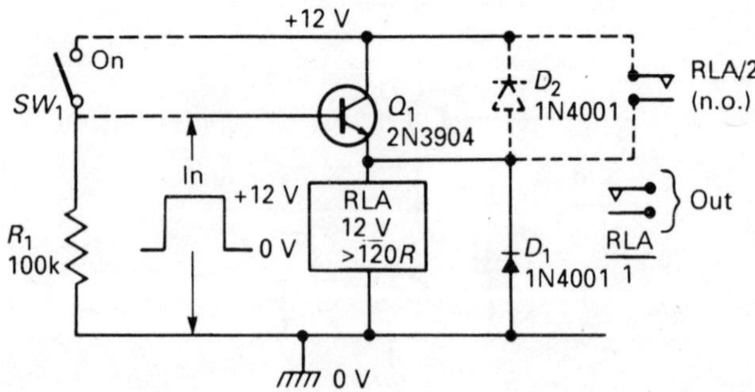

Figure 4.5 *Emitter-follower relay driver*

RLA/1 are available for external use, and the circuit can be made self-latching by wiring a spare set of normally open relay contacts (RLA/2) between Q_1's collector and emitter, as shown dotted. *Figure* 4.6 shows a pnp version of the same circuit: in this case the relay can be turned on by closing SW_1 or by applying a 'zero volt' input signal.

Note in *Figure* 4.5 that protection diode D_1 damps relay switch-off back-e.m.f.s by preventing this voltage from swinging below the zero-volts rail value; optional diode D_2 can also be used to stop this voltage going above the positive supply-rail value.

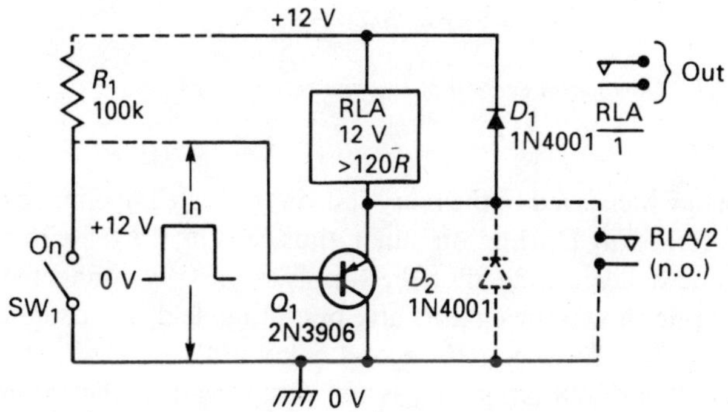

Figure 4.6 *A pnp version of the relay driver*

The *Figure* 4.5 and 4.6 circuits effectively increase the relay current sensitivity by a factor of about 200 (the h_{fe} value of Q_1), e.g. if the relay has a coil resistance of 120R and needs and activating current of 100 mA, the effective input impedance of the circuit will be 24k and the input operating current requirement will be 0.5 mA.

Circuit sensitivity can be further increased by using a Darlington or Super-Alpha pair of transistors in place of Q_1, as shown in *Figure* 4.7, but the emitter 'following' voltage of Q_2 will then be 1.2 V (two base–emitter volt drops) below the base input voltage of Q_1. This specific circuit has an input impedance of about 500k and needs an input operating current of 24 μA; C_1 protects the circuit against activation via high-impedance transient voltages, such as those induced by lightning flashes, RFI, etc.

The Darlington type of circuit is of particular value in relay-driving *C–R* time-delay designs such as those shown in *Figures* 4.8 and 4.9, in which the C_1–R_1 'divider' generates an exponentially rising or falling

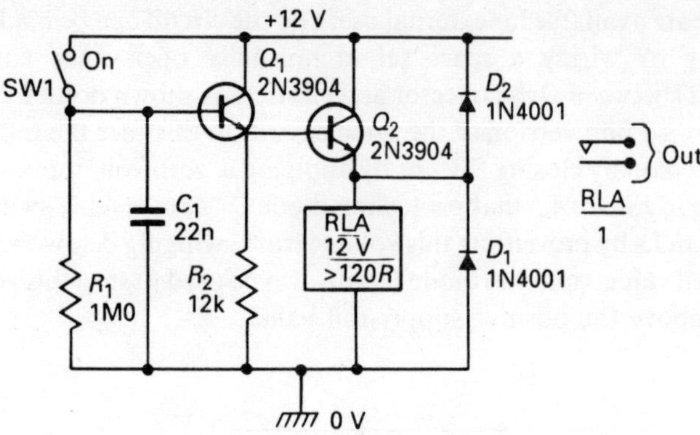

Figure 4.7 *Darlington version of the npn relay driver*

waveform which is fed to the relay coil via the high-impedance Q_1–Q_2 voltage-following Darlington buffer, thus causing the relay to change state some delayed time after the supply is initially connected: with the R_1 value shown the circuits give operating delays of roughly 0.1 s per μF of C_1 value, i.e. a 10-second delay if $C_1 = 100\,\mu$F, etc.

In the *Figure* 4.8 circuit C_1 is full discharged at the moment of power-supply connection, so the C_1–R_1 junction is initially at zero volts and the relay is off. C_1 then charges exponentially via R_1, and the resulting rising voltage is fed to the relay via Q_1–Q_2, causing it to turn on after a pre-determined delay. The *Figure* 4.9 circuit operates in a similar basic way, but in this case the C_1–R_1 junction is initially at

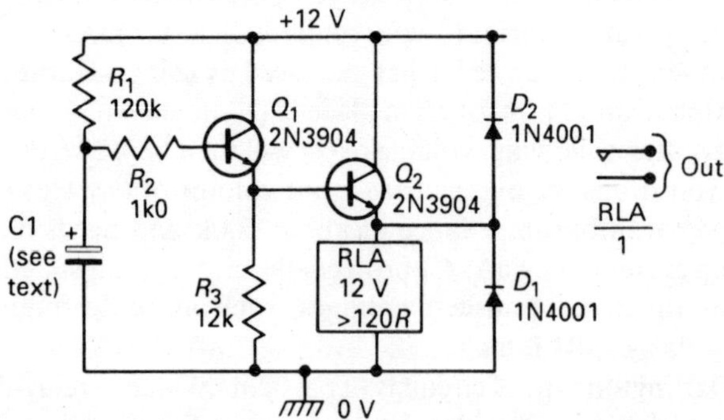

Figure 4.8 *Delayed-switch-on relay driver*

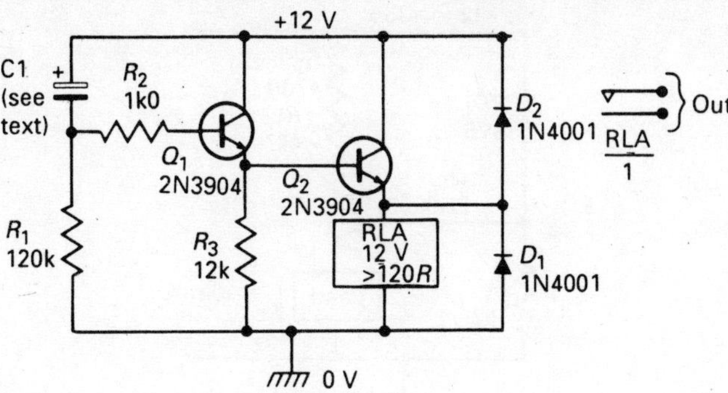

Figure 4.9 *Auto-turn-off time-delay circuit*

full supply volts and the relay is on, and the junction voltage then decays exponentially, causing the relay to turn off after a predetermined time delay.

Constant-current generators

A bipolar transistor can be used as a constant-current generator by wiring it in the basic common-collector mode and using its supply and collector terminals as the constant-current path, as shown in *Figure* 4.10. Here, R_1–ZD_1 apply a fixed 5V6 reference voltage to Q_1 base, causing 5V0 to appear (by 'follower' action) on Q_1 emitter and thus causing 5 mA to pass through R_2 via Q_1 emitter. Since Q_1's emitter and collector currents are inherently almost identical, a 5 mA

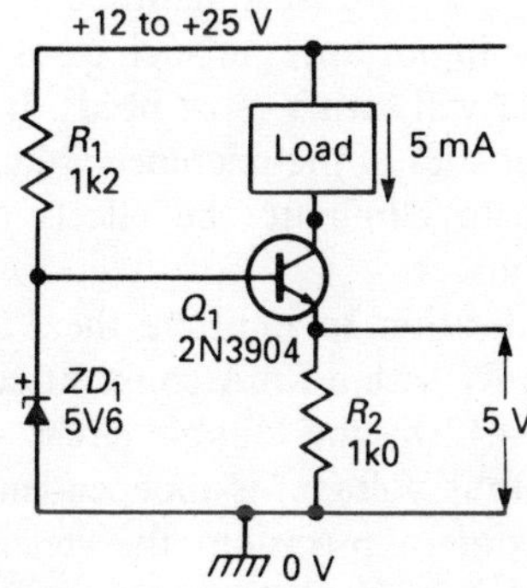

Figure 4.10 *Simple 5 mA constant-current generator*

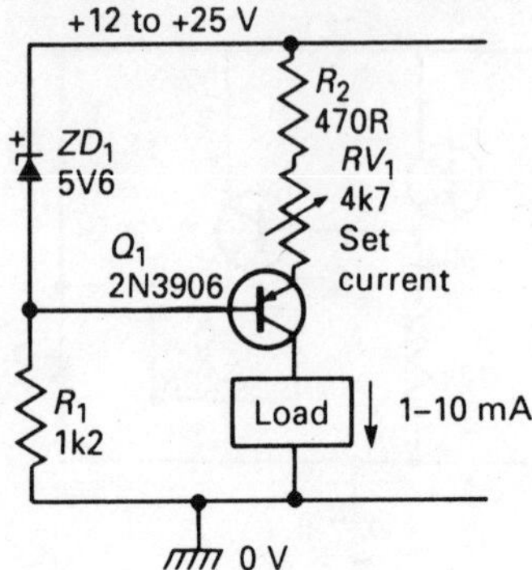

Figure 4.11 *Ground-referenced variable (1–10 mA) constant-current generator*

current also flows in any load connected between Q_1's collector and positive supply rail, almost irrespective of the load's resistance value (providing that it is not so large that Q_1 is driven into saturation); these two points thus serve as 5 mA 'constant-current' source terminals.

From the above description it can be seen that the constant-current magnitude is determined by the base reference voltage and the emitter load resistor (R_2) values, and can be altered by varying either of these. *Figure* 4.11 shows how the basic *Figure* 4.10 circuit can be 'inverted' to give a ground-referenced constant-current output that can be varied from approximately 1 mA to 10 mA via RV_1.

In most practical constant-current generator applications the circuit's most important feature is its high dynamic output impedance or 'current constancy', the precise magnitude of the constant current being of only modest importance; in such cases the basic circuits of *Figures* 4.10 and 4.11 will satisfy most needs. If greater precision is needed, the characteristics of the reference voltages of these circuits must be improved, to eliminate the effects of supply line and temperature variations.

One simple modification to improve the *Figure* 4.10 and 4.11 circuits is to replace R_1 with a 5 mA constant-current generator, as indicated in *Figure* 4.12 by the 'double circle' symbol, so that the zener current (and thus voltage) is independent of supply-voltage variations. For maximum precision, the zener reference needs a thermal coefficient of -2 mV/°C, to match that of Q_1's base–emitter junction; one way of achieving this is to use a forward-biased LED in

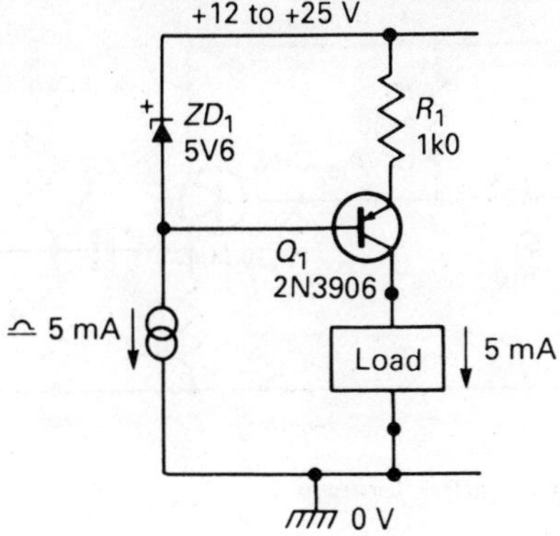

Figure 4.12 *Precision constant-current generator*

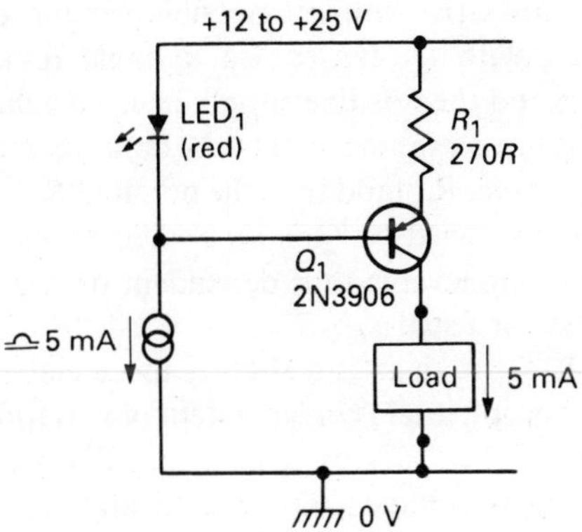

Figure 4.13 *Thermally stabilized constant-current generator, using an LED as a voltage reference*

place of the zener, as shown in *Figure* 4.13. In this case the LED voltage is roughly 2V0, so only 1V4 appears across emitter resistor R_1, which has its value reduced to about 270R to maintain the constant-current output level at 5 mA.

Analogue amplifiers

The common-collector amplifier (emitter follower) can be used as an a.c.-coupled linear (analogue) amplifier by first biasing its base to a quiescent half-supply voltage value (to accommodate maximal signal swings without distortion), and by then a.c.-coupling the input signal

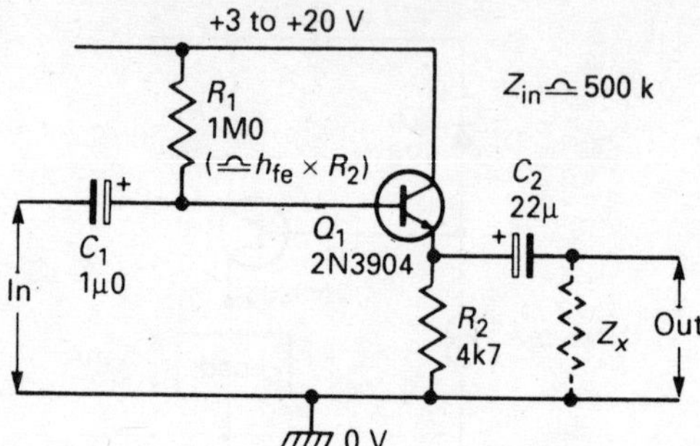

Figure 4.14 *Simple emitter follower*

to the base and taking the output signal from the emitter, as shown in *Figures* 4.14 and 4.15.

Figure 4.14 shows the simplest possible version of the analogue emitter follower, with Q_1 biased via a single resistor (R_1) wired between its base and the positive supply line. To achieve half-supply biasing, R_1 must have a value equal to the input resistance (R_{in}) of the emitter follower stage. R_{in} (and thus the nominal R_1 value) equals the R_2 value (4k7) multiplied by Q_1's h_{fe} (=200 nominal in this case). This circuit's biasing level is thus dependent on the h_{fe} value of the individual transistor used.

The *Figure* 4.15 circuit uses a slightly more elaborate method of biasing, but its biasing level is independent of variations in transistor h_{fe} values. Here R_1–R_2 act as a potential divider that applies a quiescent half-supply voltage to Q_1 base. Ideally, R_1 should equal the

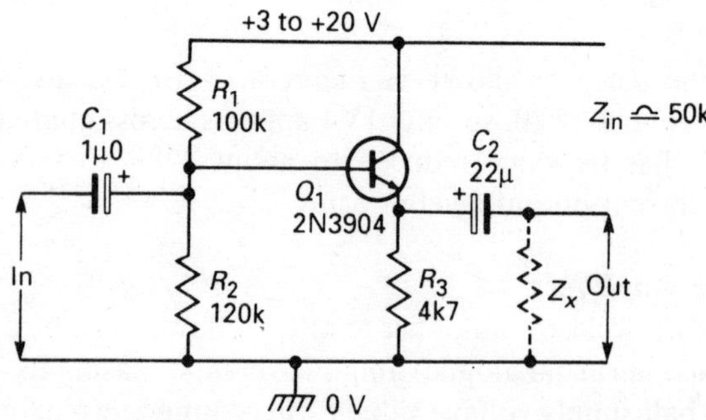

Figure 4.15 *High-stability emitter follower*

paralleled values of R_2 and R_{in}, but in practice it is adequate to simply make R_1 low relative to R_{in} and to make R_2 slightly larger than R_1.

In the *Figure* 4.14 and 4.15 circuits, the input impedance looking directly into Q_1 base equals $h_{fe} \times Z_{load}$ is equal to the combined parallel impedance of R_2 and any external load, Z_x, that is connected to the output. Thus, in these circuits the base impedance value is roughly 1M0 when Z_x is infinite. In practice, the input impedance of the complete emitter follower circuit equals the combined parallel impedance of the base impedance and the impedance of the bias network. Thus, the *Figure* 4.14 circuit gives an input impedance of about 500k, and that of *Figure* 4.15 is about 50k.

The *Figure* 4.14 and 4.15 circuits each gives a voltage gain that is slight below unity, the actual gain figures being given by:

$$A_v = Z_{load}/(Z_b + Z_{load})$$

where $Z_b = 25/I_e$ ohms, here I_e is the emitter current in milliamperes. Thus, at an operating current of 1 mA these circuits give a voltage gain of 0.995 when $Z_{load} = 4k7$, or 0.975 when $Z_{load} = 1k0$: the importance of these gain figures will be shown shortly.

Bootstrapping

The *Figure* 4.15 circuit's relatively low input impedance can be greatly increased by using the 'bootstrapping' technique of *Figure* 4.16. Here, 47k resistor R_3 is wired between the R_1–R_2 biasing network junction and Q_1 base, and the input signal is fed to Q_1 base via C_1. Note, however, that Q_1's output signal is fed back to the R_1–R_2 junction via C_2 and near-identical signal voltages thus appear at both ends of R_3; very little signal current thus flows in this resistor,

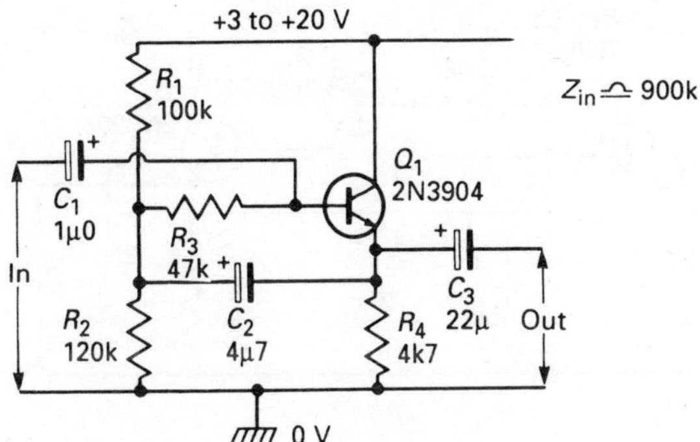

Figure 4.16 *Bootstrapped emitter follower*

which appears (to the input signal) to have a far greater impedance than its true resistance value. Suppose, for example, that the emitter follower has a voltage gain of precisely unity; in this case identical signal voltages would appear at both ends of R_3, so zero signal current would flow in this resistor, which would thus appear as an infinite impedance. The circuit's input impedance would then appear to equal R_{in}, or 1M0.

All practical emitter followers give a voltage gain slightly less than unity, and it is the precise value of gain that determines the resistor 'amplification factor', or A_R, of the circuit, as follows:

$$A_R = 1/(1 - A_v).$$

Thus, if the circuit has a gain of 0.995 (as in one example already discussed), then A_R equals 200 and the R_3 impedance is almost 10M. If, on the other hand, $A_v = 0.975$, A_R equals 40 and the R_3 impedance is only 2M0. This impedance is effectively in parallel with R_{in} so, in the former case, the complete *Figure* 4.16 circuit has an input impedance of roughly 900k.

The input impedance of the *Figure* 4.16 circuit can be increased even more by using a pair of Darlington-connected transistors in place of Q_1 and increasing the value of R_3, as shown in the example of *Figure* 4.17, which gives a measured input impedance of about 3M3.

An even greater input impedance can be obtained by using the bootstrapped 'complementary feedback pair' circuit of *Figure* 4.18, which gives an input impedance of about 10M. In this case Q_1 and Q_2 are both wired as common emitter amplifiers, but operate with

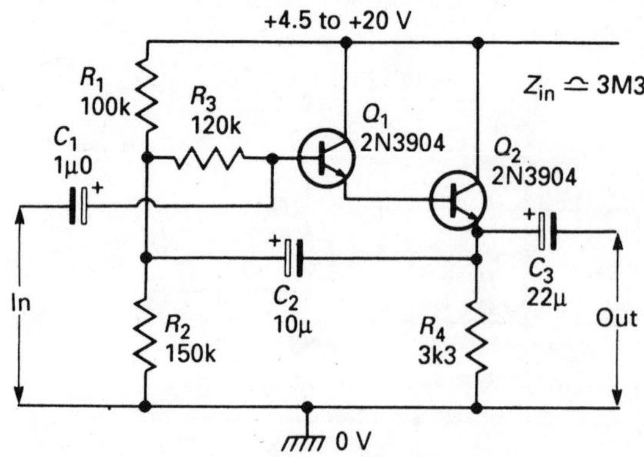

Figure 4.17 *Bootstrapped Darlington emitter follower*

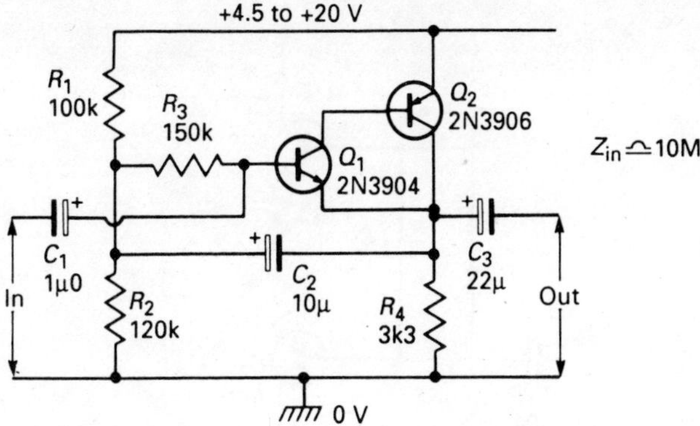

Figure 4.18 *Bootstrapped complementary feedback pair*

virtually 100 per cent negative feedback and thus give an overall voltage gain of almost exactly unity: this 'pair' of transistors thus acts like a near-perfect Darlington or Super-Alpha emitter follower.

Complementary emitter followers

It was pointed out in Chapter 3 that a standard npn emitter follower can 'source' current but can not 'sink' it, and that a pnp emitter follower can sink current but can not source it, i.e. these circuits can handle unidirectional output currents only. It was also pointed out that, in many applications, a 'bidirectional' emitter follower circuit (that can source and sink currents with equal ease) is required, and that this action can be obtained by using a complementary emitter follower configuration in which npn and pnp emitter followers are effectively wired in series. *Figures* 4.19–21 show some basic circuits of this type.

The *Figure* 4.19 circuit uses a dual ('split') power supply and has its output direct-coupled to a grounded load. The series-connected npn and pnp transistors are biased at a quiescent 'zero volts' value via the R_1–D_1–D_2–R_2 potential divider, with each transistor slightly forward biased via silicon diodes D_1 and D_2, which have characteristics inherently similar to those of the transistor base–emitter junctions; C_2 ensures that identical input signals are applied to the transistor bases, and R_3 and R_4 protect the transistors against excessive output currents. The circuit's action is such that Q_1 sources currents into the load when the input goes positive, and Q_2 sinks load current when the

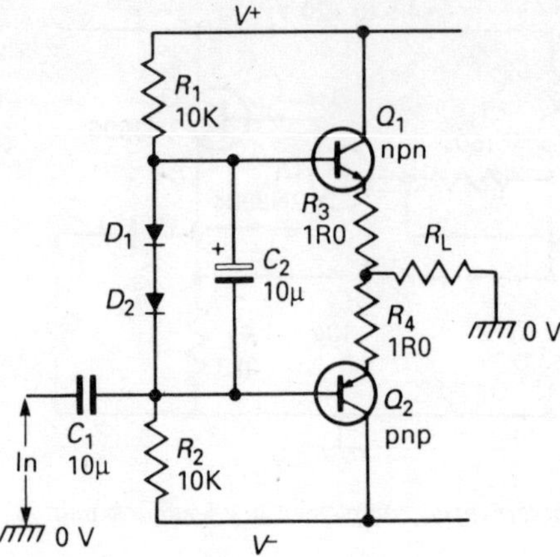

Figure 4.19 *Complementary emitter follower using split supply and direct-coupled output load*

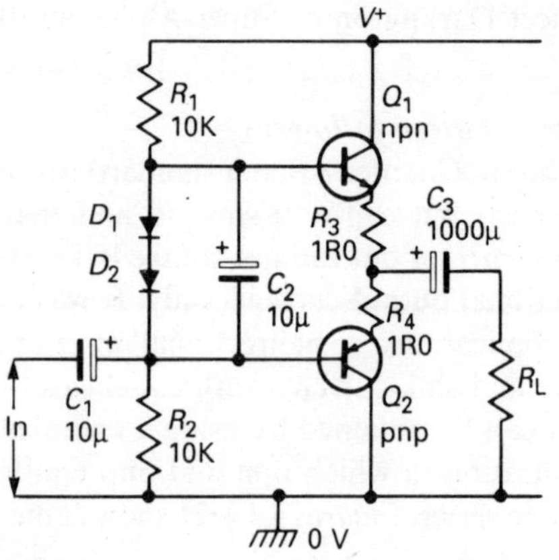

Figure 4.20 *Complementary emitter follower, using single-ended supply and a.c.-coupled load*

input goes negative. Note that input capacitor C_1 is a non-polarized type.

Figure 4.20 shows an alternative version of the above circuit, designed for use with a single-ended power supply and an a.c.-coupled output load; note in this case that C_1 is a polarized type.

In the *Figure* 4.19 and 4.20 circuits Q_1 and Q_2 are slightly forward biased (to eliminate cross-over distortion problems) via silicon diodes

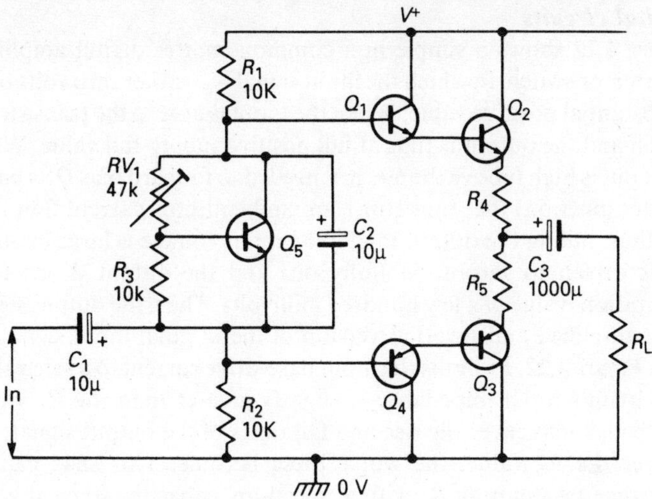

Figure 4.21 *Darlington complementary emitter follower, with biasing via an 'amplified diode'* (Q_5)

D_1 and D_2 (one per transistor); in practice, the diode currents (and thus the transistor forward bias voltages) are usually adjustable over a limited range. If these basic circuits are modified for use with Darlington transistor stages a total of four biasing diodes are needed; in such cases it is normal practice to use a one-transistor 'amplified diode' stage instead of four individual diodes, as shown in *Figure* 4.21. Here, Q_5's collector–emitter voltage equals the Q_5 base–emitter volt drop (about 600 mV) multiplied by $(RV_1 + R_3)/R_3$; thus, if RV_1 is set to zero ohms, 600 mV are developed across Q_5, which thus acts like a single silicon diode, but if RV_1 is set to 47k about 3V6 is developed across Q_5, which thus acts like six series-connected silicon diodes. RV_1 can thus be used to precisely set the Q_5 volt drop and thus adjust the quiescent current values of the Q_2–Q_3 output stages.

Common-emitter amplifier circuits

The common-emitter amplifier (also known as the common-earth or grounded-emitter circuit) has a medium value of input impedance and provides substantial voltage gain between input and output. It can be used in a wide variety of digital and analogue voltage amplifier applications. This section starts off by looking at 'digital' application circuits.

Digital circuits

Figure 4.22 shows a simple npn common-emitter digital amplifier, inverter, or switch, in which the input signal is at either zero volts or at a substantial positive value. When the input is at zero the transistor is cut off and the output is thus at full positive supply-rail value. When the input is high (above the 600 mV needed to forward bias Q_1's base–emitter junction) the transistor is on and collector current flows via R_L, thus pulling the output low; if the input voltage is large enough, Q_1 is driven to saturation (fully on) and the output drops to a 'saturation' value of a few hundred millivolts. Thus, the output signal is an amplified and inverted version of the original input signal.

In *Figure* 4.22, R_b limits the input base-drive current to a safe value; the circuit's input impedance is slightly greater than the R_b value, which also influences the rise and fall times of the output signal; the greater the R_b value, the worse these become. This snag can be overcome by shunting R_b with a 'speed-up' capacitor (typical value about 1n0), as shown dotted in the diagram. In practice, R_b should be as small as possible, consistent with safety and input-impedance requirements, and must not exceed $R_L \times h_{fe}$.

Figure 4.23 shows a pnp version of the digital inverter/switch circuit. In this case Q_1 is switched fully on, with its output a few hundred millivolts below the positive supply-rail value, when the input is at zero, and turns off (with its output at zero volts) when the input rises to within less than 600 mV of the positive supply-rail value.

Note that the sensitivity of the *Figure* 4.21 or 4.22 circuit can be greatly increased by simply replacing Q_1 with a pair of transistors wired in the Darlington or Super-Alpha mode. Alternatively, a very

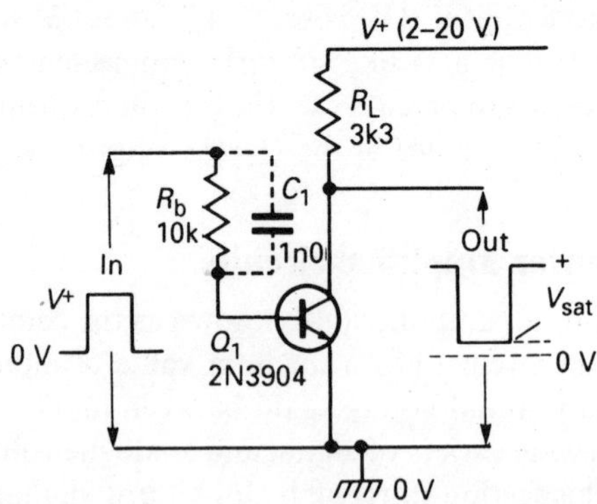

Figure 4.22 *Digital inverter/switch (npn)*

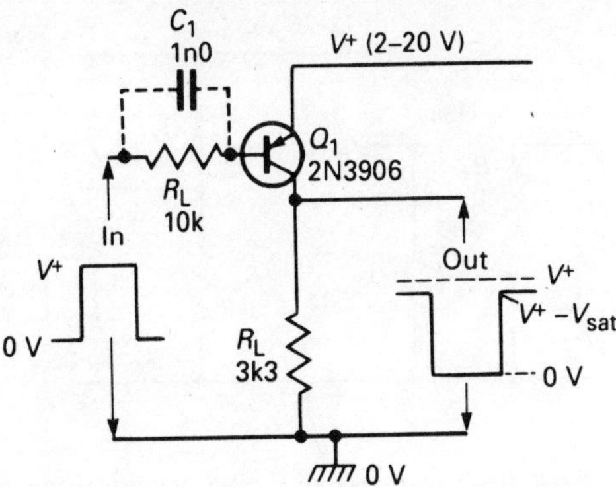

Figure 4.23 *Digital inverter/switch (pnp)*

high-gain *non*-inverting digital amplifier/switch can be made by using a pair of transistors wired in either of the configurations shown in *Figures* 4.24 or 4.25.

The *Figure* 4.24 circuit uses two npn transistors. When the input is at zero volts Q_1 is cut off, so Q_2 is driven to saturation via R_2, and the output is at near-zero. When the input is 'high', Q_1 is driven to saturation and pulls Q_2 base to less than 600 mV, so Q_2 is cut off and the output is at the full supply-voltage value.

The *Figure* 4.25 circuit uses one npn and one pnp transistor. When the input is at zero volts Q_1 is cut off, so Q_2 is also cut off (via R_2–R_3) and the output is at zero volts. When the input is 'high', Q_1 is driven on and derives most of its collector current from Q_2 base via R_3, thus

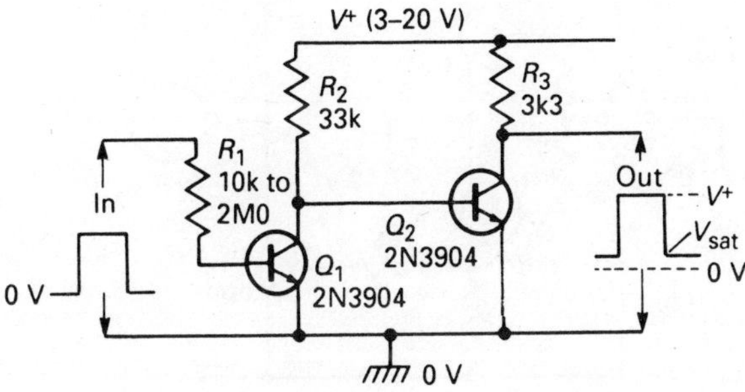

Figure 4.24 *Very-high-gain non-inverting digital amplifier/switch using npn transistors*

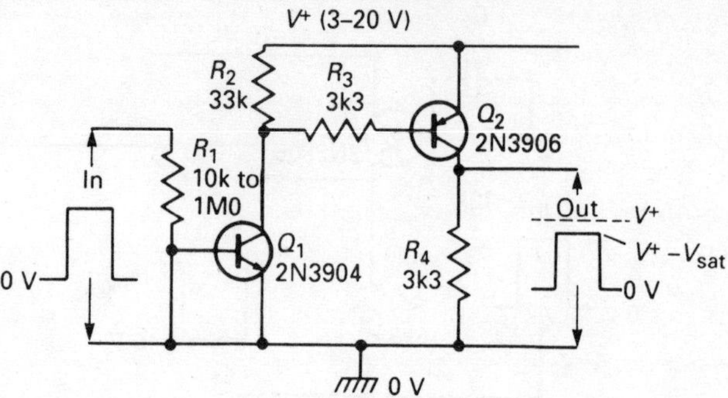

Figure 4.25 *Alternative non-inverting digital amplifier/switch using an npn–pnp pair of transistors*

driving Q_2 to saturation; under this condition the output takes up a value a few hundred millivolts below the positive supply-rail value.

Finally, to complete this look at digital common-emitter amplifier circuits, *Figure* 4.26 shows (in basic form) how a complementary pair of the *Figure* 4.25 circuits can be used to make a D.C.-motor direction-control network, using a dual power supply. The circuit operates as follows.

When SW_1 is set to *forward*, Q_1 is driven on via R_1, and Q_2 is driven on via R_3 and Q_1, but Q_3 is cut off via R_4 and Q_4 is cut off via R_5 and R_6. Thus, the 'live' side of the motor is connected (via Q_2) to the

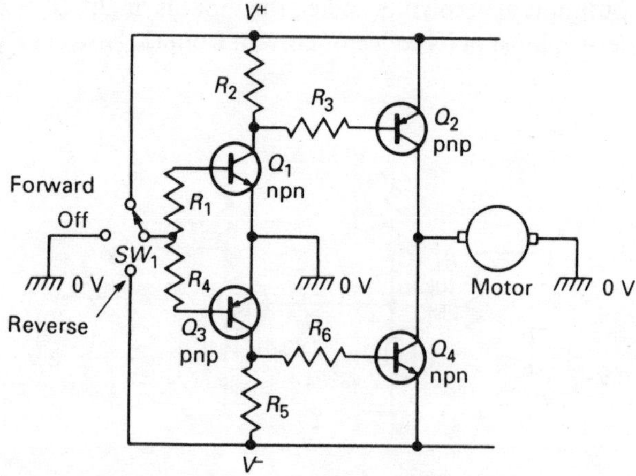

Figure 4.26 *D.c.-motor direction-control circuit*

positive supply rail under this condition, and the motor runs in a forward direction.

When SW_1 is set to *off*, Q_1 is cut off via R_1, and Q_2 is cut off via R_2–R_3, and simultaneously Q_3 is cut off via R_4 and Q_4 is cut off via R_5–R_6; the 'live' side of the motor is thus effectively open-circuit under this condition, and the motor is inoperative.

When SW_1 is set to *reverse*, Q_3 is biased on via R_4, and Q_4 is driven on via R_6 and Q_3, but Q_1 is cut off via R_1, and Q_2 is cut off via R_2–R_3. Thus, the 'live' side of the motor is connected (via Q_4) to the negative supply rail under this condition, and the motor runs in the reverse direction.

Relay drivers

If the basic digital circuits of *Figures* 4.22–5 are used to drive inductive loads such as relay coils, etc., they must be provided with simple diode protection networks to limit inductive switch-off back-e.m.f.s to safe values. Common-emitter amplifiers make far more sensitive relay drivers than do common-collector types (described earlier), and *Figures* 4.27–9 show some practical examples of such circuits.

The simple *Figure* 4.27 circuit increases a relay's operating current sensitivity by a factor of about 200 (the nominal h_{fe} value of Q_1). R_1 gives base drive protection, and can have a larger value than 1k0 if desired. The relay can be turned on either by applying a d.c. voltage to the input, or by closing SW_1 (shown dotted). The basic circuit gives non-latching operation, but can be made self-latching by wiring a spare set of relay contacts (RLA/2) between Q_1's collector and emitter, as shown dotted.

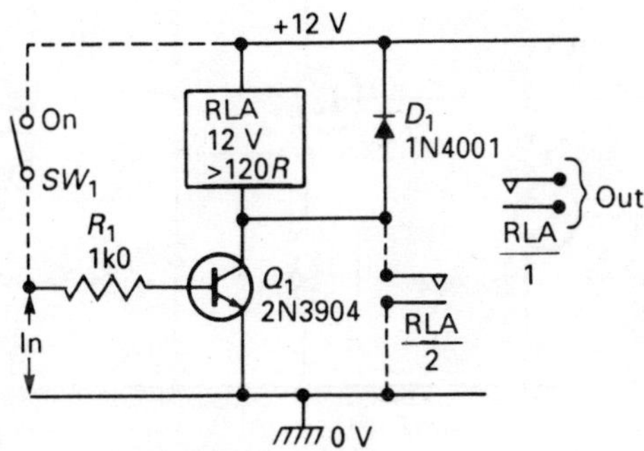

Figure 4.27 *Simple relay-driving circuit*

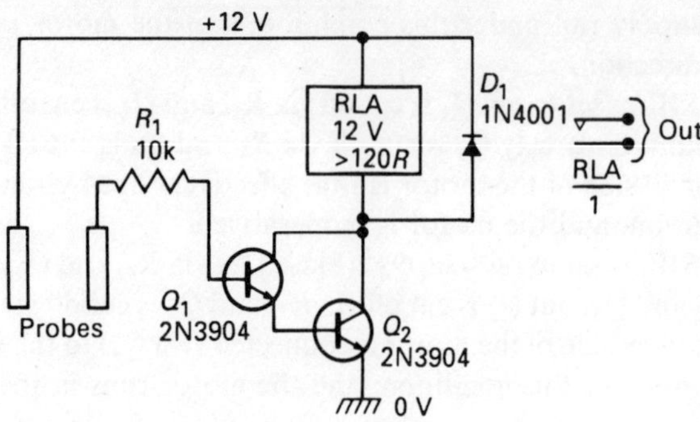

Figure 4.28 *Touch-, water- or steam-activated relay switch*

The current sensitivity of the *Figure* 4.27 circuit is limited by the current gain of Q_1; the sensitivity can be greatly increased (to a factor of about 20 000) by replacing Q_1 with a Darlington-connected pair of transistors. *Figure* 4.28 shows how this principle can be used to make a relay-driving circuit that can be activated by placing a resistance of less than 2M0 across a pair of stainless metal probes. Water, steam and skin contacts have resistances below this value, so this simple little circuit can be used as a water, steam or touch-activated relay switch.

Figure 4.29 shows another ultra-sensitive relay driver, based on the *Figure* 4.25 circuit, that needs an input of only 700 mV at 40 μA to activate the relay; R_2 ensures that Q_1 and Q_2 turn fully off when the input terminals are open circuit.

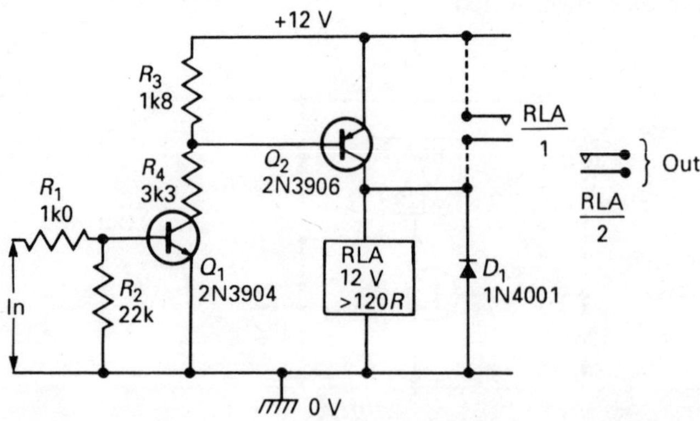

Figure 4.29 *Ultra-sensitive relay driver (needs an input of 700 mV at 40 μA)*

Linear biasing circuits

A common-emitter circuit can be used as a linear a.c. amplifier by applying a d.c. bias current to its base so that its collector takes up a quiescent half-supply voltage value (to accommodate maximal undistorted output signal swings), and by then feeding the a.c. input signal to the base and taking the a.c. output from the collector; *Figure* 4.30 shows such a circuit.

The first step in designing a circuit of the *Figure* 4.30 type is to select the value of load resistor R_2. The lower this is, the higher will be the amplifier's upper cut-off signal frequency (due to the smaller shunting effects of stray capacitance on effective impedance of the load), but the higher will be Q_1's quiescent operating current. In the diagram, R_2 has a compromise value of 5k6, which gives an upper '3 dB down' frequency of about 120 kHz and a quiescent current consumption of 1 mA from a 12 V supply. To bias the output to half-supply volts, R_1 needs a value of $R_2 \times 2h_{fe}$, and (assuming a nominal h_{fe} of 200) this works out at about 2M2 in the example shown.

The matters of input impedance and voltage gain are both determined by the forward-biased impedance of Q_1's base–emitter junction, which works out at about $25/I_c$, where I_c is the collector current value in milliamperes, e.g. this impedance is 25 ohms at 1 mA, 12.5 ohms at 2 mA, or 50 ohms at 0.5 mA. The input impedance into the transistor base equals this impedance multiplied by Q_1's h_{fe} value. Thus, in *Figure* 4.30, the input impedance equals roughly 5k0 shunted by R_1.

The voltage gain of the *Figure* 4.30 circuit equals the R_2 collector–load resistance value divided by the base–emitter junction impedance value, and works out at about 46 dB, or × 200. Note that, in theory,

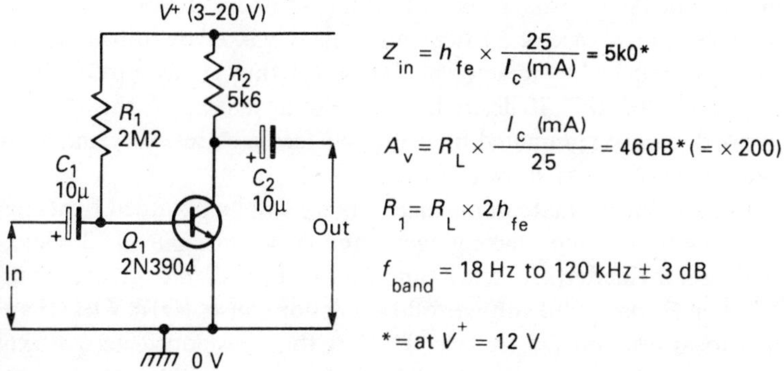

Figure 4.30 *Simple npn common-emitter amplifier*

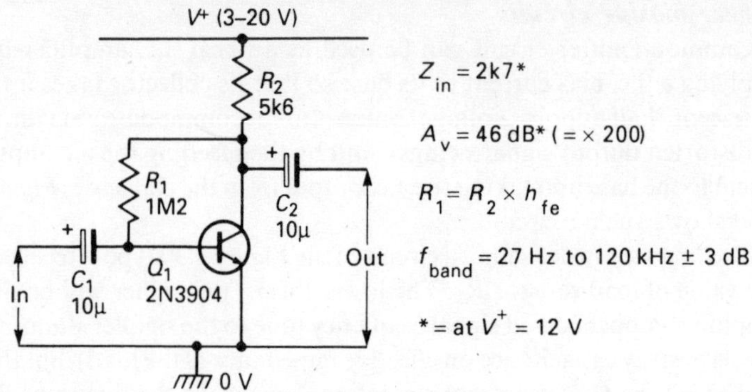

Figure 4.31 *Common-emitter amplifier with feedback biasing*

this gain figure also determines the maximum attainable upper 3 dB point of the frequency response, which equals F_T/A_v. The F_T of the 2N3904 is about 300 MHz, so the maximum attainable 3 dB point of this circuit (ignoring the effects of stray capacitance) is 1.5 MHz.

A weakness of the *Figure* 4.30 circuit is that its quiescent biasing point is dependent on Q_1's h_{fe} value. This weakness can be overcome by modifying the circuit as in *Figure* 4.31, where biasing resistor R_1 is wired in a d.c. feedback mode between base and collector and has a value of $R_2 \times h_{fe}$. The feedback action is such that any shift in the output biasing point (due to variations in h_{fe}, temperature, or component values) causes a counter-change in the base-current biasing level, thus tending to cancel the original shift.

The *Figure* 4.31 circuit provides the same values of bandwidth and voltage gain as the *Figure* 4.30 design, but has a lower total value of input impedance. This is because its a.c. feedback action causes the apparent impedance of R_1 (which shunts the 5k0 base impedance of Q_1) to be reduced by a factor of 200 ($=A_v$), thus giving a total input impedance of 2k7. If desired, the shunting effects of the biasing network can be eliminated by using two feedback resistors and a.c.-decoupling them as shown in *Figure* 4.32.

Finally, the ultimate in biasing stability can be obtained by using the 'potential-divider biasing' technique shown in *Figure* 4.33. Here, potential divider R_1–R_2 sets a quiescent voltage slightly greater than $V^+/3$ on Q_1 base, and voltage follower action causes 600 mV less than this to appear on Q_1 emitter. $V^+/3$ is thus developed across 5k6 emitter resistor R_3, and (since Q_1's emitter and collector currents are

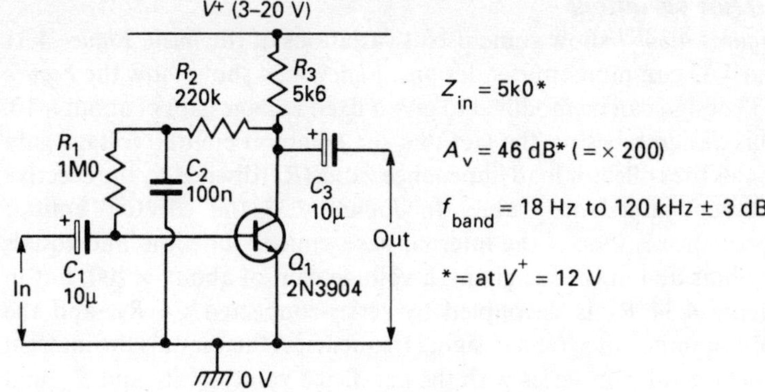

Figure 4.32 *Amplifier with a.c.-decoupled feedback biasing*

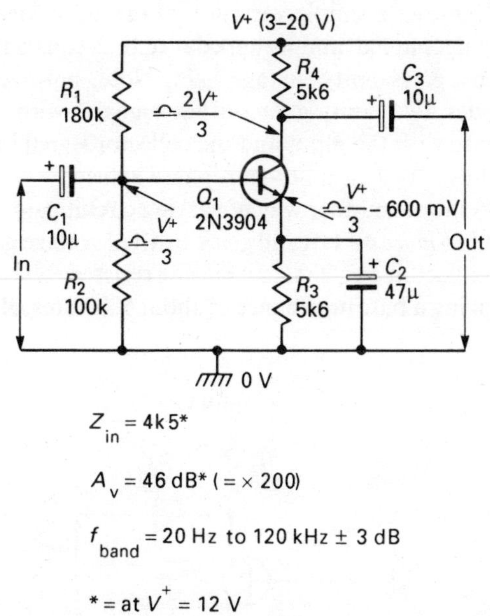

Figure 4.33 *Amplifier with voltage-divider biasing*

almost identical) a similar voltage is dropped across R_4, which also has a value of 5k6, thus setting the collector at a quiescent value of $2V^+/3$. Note that R_3 is a.c.-decoupled via C_2, enabling the circuit to give an a.c. voltage gain of 46 dB.

Circuit variations

Figures 4.34–7 show some useful variations of the basic *Figure* 4.31 and 4.33 common-emitter designs. *Figure* 4.34 shows how the *Figure* 4.33 design can be modified to give a fixed voltage gain of about × 10. This design relies on the fact that the common-emitter voltage gain equals the collector load impedance value (R_4) divided by the effective 'emitter' impedance value. In *Figure* 4.33 the effective emitter impedance is that of the internal base–emitter junction, and equals 25 ohms at 1 mA, thus giving a voltage gain of about × 200, but in *Figure* 4.34 R_3 is decoupled by series-connected C_2–R_5, and the emitter impedance (at a.c. signal frequencies) thus equals the internal junction value in series with the paralleled values of R_3 and R_5, and works out at roughly 560 ohms, thus giving a final voltage gain value of × 10. Alternative gain values can be obtained by altering the R_5 value.

Figure 4.35 shows a simple variation of the above design. In this case R_3 is not decoupled, and its impedance thus equals the R_4 value and the circuit gives unity voltage gain. Note, however, that this circuit provides two unity-gain output signals, with the emitter output in phase with the input and the collector signal in antiphase; this circuit thus acts as a unity-gain phase splitter.

Figure 4.36 shows another way of varying circuit gain. This design is a variation of *Figure* 4.31; it still gives 46 dB of voltage gain between Q_1 base and collector, but feedback biasing resistor R_3 is a.c.-shunted by R_2, thus giving a base impedance of about 500 ohms; R_1 is wired in

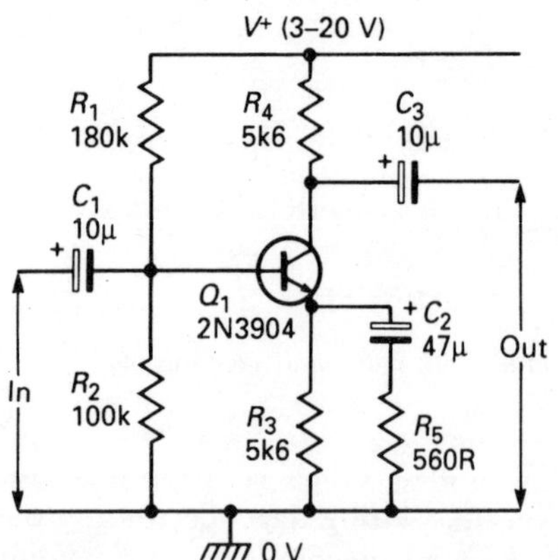

Figure 4.34 *Fixed-gain (× 10) common-emitter amplifier*

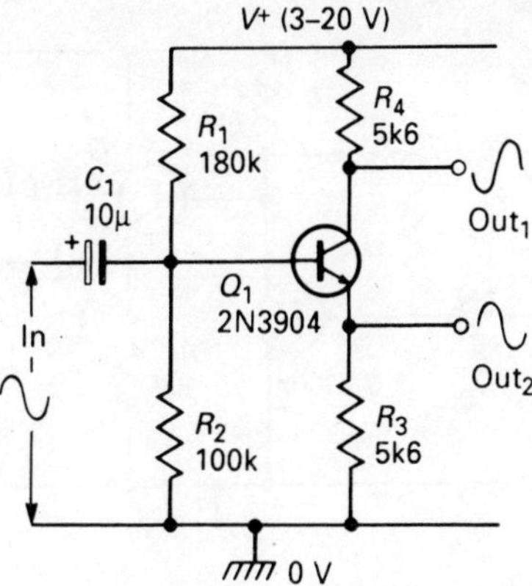

Figure 4.35 *Unity-gain phase splitter*

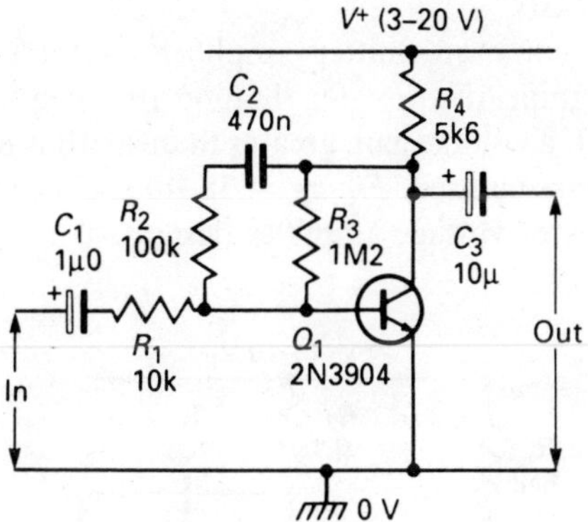

Figure 4.36 *Alternative fixed-gain* (× *10) amplifier*

series between the input signal and Q_1 base, and thus (in conjunction with the base impedance) gives signal attenuation between the input and base. The net effect is that the circuit's voltage gain equals R_2/R_1, and works out at × 10 in this particular case. Alternative gain values can be obtained by altering the R_1 or R_2 values.

Finally, *Figure* 4.37 shows how the *Figure* 4.31 design can be modified to give a wide-band performance by simply wiring a direct-coupled emitter follower stage (Q_2) between Q_1 collector and the output terminal, thus minimizing the shunting effects of stray capacitance on R_2 and thus extending the upper bandwidth to several hundred kilohertz.

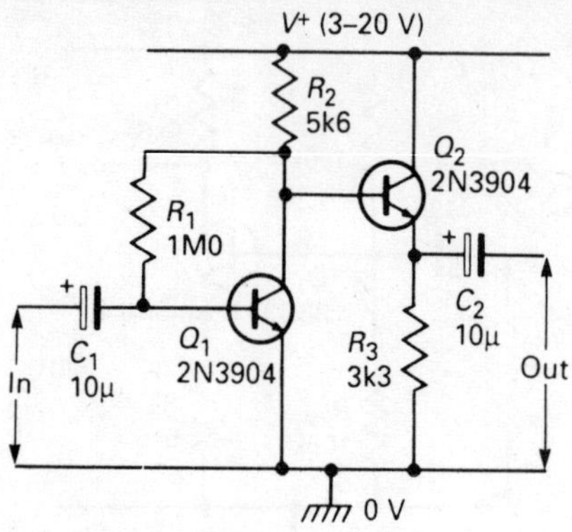

Figure 4.37 *Wide-band amplifier*

High-gain circuits

A single-stage common-emitter amplifier circuit can not give a voltage gain significantly greater than 46 dB when using a resistive collector load. If a voltage gain greater than 46 dB is needed, a multi-stage circuit must be used. *Figures* 4.38–40 show three useful high-gain two-transistor voltage amplifier designs.

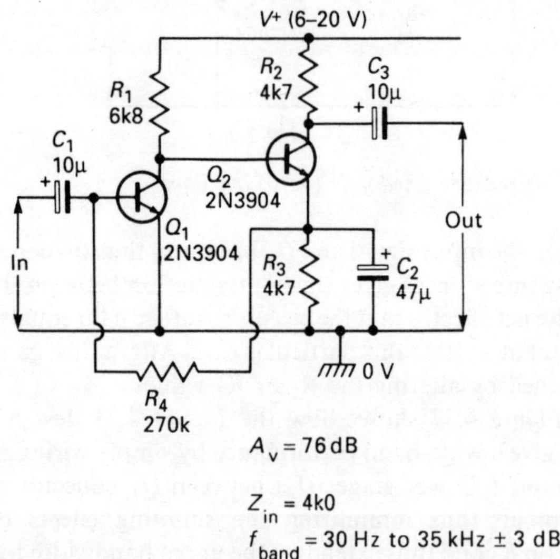

Figure 4.38 *High-gain two-stage amplifier*

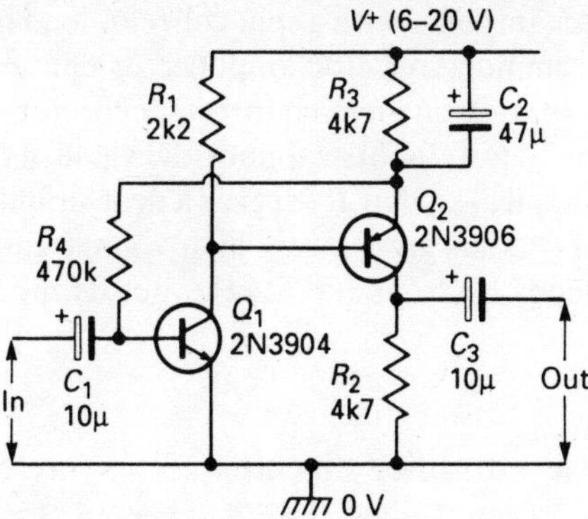

Figure 4.39 *Alternative high-gain two-stage amplifier*

The *Figure* 4.38 circuit acts like a direct-coupled pair of common-emitter amplifiers, with Q_1's output feeding directly into Q_2 base, and gives an overall voltage gain of 76 dB (about ×6150) and an upper −3 dB frequency point of 35 kHz. Note that feedback biasing resistor R_4 is fed from Q_2's a.c.-decoupled emitter (which 'follows' the quiescent collector voltage of Q_1), rather than directly from Q_1 collector, and that the bias circuit is thus effectively a.c.-decoupled. *Figure* 4.39 shows an alternative version of the above design, using a pnp output stage; the performance of this circuit is the same as that of *Figure* 4.38.

The Figure 4.40 circuit uses a very different way of giving a high voltage gain (about 66 dB, or ×2000). In this case Q_1 is wired as a

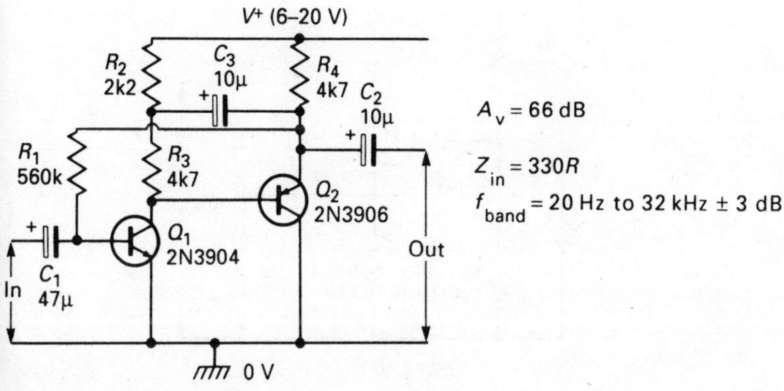

Figure 4.40 *Bootstrapped high-gain amplifier*

common-emitter amplifier with a split collector load (R_2–R_3), and Q_2 is wired as a common-collector amplifier or emitter follower, and feeds the a.c. output signal (derived from Q_1 collector) back to the R_2–R_3 junction via C_3, thus 'bootstrapping' the value of R_3 (as described earlier in this chapter) so that R_3 acts as a near-infinite impedance to a.c. signals and Q_1 thus gives a very high voltage gain. This circuit's bandwidth extends up to about 32 kHz, but its input impedance is only 330 ohms.

Common-base amplifier circuits

The common-base amplifier has a very low input impedance, gives near-unity current gain and a high voltage gain, and is used mainly in wide-band or high-frequency voltage amplifier applications. *Figure* 4.41 shows an example of a common-base amplifier that gives a good wide-band response. This circuit is biased in the same way as *Figure* 4.33; note, however, that the base is a.c.-decoupled via C_1, and the input signal is applied to the emitter via C_3. The circuit has a very low input impedance (equal to that of Q_1's forward-biased base–emitter junction), gives the same voltage gain as the common-emitter amplifier (about 46 dB), gives zero phase shift between input and output, and has a −3 dB bandwidth extending to a few megahertz.

Figure 4.42 shows a really good wideband amplifier, the 'cascode' amplifier, which gives the wide bandwidth benefit of the common-base amplifier together with the medium input impedance advantage

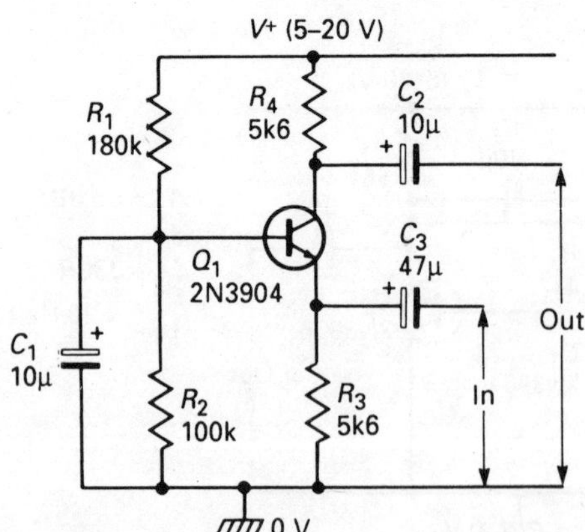

Figure 4.41 *Common-base amplifier*

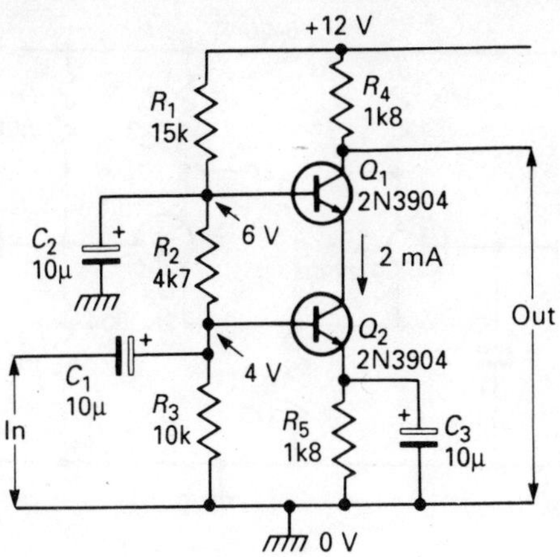

Figure 4.42 *Wide-band cascode amplifier*

of the common-emitter amplifier. This is achieved by wiring Q_1 and Q_2 in series, with Q_1 connected in the common-base mode and Q_2 in the common-emitter mode. The input signal is applied to the base of Q_2, which uses Q_1 emitter as its collector load and thus gives unity voltage gain and a very wide bandwidth, and Q_1 gives a voltage gain of about 46 dB. Thus, the complete circuit has an input impedance of about 1.8k, a voltage gain of 46 dB, and a −3 dB bandwidth that extends to a few megahertz.

Figure 4.43 shows a circuit that is a close relative of the common-base amplifier, this being a two-transistor 'long-tailed pair' phase splitter, which gives a pair of anti-phase outputs when driven from a single-ended input signal. Note that Q_1 and Q_2 share a common-emitter resistor (the 'tail'), and the circuit bias point is adjusted via RV_1 so that the two transistors pass identical collector currents (giving zero difference between the two collector voltages) under quiescent conditions. Also note that Q_1 base is firmly a.c.-grounded via C_1, and that a.c.-input signals are applied to Q_2 base. The circuit acts as follows.

Suppose that a sine-wave input signal is fed to Q_2 base. Q_2 is wired as a common-emitter amplifier, giving an inverting amplifier action, and when the signal drives its base upwards its collector inevitably swings downwards, and vice versa; at the same time, Q_2's emitter 'follows' the input signal, and as its emitter voltage rises it inevitably reduces the base–emitter bias of Q_1 (its base is a.c.-grounded via C_1),

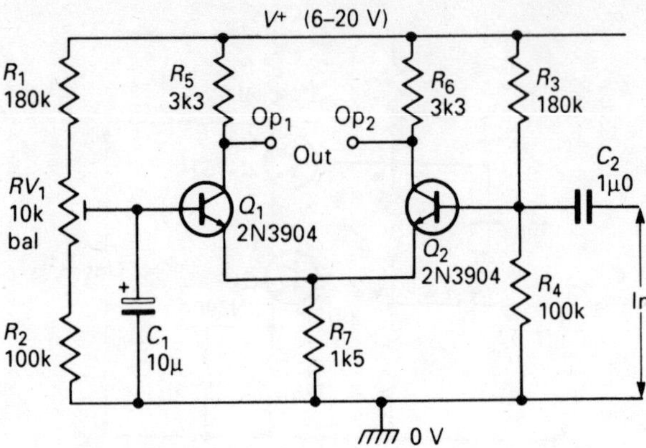

Figure 4.43 *Phase splitter*

thus causing Q_1 collector voltage to rise, etc. Q_1 thus operates in the common-base mode and gives the same voltage gain as Q_2, but gives a non-inverting amplifier action; this 'phase-splitter' circuit thus generates a pair of balanced antiphase output signals.

Finally, *Figure* 4.44 shows how the above circuit can be made to act as a differential amplifier that gives a pair of antiphase output signals, each of which is proportional to the *difference* between two input signals; if identical signals are applied to both inputs the circuit will (ideally) give zero output. The second input signal is fed to Q_1 base via C_1, and the R_7 'tail' provides the coupling between the two transistors.

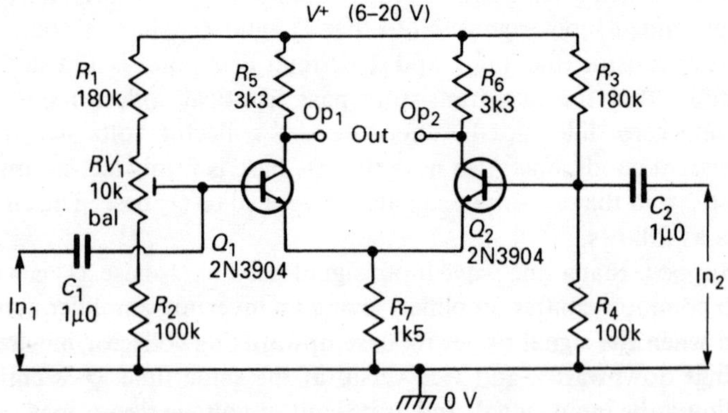

Figure 4.44 *Simple differential amplifier or long-tailed pair*

5 Transistor waveform generators

Bipolar transistors waveform generator circuits can be roughly divided into two basic classes. Those used to generate sine waves are usually known as 'oscillators' and use the transistors as linear amplifying elements. Those used to generate square or rectangular waveforms are usually known as 'multivibrators', and use the transistors as digital switching elements. Both classes of generator are described in this chapter.

Oscillator basics

Transistor oscillator circuits are usually designed to generate fairly pure sine-wave outputs. Two basic requirements must be satisfied to make such an oscillator, as shown in *Figure* 5.1. First, the output of the amplifying device (A_1) must be fed back to its input via a frequency-selective network (A_2) in such a way that the sum of the amplifier feedback network phase shifts equals zero degrees (or 360°) at the desired oscillation frequency, i.e. so that $x° + y° = 0°$ (or 360°). Thus, if the transistor stage generates 180° of phase shift between input and output, an additional 180° of phase shift must be introduced by a frequency-selective network connected between input and output in order to meet the first requirement of a sine-wave oscillator.

The second requirement is that the gain of the amplifying device must exactly counter the losses of the frequency-selective feedback network at the desired oscillation frequency, to give an overall system gain of precisely unity, e.g. $A_1 \times A_2 = 1$. If the gain is less than unity the circuit will not oscillate, and if greater than unity it will be over-

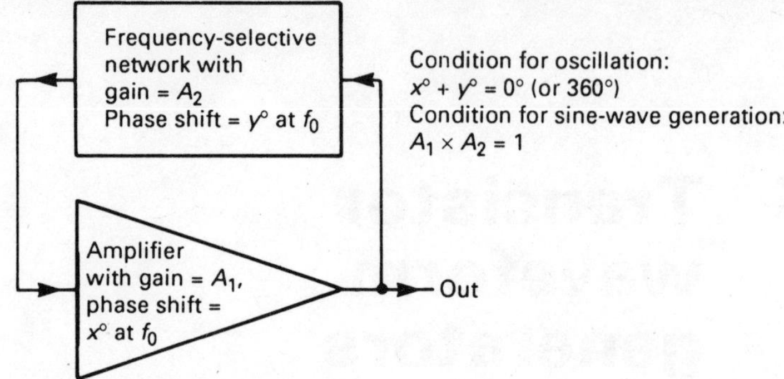

Figure 5.1 *Essential circuit and conditions needed for sine-wave generation*

driven and will generate distorted (non-sinusoidal) waveforms. The frequency-selective feedback network usually consists of either a *C–R* or *L–C* filter or of a tuned transformer or a crystal filter; networks of all of these types are described in this chapter.

C–R oscillators

Figure 5.2 shows the practical circuit of one of the crudest types of *C–R* sine-wave oscillator, the so-called 'phase-shift' type. Here, Q_1 is wired as a common-emitter amplifier and has its output (collector) signal fed back to its input (base) via a three-stage *C–R* ladder network, essentially comprising C_1–R_1, C_2–R_2, and C_3–R_3.

Each *C–R* stage of the ladder generates a phase shift between its input and output; the size of shift varies with frequency, and has a maximum value of 90°. The ladder's total phase shift equals the sum of the three stage shifts, and in *Figure* 5.2 (in which $C_1 = C_2 = C_3 = C$, and $R_1 = R_2 = R_3 = R$) equals 180° at a frequency of $1/14CR$; since the transistor stage itself generates a phase shift of 180°, the circuit oscillates at this frequency. The three-stage ladder has an attenuation factor of 29 at the oscillation frequency, and the gain of the Q_1 stage must be adjusted (via RV_1) to counter this signal loss and give an overall circuit gain of unity if stable sine-wave generation is to be obtained. In practice, the *Figure* 5.2 circuit oscillates at about 800 Hz, and RV_1 should, to ensure stable operation, be adjusted so that a slightly distorted sine wave is generated; the amplitude of the output signal can be varied via RV_2.

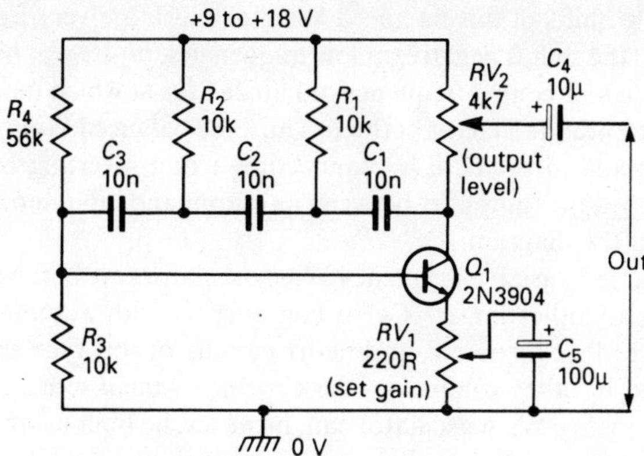

Figure 5.2 *800 Hz phase-shift oscillator circuit*

The simple phase-shift oscillator circuit has the advantage of simplicity, but it has poor gain stability and its operating frequency can not easily be varied (unless a three-gang *R* or *C* component is used). A far more versatile *C–R* oscillator circuit, which can easily have its operating frequency varied via a two-gang component, can be built using a Wien bridge network connected in the basic form shown in *Figure* 5.3.

The Wien network comprises R_1–C_1 and R_2–C_2, which normally have their values 'balanced' so that $C_1 = C_2 = C$, and $R_1 = R_2 = R$.

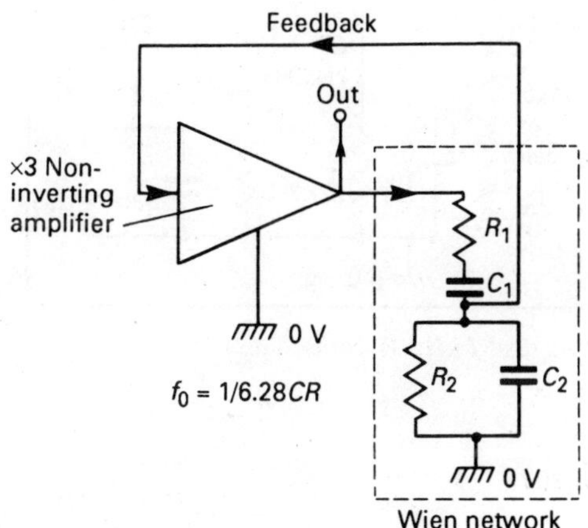

Figure 5.3 *Basic Wien bridge sine-wave oscillator*

The phase shifts of this balanced Wien network are very frequency-sensitive; the shift is negative at low frequencies, positive at high ones, and is zero at a 'centre' frequency of $1/(6.28CR)$, at which the network has an attentuation factor of three. Thus, the balanced Wien network can be made to oscillate by connecting a non-inverting $\times 3$ high-input-impedance amplifier between its output and input terminals, as shown in the diagram.

In practice, variable-frequency Wien oscillators are best built using op-amps or other linear ICs, in conjunction with automatic-gain-control feedback systems, and many circuits of this type are in fact published in other volumes of the *Circuits Manual* series. A simple fixed-frequency Wien oscillator can, however, be built using a couple of bipolar transistors, as shown in *Figure* 5.4, where Q_1 and Q_2 are both wired as low-gain common-emitter amplifiers. Q_2 gives a voltage gain slightly greater than unity and uses Wien network resistor R_1 as its collector load, and Q_1 presents a high input impedance to the output of the Wien network and has its gain variable via RV_1. With the component values shown the circuit oscillates at about 1 kHz; in use, RV_1 should be adjusted so that a slightly distorted output sine wave is generated.

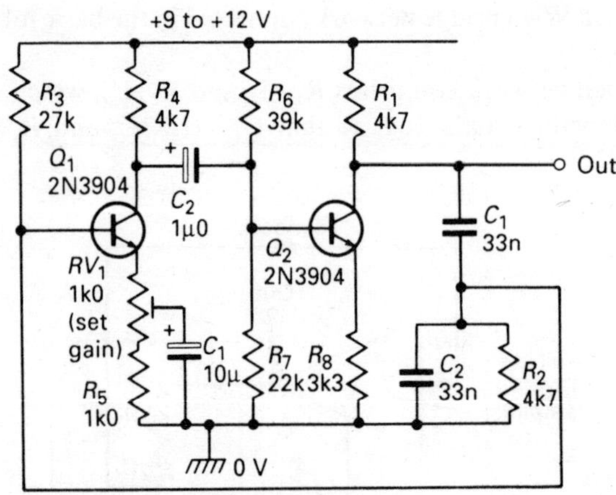

Figure 5.4 *Practical 1 kHz Wien oscillator*

L–C oscillators

C–R sine-wave oscillators are useful for generating signals ranging from a few hertz up to several tens or hundreds of kilohertz. *L–C* oscillators, on the other hand, are useful for generating signals from a few tens of kilohertz to hundreds of megahertz. An *L–C* oscillator consists, in essence, of an amplifying device that gives significant gain between input and output, and an *L–C* network that provides frequency-selective feedback between the output and input terminals of the amplifier. Because of the inherently high *Q* or frequency selectivity of *L–C* networks, *L–C* oscillators usually produce reasonably pure sine-wave outputs, even when the loop gain of the circuit is far greater than unity.

Many different versions of the *L–C* transistor oscillator are in common use. The simplest is the 'tuned collector feedback' type shown in *Figure* 5.5. Q_1 is wired as a common-emitter amplifier, with base bias provided via R_1–R_2 and with emitter resistor R_3 a.c.-decoupled via C_2. The tuned collector circuit is formed by L_1–C_1, and collector-to-base feedback is provided via L_2, a small winding inductively coupled to L_1 which thus provides a 'transformer' action; by selecting the phase of this feedback signal the circuit can be made to give zero loop phase shift at the tuned frequency, so that it will oscillate if the loop gain (determined by the turns ratio of T_1) is greater than unity.

A feature of any *L–C* tuned circuit is that the phase relationship between its energizing current and induced voltage varies from $-90°$ to $+90°$, and is zero at a 'centre' frequency given by $f=1/(2\pi\sqrt{(LC)})$. Thus, the *Figure* 5.5 circuit gives zero overall phase shift, and oscillates, at this centre frequency; with the component values shown,

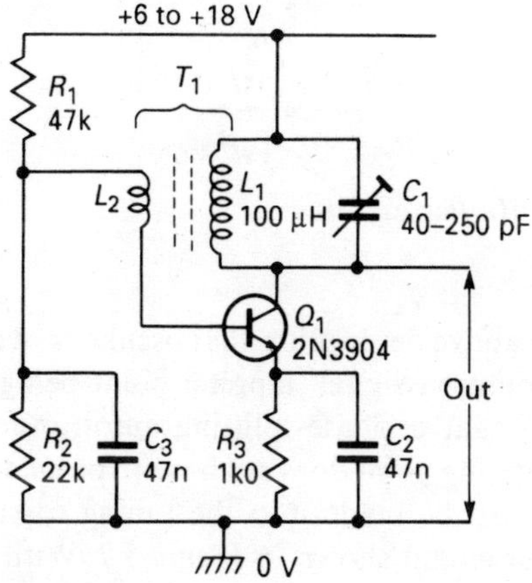

Figure 5.5 *Tuned collector feedback oscillator*

the frequency can be varied from 1 MHz to 2 MHz via C_1. This basic circuit can be designed to operate at frequencies ranging from a few tens of hertz by using a laminated iron-cored transformer, up to tens or hundreds of megahertz using RF techniques.

Circuit variations

Figure 5.6 shows a simple variation of the *Figure* 5.5 design, this being known as a Hartley oscillator. Its collector load inductor L_1 is tapped roughly 20 per cent down from its top, and the circuit's positive supply rail is connected to this point; L_1 thus gives an autotransformer action, in which the signal voltage appearing at the top of L_1 is 180° out of phase with that at its low (Q_1 collector) end. The signal from the top of the coil is coupled to the base (input) of Q_1 via C_2, and the circuit thus oscillates at a centre frequency determined by the L–C values.

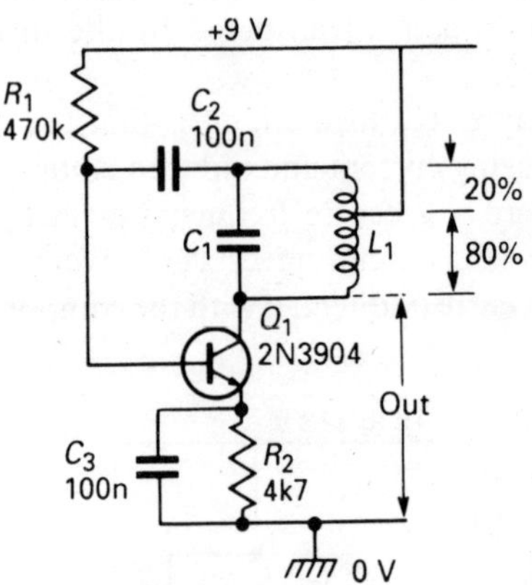

Figure 5.6 *Basic Hartley oscillator*

Note from the above description that oscillator action depends on some kind of 'common signal' tapping point being made into the tuned circuit, so that a phase-splitting autotransformer action is obtained. This tapping point does not have to be made into the actual tuning coil, but can be made into the tuning capacitor, as in the Colpitts oscillator circuit shown in *Figure* 5.7. With the component values shown, this particular circuit oscillates at about 37 kHz.

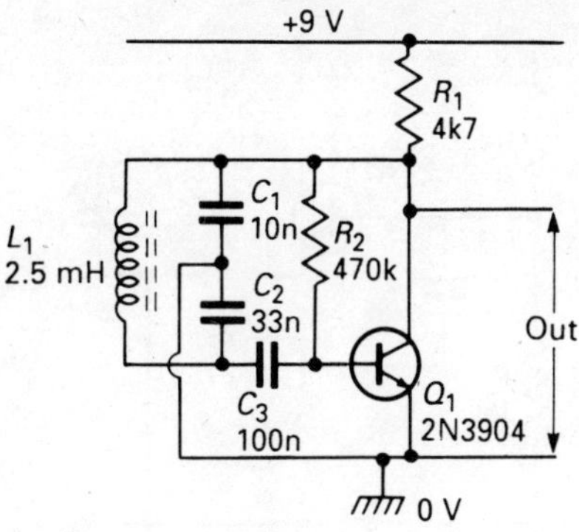

Figure 5.7 *37 kHz Colpitts oscillator*

Note in *Figure* 5.7 that C_1 is in parallel with Q_1's output capacitance, and C_2 is in parallel with its input capacitance; consequently, changes in Q_1 capacitance (due to thermal shifts, etc.) cause a change in frequency. This effect can be minimized (and good frequency stability obtained) by making C_1 and C_2 large relative to Q_1's internal capacitances.

A modification of the Colpitts design, known as the Clapp or Gouriet oscillator, is shown in *Figure* 5.8. Here, a further capacitor (C_3) is wired in series with L_1 and has a value that is small relative to C_1 and C_2. Consequently, the circuit's resonant frequency is set mainly by L_1 and C_3 and is almost independent of variations in transistor capacitances. This circuit thus gives excellent frequency

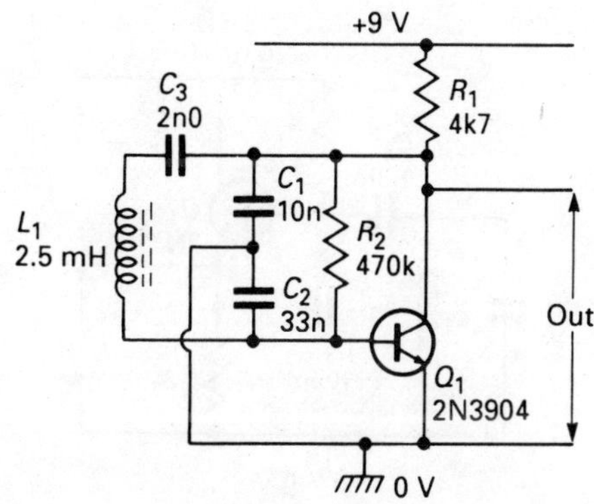

Figure 5.8 *80 kHz Gouriet or Clapp oscillator*

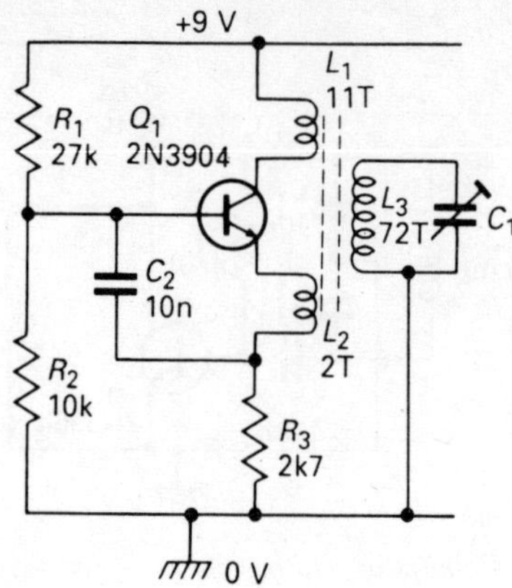

Figure 5.9 *Basic Reinartz oscillator*

stability; with the component values shown it oscillates at about 80 kHz.

Figure 5.9 shows a Reinartz oscillator, in which the tuning coil has three inductively coupled windings. Positive feedback is obtained by coupling the transistor's collector and emitter signals via windings L_1 and L_2. Both of these inductors are coupled to L_3, and the circuit oscillates at a frequency determined by L_3–C_1. The diagram shows typical coil-turns ratios for a circuit designed to oscillate at a few hundred kilohertz.

Finally, *Figures* 5.10 and 5.11 show emitter follower versions of Hartley and Colpitts oscillators. In these circuits the transistors and

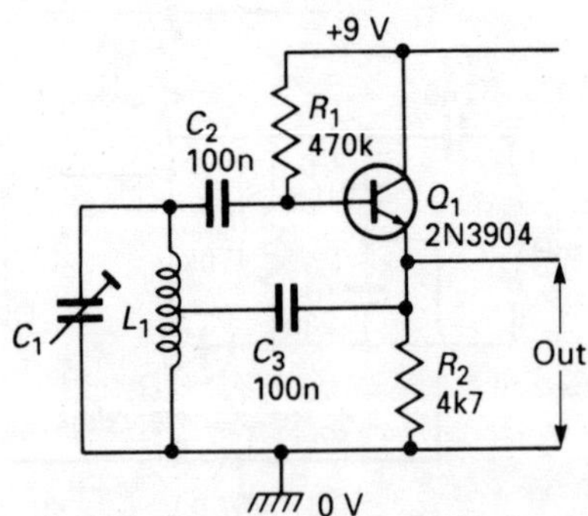

Figure 5.10 *Emitter follower version of the Hartley oscillator*

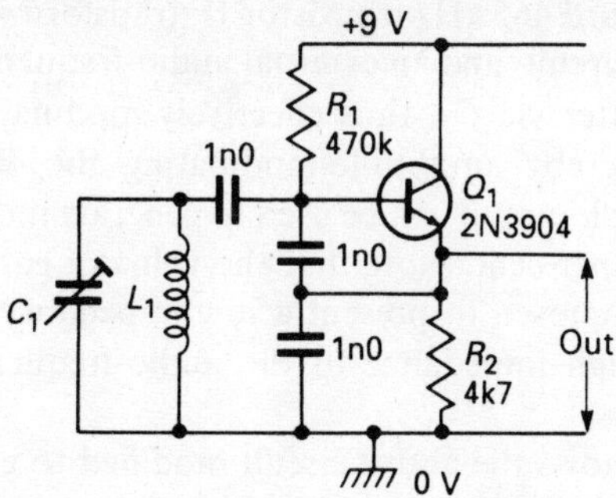

Figure 5.11 *Emitter follower version of the Colpitts oscillator*

L_1–C_1 tuned circuits each give zero phase shift at the oscillation frequency, and the tuned circuit gives the voltage gain necessary to ensure oscillation.

Modulation

The *L–C* oscillator circuits of *Figures* 5.5–11 can easily be modified to give modulated (AM or FM) rather than continuous-wave (CW) outputs. *Figure* 5.12, for example, shows how the *Figure* 5.5 circuit can be modified to act as a 465 kHz beat-frequency oscillator (BFO) with an amplitude-modulation (AM) facility.

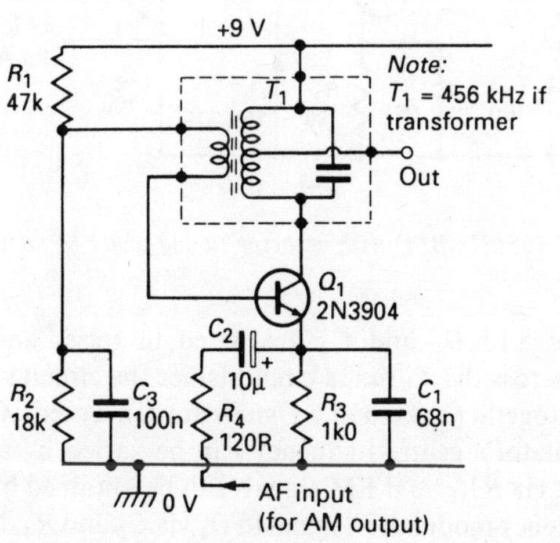

Figure 5.12 *465 kHz BFO with AM facility*

Here, a standard 465 kHz transistor IF transformer (T_1) is used as the L–C tuned circuit, and an external audio-frequency signal can be fed to Q_1's emitter via C_2, thus effectively modulating Q_1's supply voltage and thereby amplitude-modulating the 465 kHz 'carrier' signal. This simple circuit can be used to generate modulation depths up to about 40 per cent. Note that the value of emitter-decoupling capacitor C_1 is chosen to present a low impedance to the 465 kHz carrier but a high impedance to the audio-frequency modulation signal.

Figure 5.13 shows the above circuit modified to give a frequency-modulation (FM) facility, together with 'varactor' tuning via potentiometer RV_1. In this circuit silicon diode D_1 (an IN4001 type) is used as an inexpensive varactor diode or voltage-variable capacitor which (as already pointed out in Chapters 1 and 2), when reverse biased, exhibits a modest capacitance (typically a few tens of picofarads) that decreases with applied (reverse) voltage.

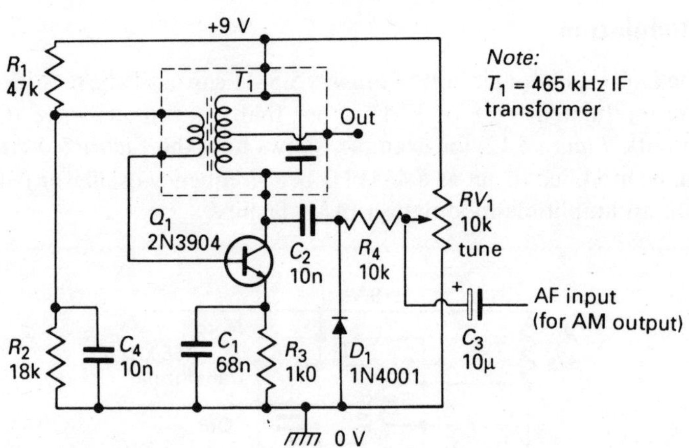

Figure 5.13 *465 kHz BFO with varactor tuning and FM facility*

In *Figure* 5.13 D_1 and C_2 are wired in series and effectively connected across the T_1 tuned circuit (since the circuit's supply rails are shorted together as far as a.c. signals are concerned). Consequently, the oscillator's centre frequency can be varied by altering D_1's capacitance via RV_1, and FM signals can be obtained by feeding an audio-frequency modulation signal to D_1 via C_3 and R_4. Note that C_2 provides d.c. isolation between Q_1 and D_1.

Crystal oscillators

Crystal-controlled oscillator circuits give very high levels of frequency accuracy and stability. They use piezo-electric quartz crystals as high-precision electromechanical resonators or tuned circuits; these crystals have typical *Q*s of about 100 000 and provide about 1000 times greater frequency stability than a conventional *L–C* tuned circuit. Their operating frequency (which may vary from a few kilohertz to 100 MHz) is determined by the mechanical dimensions of the crystal, which may be cut to give either series or parallel resonant operation; series-mode devices present a low impedance at resonance, while parallel-mode ones present a high impedance at resonance.

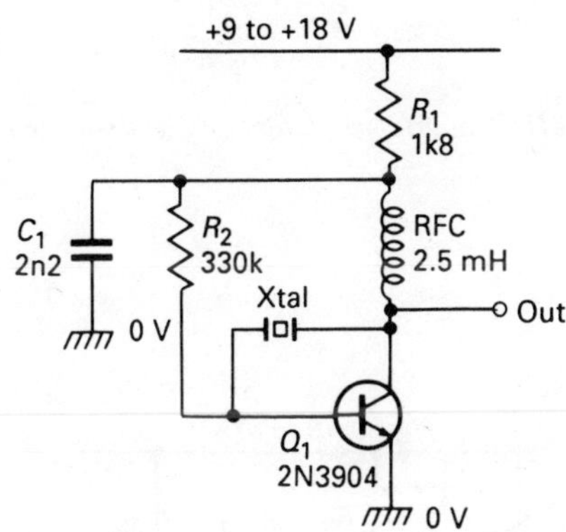

Figure 5.14 *Wide-range Pierce oscillator uses parallel-mode crystal*

Figure 5.14 shows the practical circuit of a wide-range crystal oscillator designed for use with a parallel-mode crystal. This is actually a Pierce oscillator circuit, and can be used with virtually any good 100 kHz to 5 MHz parallel-mode crystal without need for circuit modification.

Alternatively, *Figure* 5.15 shows a 100 kHz Colpitts oscillator designed for use with a series-mode crystal. Note that the L_1–C_1–C_2 tuned circuit is designed to resonate at the same frequency as the crystal, and that its component values must be changed if other crystal frequencies are used.

Finally, *Figure* 5.16 shows an exceptionally useful two-transistor

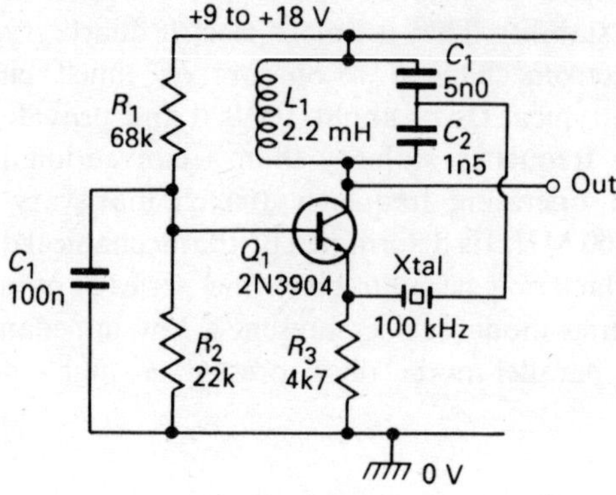

Figure 5.15 *100 kHz Colpitts oscillator uses series-mode crystal*

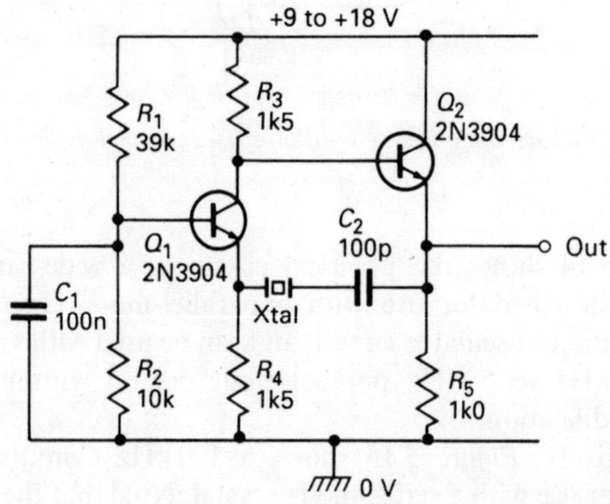

Figure 5.16 *Wide-range (50 kHz to 10 MHz) oscillator can be used with any series-mode crystal*

oscillator that can be used with any 50 kHz to 10 MHz series-resonant crystal. Q_1 is wired as a common-base amplifier and Q_2 is an emitter follower, and the output signal (from Q_2 emitter) is fed back to the input (Q_1 emitter) via C_2 and the series-resonant crystal. This excellent circuit will oscillate with any crystal that shows the slightest sign of life.

White-noise generator

One useful 'linear' but non-sinusoidal waveform is that known as 'white noise', which can be simply described as a signal containing a full spectrum of randomly generated frequencies, each having equal mean power when averaged over a unit of time. White noise is of value in testing AF and RF amplifiers, and is widely used in special-effects sound generator systems.

Figure 5.17*a* shows a simple but useful white-noise generator, which relies on the fact that all 'reverse-biased' zener diodes inherently generate substantial white noise. In the circuit, R_2 and ZD_1 are wired in a negative-feedback loop between the collector and base of common-emitter amplifier Q_1, thus stabilizing the circuit's d.c. working levels; the loop is a.c. decoupled via C_1. Consequently, the zener diode acts as a white-noise source that is wired in series with the base of Q_1, which amplifies the zener noise to a useful level of about 1V0 peak-to-peak. Any 5V6 to 12 V zener diode can be used in this circuit.

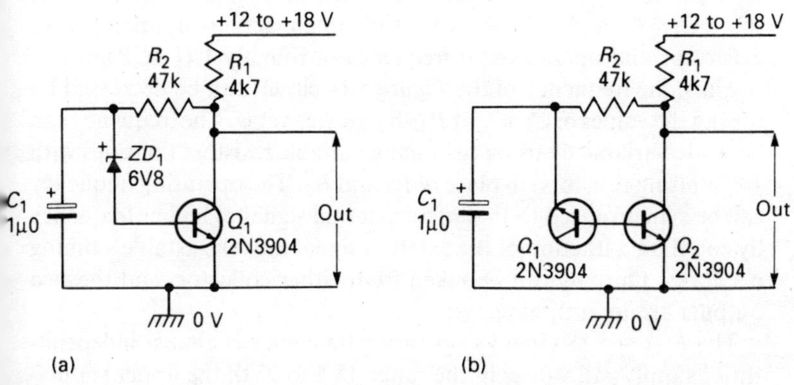

Figure 5.17 *Transistor-zener (a) and two-transistor (b) white noise generators*

In practice, the base–emitter junction of any silicon transistor can be used as a noise-generating zener diode by simply reverse-biasing it to its breakdown point. In the 2N3904 this breakdown occurs at about 6 V, and a 'two-transistor' white-noise generator can thus be made by using the circuit of *Figure* 5.17*b*, in which Q_1 acts as a zener diode.

Multivibrator circuits

Multivibrators are two-state circuits that can be switched between one state and the other by the application of a suitable trigger signal, which may be generated either internally or externally. There are four basic types of multivibrator circuit (already shown and briefly described in Chapter 3), and they are all useful in waveform-generating applications. Of these four, the 'astable' is useful as a free-running square-wave generator, the 'monostable' as a triggered pulse generator, the 'bistable' as a stop/go waveform generator, and the 'Schmitt' as a sine-to-square waveform converter.

Astable basics

The transistor astable multivibrator is of great value in generating free-running square or rectangular waveforms. *Figure* 5.18 shows a practical circuit of this kind, which acts as a self-oscillating regenerative switch in which the on and off periods are controlled by the C_1–R_1 and C_2–R_2 time constants. If these time constants are equal ($C_1 = C_2 = C$, and $R_1 = R_2 = R$), the circuit acts as a square-wave generator and operates at a frequency of roughly $1/(1.4CR)$.

Thus, the frequency of the *Figure* 5.18 circuit can be decreased by raising the values of C_1–C_2 or R_1–R_2, or vice versa. The frequency can be made variable by using twin-gang variable resistors (in series with 10k limiting resistors) in place of R_1 and R_2. The operating frequency can be synchronized to that of an external signal of higher frequency by coupling a fraction of the external signal into the astable's timing networks. Outputs can be taken from either collector, and the two outputs are in antiphase.

The *Figure* 5.18 circuit's operating frequency is almost independent of supply-rail values in the range 1V5 to 9V0; the upper supply-voltage limit is set by the fact that, as the transistors change state at the end of each half-cycle, the base–emitter junction of one transistor

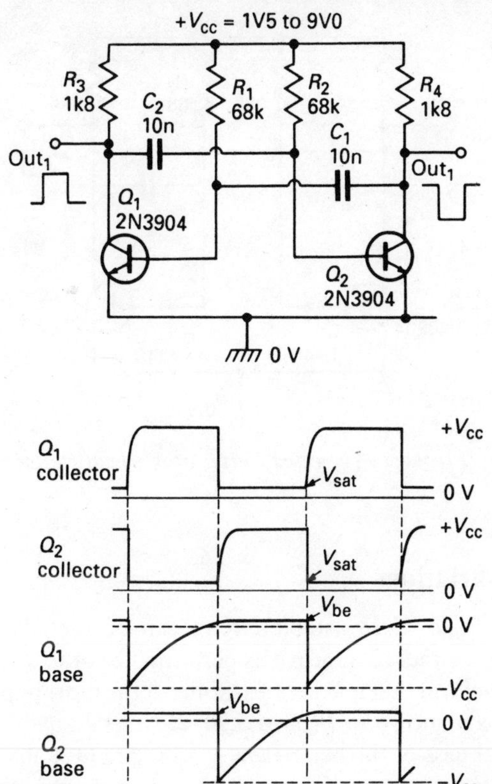

Figure 5.18 *Circuit and waveforms of basic 1 kHz astable multivibrator*

is reverse-biased by an amount almost equal to the supply voltage. Consequently, if the supply voltage exceeds the transistor's base–emitter reverse breakdown voltage (typically only a few volts), the circuit's timing operations will be upset. This problem can be overcome by using the modifications shown in *Figure* 5.19.

Here, a silicon diode is wired in series with the base input terminal of each transistor, and raises its effective base–emitter reverse breakdown voltage to a value greater than that of the diode. The 'protected' *Figure* 5.19 circuit can be used with any supply in the range 3–20 V, and gives a frequency variation of only 2 per cent when the supply is varied from 6V0 to 18V. This variation can be reduced to a mere 0.5 per cent by wiring an additional 'compensation' diode in series with the collector of each transistor, as shown in the diagram.

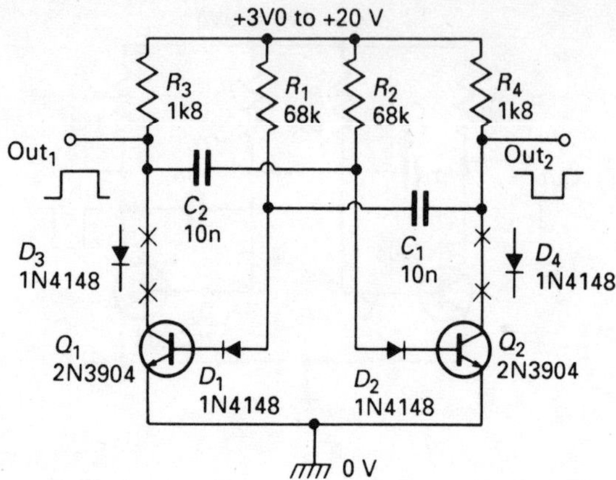

Figure 5.19 *Frequency-corrected 1 kHz astable multivibrator*

Astable variations

The basic *Figure* 5.18 astable circuit can be usefully modified in several ways, either to improve its performance or to alter the type of output waveform that it generates. Some of the most popular of these variations are shown in *Figures* 5.20–25.

One weakness of the basic *Figure* 5.18 circuit is that the leading edges of its output waveforms are slightly rounded; the lower the values of timing resistors R_1–R_2 relative to collector load resistors R_3–R_4, the worse this rounding becomes; conversely, the larger the values of R_1–R_2 relative to R_3–R_4, the better the waveforms. The maximum R_1–R_2 values are in fact set by the current gains of the transistors, and equal $h_{fe} \times R_3$ (or R_4). One obvious way of improving the waveforms, therefore, is to replace Q_1 and Q_2 with Darlington of Super-Alpha connected pairs of transistors and to then use the largest values of timing resistance that are permissible, as shown in the long-period astable circuit of *Figure* 5.20.

In *Figure* 5.20, R_1 and R_2 can be given any values from 10k to 12M, and the circuit can use any supply from 3V0 to 18 V. With the specific R_1–R_2 values shown the circuit gives a total period or cycling time of about 1 s per μF when C_1 and C_2 have equal values, and generates an excellent square-wave output.

The leading-edge rounding of the *Figure* 5.18 circuit occurs because, at the moment of transistor switch-off, the collector resistor

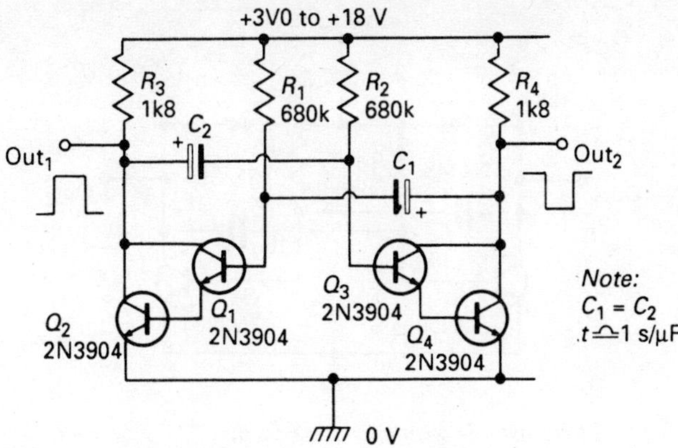

Figure 5.20 *Long-period astable multivibrator*

and timing capacitor (which is connected between the collector of one transistor and the base of the other) form an *R–C* 'divider' that prevents the collector of the off-switching transistor from going abruptly positive. This action can be altered and excellent square waves obtained by effectively disconnecting the timing capacitor from the collector of its transistor as it turns off, as shown in the 1 kHz generator circuit of *Figure* 5.21. Here, D_1 and D_2 are used to disconnect the timing capacitors at the moment of switching. The circuit's main time constants are again determined by C_1–R_1 and C_2–R_2. The effective collector loads of Q_1 and Q_2 are equal to the parallel resistances of R_3–R_4 and R_5–R_6 respectively.

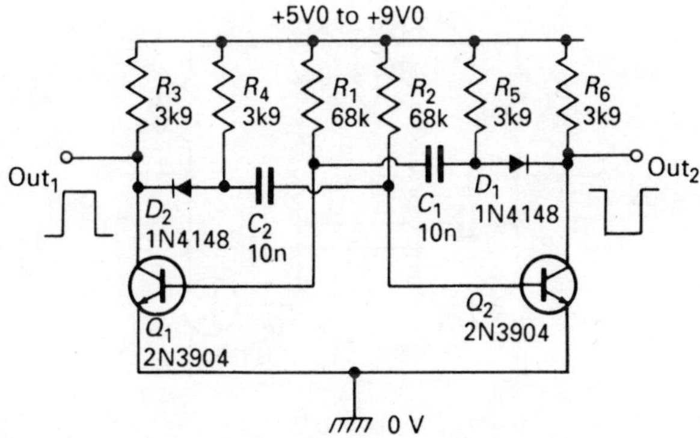

Figure 5.21 *1 kHz astable with waveform correction*

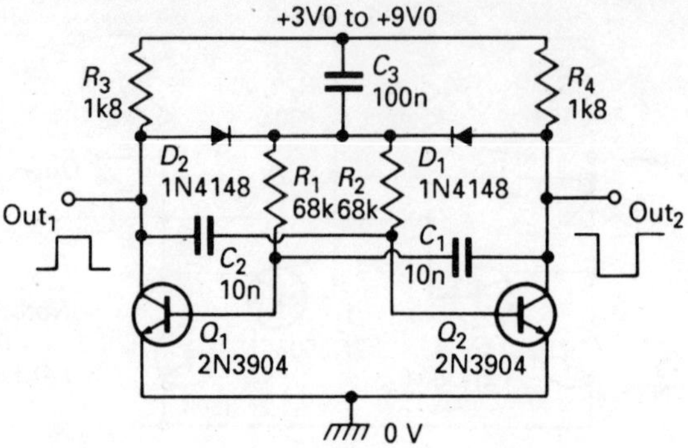

Figure 5.22 *1 kHz astable with sure-start facility*

The basic astable multivibrator operation relies on slight imbalances of the transistor characteristics, which cause one transistor to turn on slightly faster than the other when power is first applied, thus initiating the oscillatory action; if the supply voltage is applied too slowly, both transistors may turn on simultaneously, and the oscillator will not 'start'. This snag can be overcome by using the 'sure-start' circuit of *Figure* 5.22, in which the timing resistors are connected to the transistor collectors in such a way that only one transistor can be on at a time.

The astable circuits shown so far all give symmetrical output waveforms, with a 1:1 mark–space ratio. A non-symmetrical waveform can be obtained by simply making one set of astable time constant components larger than the other. *Figure* 5.23 shows a fixed-

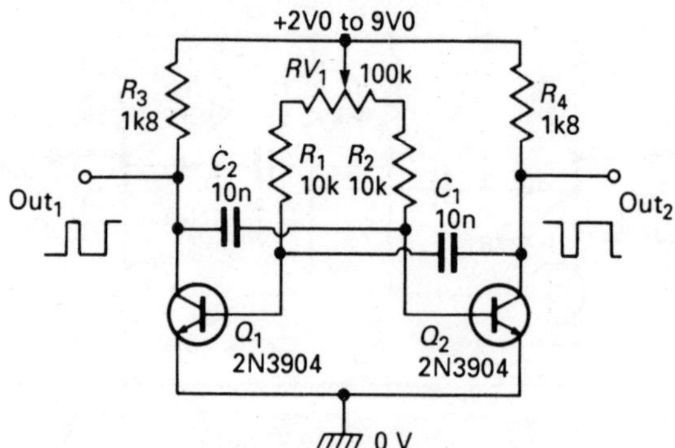

Figure 5.23 *1100 Hz variable mark–space ratio generator*

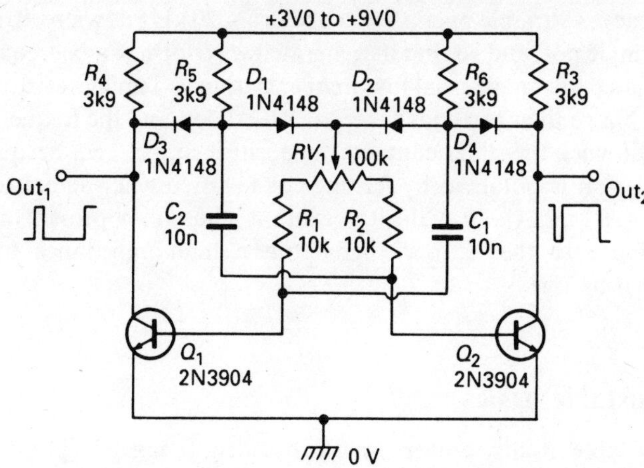

Figure 5.24 *1100 Hz variable mark–space ratio generator with waveform correction and sure-start facility*

frequency (1.1 kHz) variable mark–space ratio generator in which the ratio is variable from 1:10 to 10:1 via RV_1.

The leading edges of the output waveforms of the above circuit may be objectionably rounded when the mark–space control is set to its extreme positions; also, the circuit may not start if its supply is applied too slowly. Both of these snags can be overcome by using the circuit of *Figure* 5.24, which is fitted with both sure-start and waveform-correction diodes.

Finally, *Figure* 5.25 shows the basic astable modified so that its

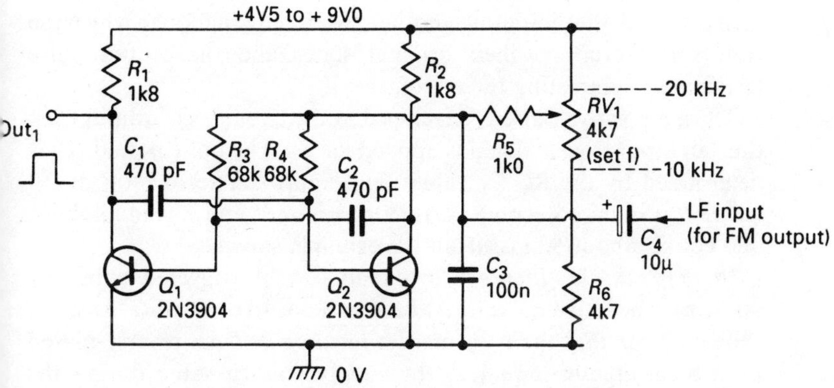

Figure 5.25 *Astable with variable-frequency and FM facility*

frequency is variable over a 2:1 range (from 20 kHz down to 10 kHz) via a single pot, and so that its generated waveform can be frequency modulated via an external low-frequency signal. Timing resistors R_3 and R_4 have their top ends taken to RV_1 slider, and the frequency is greatest when the slider contacts the positive supply line. Frequency modulation is obtained by feeding the low-frequency signal to the tops of R_3–R_4 via C_4; the C_3 value is chosen to present a low impedance to the 'carrier' signal but a high impedance to the modulating one.

Monostable basics

Monostable multivibrators make excellent triggered pulse generators, and may be triggered either electronically or manually. *Figure* 5.26 shows a circuit of the latter type, which is triggered by feeding a positive pulse to Q_2 base via S_1 and R_6. This circuit operates as follows.

Normally, Q_1 is driven to saturation via R_5, so the output (taken from Q_1 collector) is low; Q_2 (which derives its base-bias from Q_1 collector via R_3) is cut off under this condition, and its collector is at full supply-rail voltage. When a *start* signal is applied to Q_2 base by briefly closing S_1, Q_2 is driven on and its collector goes low, reverse biasing Q_1 base via C_1 and thus initiating a regenerative switching action in which Q_1 is turned off (and its output switches high) via C_1's negative charge, and Q_2 is driven on via R_1–R_3 after S_1 is released. As soon as the regenerative action is complete C_1 starts to discharge via R_5, until eventually its charge falls to such a low value that Q_1 starts to turn on again, thus initiating another regenerative action in which the transistors revert to their original states and the output pulse terminates, completing the action.

Thus, a positive pulse is developed at the circuit's Q_1 output each time an input trigger signal is applied via S_1. The pulse period (P) is determined by the R_5–C_1 values, and approximates $0.7 \times R_5 \times C_1$, where P is in microseconds, C is in microfarads and R is in kilohms, and equals about 50 ms/μF in the example shown.

In practice, the *Figure* 5.26 circuit can be triggered either by applying a negative pulse to Q_1 base or a positive one to Q_2 base (as shown). Note that the base–emitter junction of Q_1 is reverse-biased by a peak amount equal to the supply voltage value during the operating cycle, thus limiting the maximum usable supply voltage to

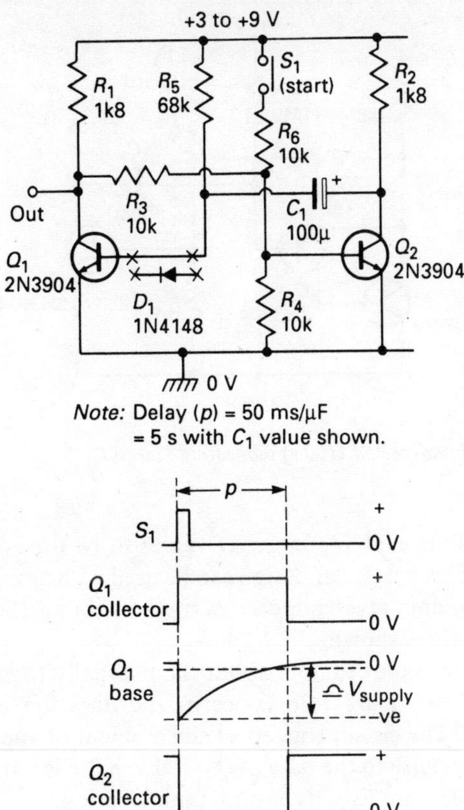

Figure 5.26 *Basic manually triggered monostable pulse generator*

about 9 V (Q_1's base–emitter reverse-breakdown voltage rating). Greater supply voltages can be used by simply wiring a silicon diode in series with Q_1 base, as shown in the diagram, to give the same 'frequency correction' action as described earlier for the astable circuit.

Long delays

The value of timing resistor R_5 used in the basic monostable circuit of *Figure* 5.26 must be large relative to R_2, but must be less than the product of R_1 and the h_{fe} of Q_1. Very long timing periods can be obtained by using a Darlington or Super-Alpha pair of transistors in

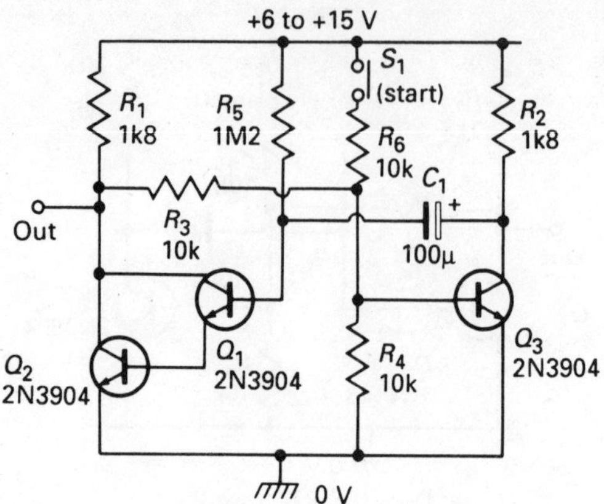

Figure 5.27 *Long-period (100 s) monostable circuit*

place of Q_1, thus enabling large R_5 values to be used, as shown in *Figure* 5.27. This particular design can be used with any supply in the range 6–15 V and gives a pulse period of about 100 s with the component values shown.

An important point to note about the manually triggered monostable circuit of *Figure* 5.26 concerns the duration of the input trigger signal. The circuit triggers at the moment of application of a positive-going pulse to the base of Q_2; if this pulse is removed before the monostable completes its natural timing period the pulse will end regeneratively in the way already described, but if the trigger pulse is not removed at this time the monostable period will end non-regeneratively and will have a longer period and fall-time than normal.

Electronic triggering

Figures 5.28 and 5.29 show alternative ways of applying electronic (rather than manual) triggering to the monostable pulse generator circuit. In each case, the circuit is triggered by a square-wave input with a short rise time; this waveform is differentiated by C_2–R_6, to produce a brief trigger pulse. In the *Figure* 5.28 circuit the differentiated input signal is discriminated by diode D_1, to provide a positive trigger pulse on Q_2 base each time an external trigger signal is applied. In the *Figure* 5.29 circuit the differentiated signal is fed to gate

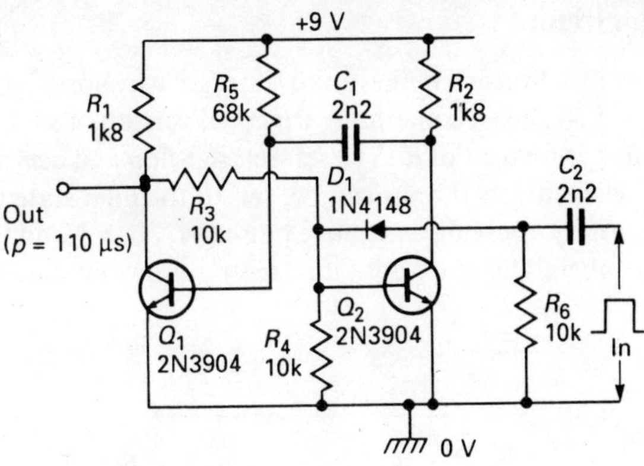

Figure 5.28 *Electronically triggered monostable*

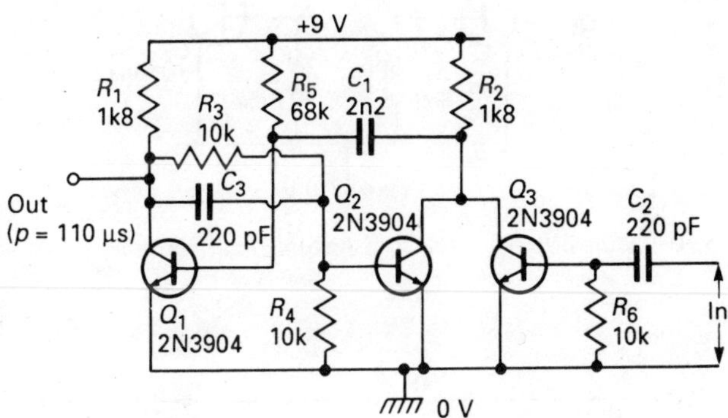

Figure 5.29 *Monostable with gate-input triggering*

transistor Q_3, which enables the trigger signal to be quite independent of Q_2. Note in the latter circuit that 'speed up' capacitor C_3 is wired across feedback resistor R_3, to help improve the shape of the circuit's output pulse.

The *Figure* 5.28 and 5.29 circuits each gives an output pulse period of about 110 μs with the component values shown. The period can be varied from a fraction of a microsecond to many seconds by choice of the C_1–R_5 values. The circuits can be triggered by sine or other non-rectangular waveforms by feeding them to the monostable input via a Schmitt trigger or similar sine/square converter circuit (see *Figure* 5.32).

Bistable circuits

Bistable multivibrators make good stop/go waveform generators, and *Figure* 5.30 shows a manually triggered version of such a circuit, which is also known as an *R–S* (reset–set) flip-flop and acts as a crude 'memory' element; its output can be 'set' to the high state by briefly closing S_1 (or by applying a negative pulse to Q_1 base), and the circuit then 'remembers' this state until it is 'reset' to the low state by briefly

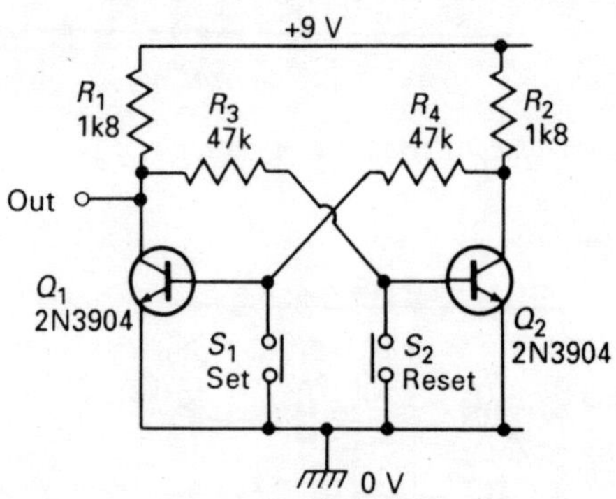

Figure 5.30 *Manually triggered* R–S *bistable multivibrator*

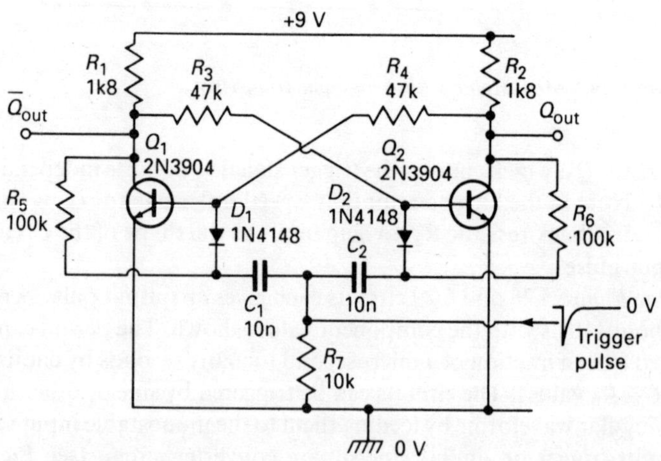

Figure 5.31 *Divide-by-two bistable circuit*

closing S_2 (or by applying a negative pulse to Q_2 base); the circuit then 'remembers' this new state until it is again set via S_1, and so on.

The above circuit can, by connecting two 'steering' diodes and associated components as shown in *Figure* 5.31, be modified to give a divide-by-two or 'counting' action in which it changes state each time a negative-going trigger pulse is applied; thus, if the input pulses are derived from a square wave it will generate a square-wave output at half of the input signal frequency. Note that the circuit generates a pair of antiphase outputs, known as the Q and not-Q. Also note that the introduction of very inexpensive CMOS IC versions of the bistable counter has made the *Figure* 5.31 transistor circuit almost obsolete.

The Schmitt trigger

The final member of the multivibrator family is the Schmitt trigger. This is a voltage-sensitive switching circuit that changes its output state when the input goes above or below pre-set upper and lower threshold levels; *Figure* 5.32 shows it used as a sine-to-square waveform converter. The Schmitt uses both emitter coupling and cross-coupling between Q_1 collector and Q_2 base to provide regenerative switching operation; C_2 helps speed up the switching actions by shunting R_4. The sine wave input is superimposed on a d.c. voltage (determined by RV_1–R_1 and R_2) applied to Q_1 base.

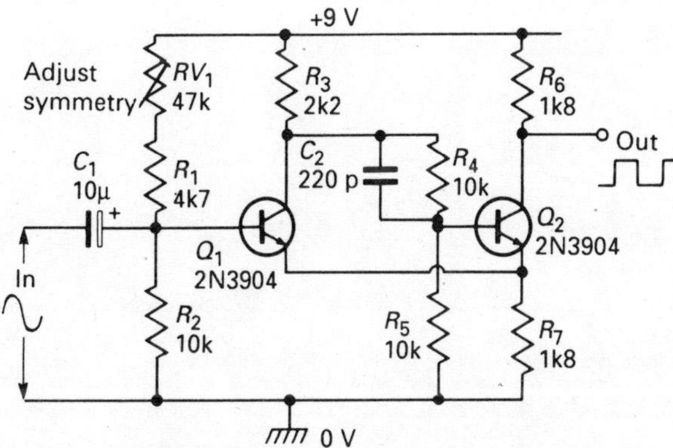

Figure 5.32 *Schmitt sine/square converter*

The *Figure* 5.32 circuit acts as a good sine/square converter at frequencies up to a few hundred kilohertz, needs a sine-wave input signal amplitude of at least 0.5 V r.m.s., and produces square waves with rise times of only a fraction of a microsecond. The output signal symmetry varies with input signal amplitude; RV_1 should be adjusted to give best results.

6 Transistor audio amplifiers

Chapter 4 showed various ways of using bipolar transistors in the three basic amplifying modes; this present chapter looks at ways of using them in audio pre-amp, tone control, and power amplifier applications.

Audio amplifier basics

A modern stereo amplifier system consists of two virtually identical hi-fi audio amplifier channels, each with a switch-selectable option of several input signal sources (radio tuner, tape player, disc player, auxiliary input, etc.), and giving a single output to a high-power loudspeaker. For most practical purposes, each channel can be broken down into three distinct circuit sections or blocks, as shown in *Figure* 6.1.

The first section is the selector/pre-amplifier block. It enables the user to select the desired type of input signal source and applies an appropriate amount of amplification and frequency correction to the

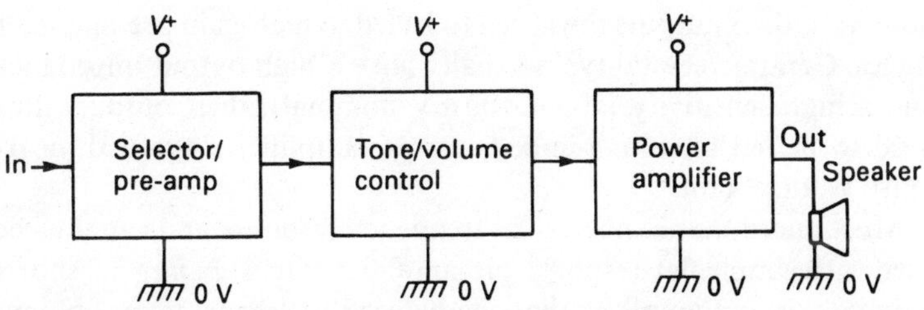

Figure 6.1 *Basic elements of one channel of an audio-amplifier system*

signal, so that the resulting output signal is suitable for use by the second circuit block.

The second section is the tone-/volume-control block, which enables the user to adjust the system's frequency characteristics and output signal amplitude to suit personal tastes. This section may also contain additional filter circuits and gadgets, such as scratch and rumble filters and audio mixer circuitry, etc.

The system's final section is the power amplifier, which may be designed to handle maximum levels ranging from a few hundred milliwatts up to hundreds of watts. These amplifiers span the full audio-frequency range and generate minimal signal distortion, and almost invariably incorporate some form of automatic overload and thermal-runaway protection, etc.

All three-audio amplifier sections are powered from a single source, and incorporate supply decoupling networks to prevent unwanted signal interactions.

Simple pre-amplifiers

The basic function of an audio pre-amplifier is that of modifying the input signal characteristics so that they give the level frequency response and nominal 100 mV mean output amplitude needed to drive the amplifier's tone-control system. If the input is derived from a radio tuner or a tape player, etc., the signal characteristics are usually such that they can be fed directly to the tone-control sections, bypassing the preamplifier circuit, but if derived from a microphone or pick-up device they will almost certainly need modification via a pre-amplifier stage.

Microphones and pick-ups come in two basic types; they are either magnetic or ceramic/crystal devices. Magnetic types usually have a low output impedance and a low signal sensitivity (about 2 mV nominal); their outputs thus need to be fed to high-gain pre-amplifier stages. Ceramic/crystal types usually have a high output impedance and a high sensitivity (about 100 mV nominal); their outputs thus need to be fed to a high-impedance pre-amplifier stage with near-unity voltage gain.

Most microphones have a flat frequency response and can thus be used with simple flat-response pre-amplifier stages. *Figure* 6.2 shows a unity-gain pre-amplifier that can be used with most types of high-impedance ceramic/crystal microphones. This is an emitter follower

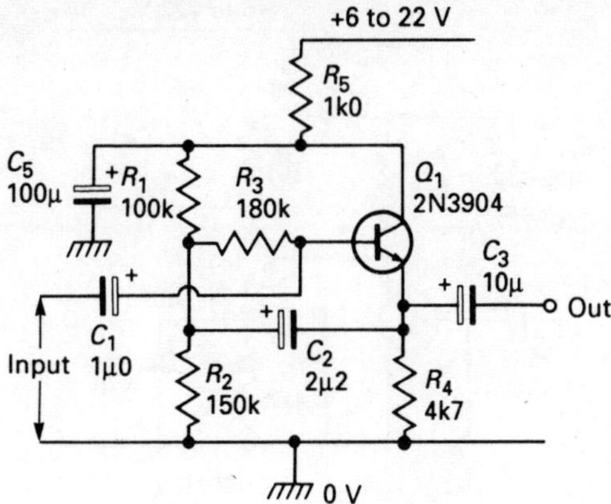

Figure 6.2 *High-impedance pre-amplifier for use with ceramic/crystal microphones*

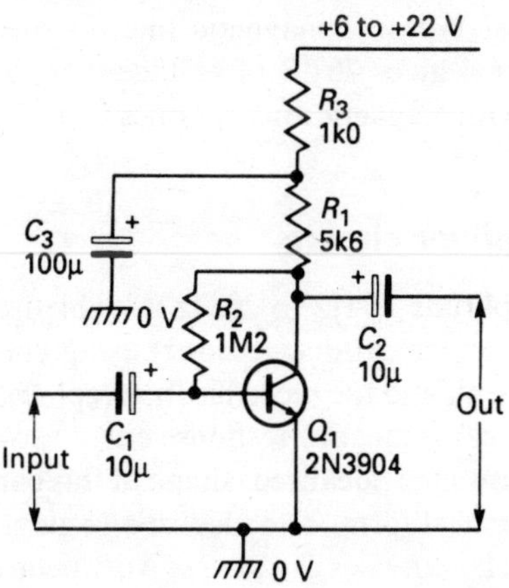

Figure 6.3 *Magnetic microphone pre-amplifier, giving 46 dB of gain*

circuit with a bootstrapped (via C_2–R_3) input network, and has a typical input impedance of about 2M0; its supply is decoupled via C_5–R_5.

Figures 6.3 and 6.4 show alternative pre-amplifier circuits that can be used with low-sensitivity magnetic microphones. The single-stage circuit of *Figure* 6.3 gives 46 dB (× 200) of voltage gain, and is suitable

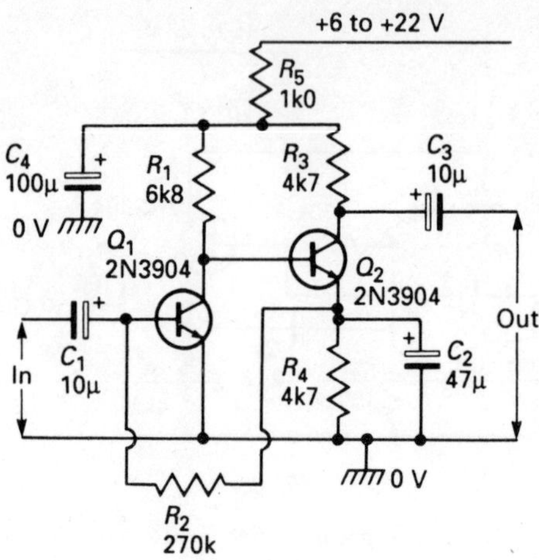

Figure 6.4 *Magnetic microphone pre-amplifier, giving 76 dB of gain*

for use with most types of magnetic microphone. The two-stage circuit of *Figure* 6.4 gives 76 dB of voltage gain, and is specifically intended for use with magnetic microphones with very low sensitivity.

RIAA pre-amplifier circuits

If a constant-amplitude 20 Hz to 20 Hz variable-frequency signal is recorded on a phonograph disc (record) using conventional stereo recording equipment, and the record is then replayed, it will generate the highly non-linear frequency response curve shown in *Figure* 6.5; the dotted line shows the 'idealized' shape of this curve, and the solid line shows its practical form. The idealized response is flat between 500 Hz and 2120 Hz, but rises at a rate of 6 dB/octave (20 dB/decade) above 2120 Hz, and falls at a 6 dB/octave rate between 500 Hz and 50 Hz; the response is flat to frequencies below 50 Hz.

These specific response curves are used because they enable disc recordings to be made with excellent signal-to-noise ratios and wide dynamic ranges, and are used on all normal records. Consequently, when a disc is replayed the output of the pick-up device must be passed to the power amplifier circuitry via a pre-amplifier that has a frequency equalization curve that is the exact inverse of that used to make the original disc recording, so that a linear overall record-to-replay response is obtained.

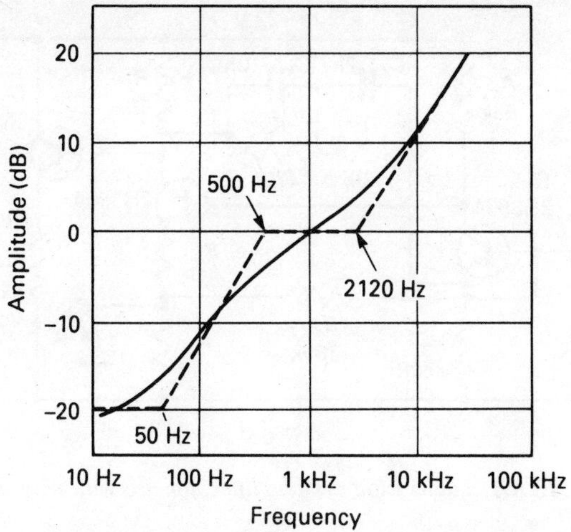

Figure 6.5 *Typical phono' disc frequency response playback curve*

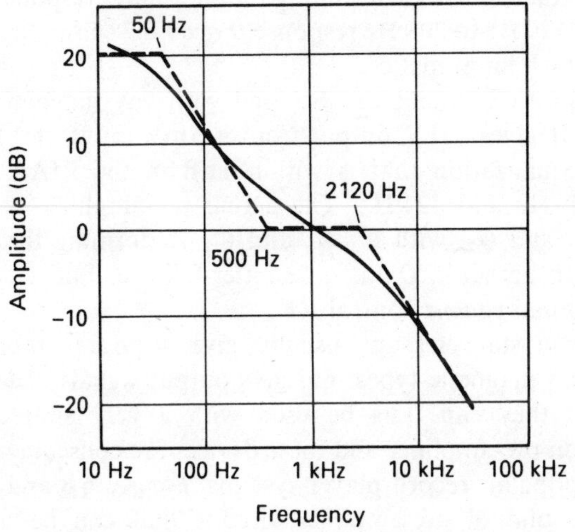

Figure 6.6 *RIAA playback equalization curve*

Figure 6.6 shows the internationally standardized shape of the necessary 'RIAA' (Record Industry Association of America) equalization curve. A practical RIAA equalization pre-amplifier can be made by wiring a pair of frequency-dependent *C–R* feedback networks into a standard pre-amplifier circuit (so that the gain falls as the frequency

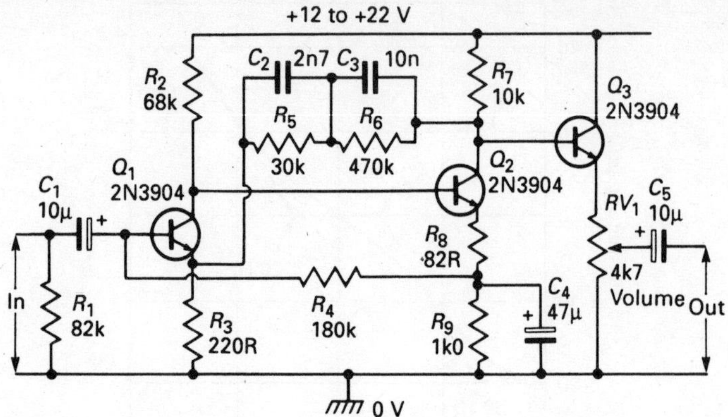

Figure 6.7 *RIAA equalization pre-amplifier, for use with magnetic pick-up cartridges*

rises), with one network controlling the 50–500 Hz response, and the other the 2120 Hz to 20 kHz response. *Figure* 6.7 shows the practical circuit of such an amplifier.

The *Figure* 6.7 circuit can be used with any magnetic pick-up cartridge. It gives a 1 V output from a 6 mV input at 1 kHz, and provides equalization that is within 1 dB of the RIAA standard between 40 Hz and 12 kHz. The actual pre-amplifier is designed around Q_1 and Q_2, with C_2–R_5 and C_3–R_6 forming the feedback equalization network. Q_3 as an emitter-follower buffer stage, and drives optional *volume* control RV_1.

Ceramic/crystal pick-ups usually give a poorer reproduction quality than magnetic types, but give output signals of far greater amplitude: they can thus be used with a very simple type of equalization pre-amplifier and these devices are consequently found in many 'popular' record player systems. *Figures* 6.8 and 6.9 show alternative phono' pre-amplifier circuits that can be used with ceramic or crystal pick-up cartridges: in each case, the pre-amplifier/equalizer circuit is designed around Q_1, and Q_2 is an emitter follower output stage that drives optional *volume* control RV_1.

The *Figure* 6.8 circuit can be used with any pick-up cartridge that has a capacitance in the 1000–10 000 pF range. Two-stage equalization is provided via C_2–R_2 and C_2–R_3, and is typically within 1.6 dB of the RIAA standard between 40 Hz and 12 kHz.

The alternative *Figure* 6.9 circuit can be used only with pick-ups

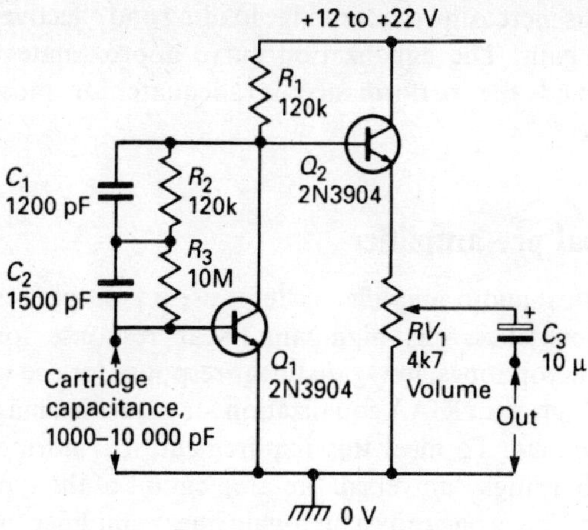

Figure 6.8 *RIAA phono' equalizer for ceramic cartridges*

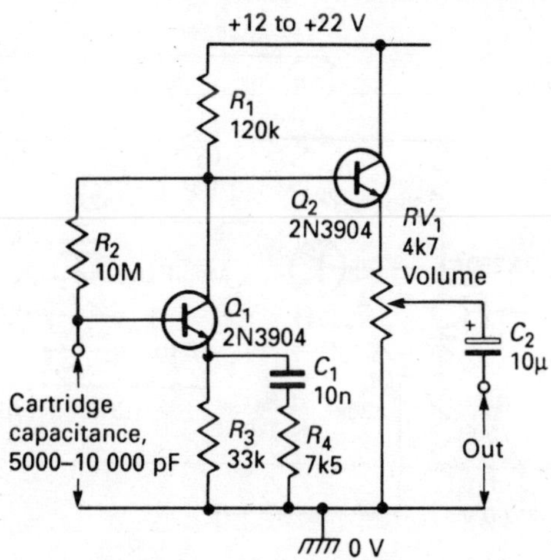

Figure 6.9 *Alternative RIAA phono' equalizer for ceramic cartridges*

with capacitance values in the range 5000–10 000 pF, since this capacitance forms part of the frequency-response network: the other part is formed by C_1–R_3. At 50 Hz, this circuit has a high input impedance (about 600k), and causes only slight cartridge loading: as the frequency is increased, however, the input impedance decreases sharply, thus increasing the cartridge loading and effectively reducing the circuit gain. The equalization curve approximates the RIAA standard, and the performance is adequate for most practical applications.

A universal pre-amplifier

Most practical audio-amplifier systems use pre-amplifiers with variable characteristics, e.g. high-gain linear response for use with magnetic microphones, low-gain linear response for use with a radio tuner, and high-gain RIAA equalization for use with a magnetic pick-up cartridge, etc. To meet this requirement, it is normal to fit the system with a single 'universal' pre-amp circuit of the type shown in *Figure* 6.10. This is basically a high-gain linear amplifier that can have its characteristics altered by switching alternative types of resistor/filter network into its feedback loops.

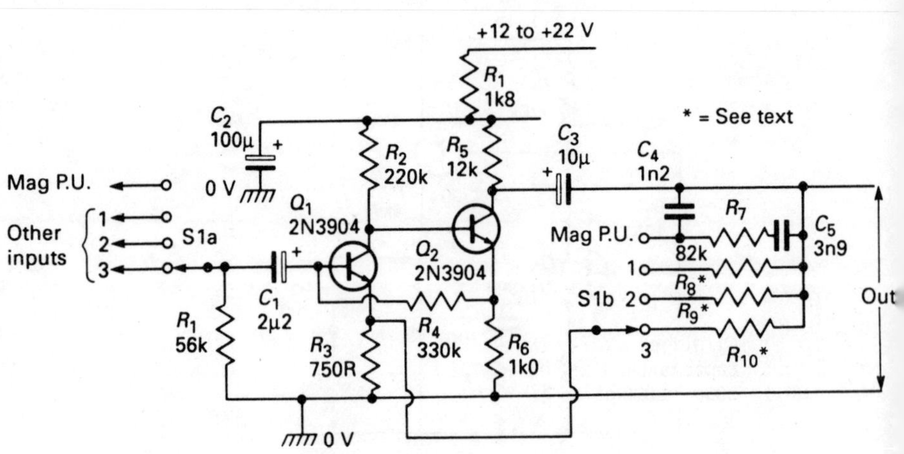

Figure 6.10 *'Universal' pre-amplifier circuit*

Thus, when the selector switch is set to the 'MAG P.U' position, S_{1a} connects the input to the magnetic pick-up cartridge, and S_{1b} connects the C_4–R_7–C_5 RIAA equalization network into the feedback loop. In the remaining switch positions, alternative input sources are selected via S_{1a}, and appropriate linear-response gain-controlling feedback resistors (R_8, R_9 and R_{10}) are selected via S_{1b}.

The values of these feedback resistors should be selected (between 10k and 10M) to suit individual requirements; the circuit gain is proportional to the feedback resistor value.

Volume control

The volume control circuitry of an audio amplifier system is normally placed between the output of the pre-amplifier and the input of the tone-control circuitry, and usually consists of a variable potential divider or 'pot'. This pot can form part of an active circuit, as shown in *Figures* 6.7–9, but a snag here is that rapid variation of the control can briefly apply d.c. potentials to the next circuit, possibly upsetting its bias and generating severe signal distortion.

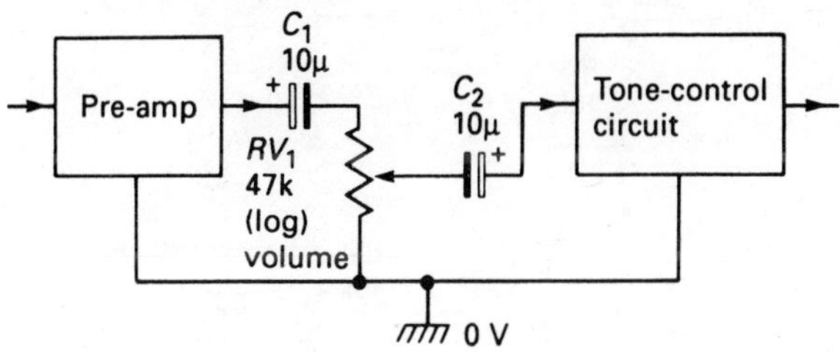

Figure 6.11 *Ideal form and location of the volume control*

Figure 6.11 shows the ideal form and location of the volume control. It is fully d.c.-isolated from the pre-amplifier's output via C_1, and from the input of the tone-control circuitry via C_2; variation of RV_1 slider thus has no effect on the d.c. bias levels of either circuit. RV_1 should be a 'log' type of pot.

Passive tone control

A tone control network lets the user alter the frequency response of the amplifier system to suit his personal mood or requirement. He can, for example, use it to boost or cut the low-frequency (bass) or high-frequency (treble) parts of a musical piece, to emphasize the effects of certain sections of the orchestra, etc.

Simple tone control networks consist, in essence, of collections of C–R filters, through which the audio signals are passed; these

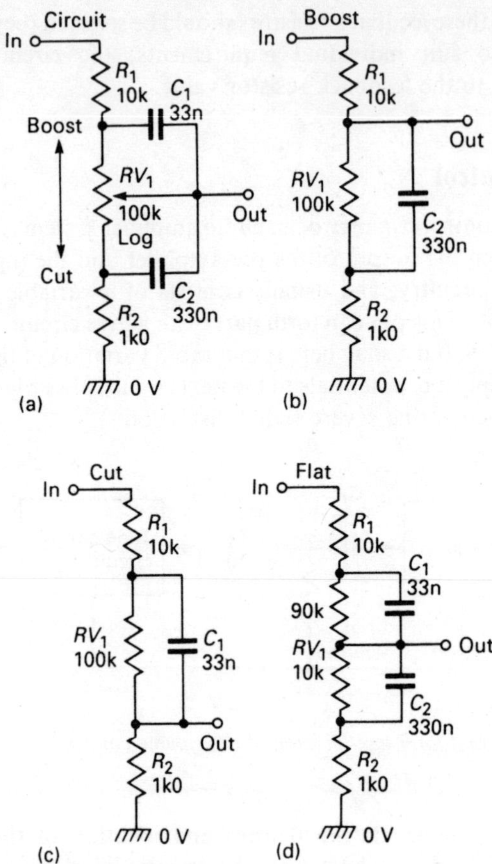

Figure 6.12 *Circuit and equivalents of bass tone control network*

networks are passive, and cause some degree of signal attenuation. Tone control networks can also be wired into the feedback loops of simple transistor amplifiers, to enable the systems to give an overall signal gain; in this case they are known as 'active' tone control circuits.

Figure 6.12*a* shows a typical passive bass tone control network, and *Figures* 6.12*b–d* show the circuit's equivalent when RV_1 is set to the maximum boost, maximum cut, and flat positions respectively. C_1 and C_2 are effectively open circuit when the frequency is at its lowest bass value, so it can be seen from *Figure* 6.12*b* that the boost circuit is equal to a 10k-over-101k potential divider, and gives only slight bass attenuation. The *Figure* 6.12*c* cut circuit is equal to a 110k-over-1k0 divider, and gives roughly 40 dB of signal attenuation. Finally, when RV_1 is set to the flat position shown in *Figure* 6.12*d* (with 90k of RV_1 above the slider, and 10k below it), the circuit is equal to a 100k-over-11k divider, and gives about 20 dB of signal attenuation at all frequencies. Thus, this bass control circuit gives a maximum of about 20 dB of bass boost or cut relative to the flat signals.

Figure 6.13 shows the typical circuit of a passive treble tone control network, together with its equivalent circuits under the maximum boost, maximum cut, and flat operating conditions. This circuit also

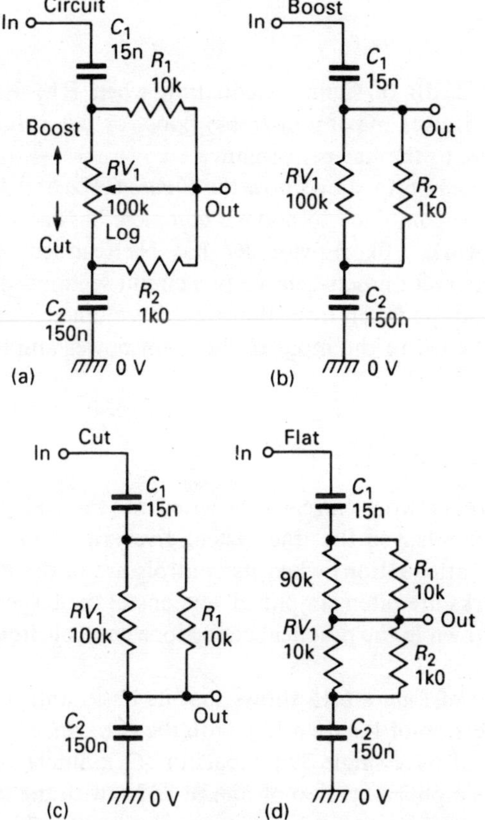

Figure 6.13 *Circuit and equivalents of treble tone control network*

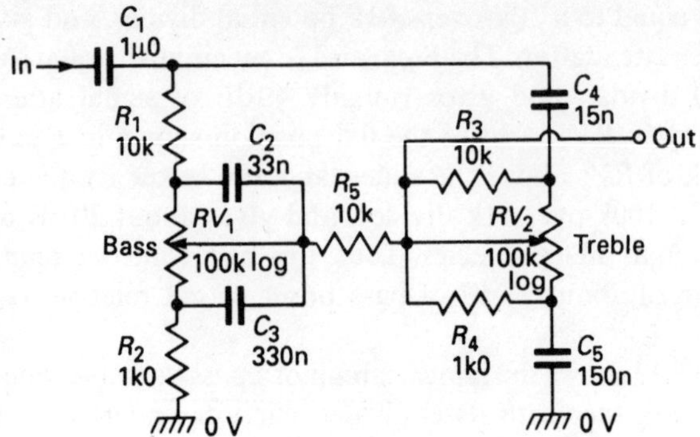

Figure 6.14 *Passive bass and treble tone control network*

gives about 20 dB of signal attenuation when RV_1 is in the flat position, and gives maximum treble boost or cut values of about 20 dB relative to the flat performance.

Finally, *Figure* 6.14 shows how the *Figure* 6.12*a* and *Figure* 6.13*a* circuits can be combined to make a complete bass and treble tone-control network; 10k resistor R_5 has been added to minimize unwanted interaction between the two circuit sections. The input to this circuit can be taken from the circuit's volume control, and the output can be fed to the input of the main power amplifier.

Active tone controls

A tone control network can easily be wired into the feedback path of a transistor amplifier so that the system gives an overall signal gain (rather than attenuation) when its controls are in the flat position. Such networks are often simplified versions of the basic *Figure* 6.14 circuit, as shown in the practical active tone control circuit of *Figure* 6.15.

Inspection of *Figure* 6.15 shows that its bass control section is a simplified version of *Figure* 6.12*a*, with the two capacitors of *Figure* 6.12*a* replaced by a single 39n capacitor (C_2). Similarly, the treble section is a simplified version of *Figure* 6.13*a*, with the two resistors (R_1 and R_2 of *Figures* 6.13*a*) eliminated. R_3 and R_4 balance the performances of the two sections of the *Figure* 6.15 circuit.

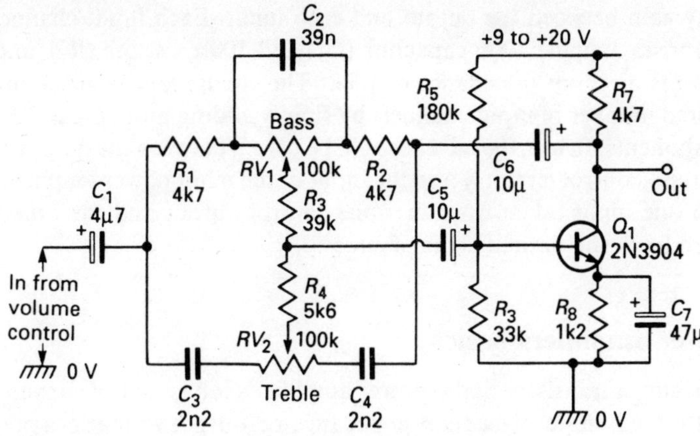

Figure 6.15 *Active bass and treble tone control circuit*

An audio mixer

One useful gadget that can be fitted in the area of the volume-/tone-control section of an audio-amplifier is a multichannel audio mixer. As the title implies, this gadget enables several different audio signals to be mixed together, to form a single composite output signal. This can be useful if, for example, you wish to be able to hear the 'emergency' sounds of a front-door or baby-room microphones, etc., while listening to normal entertainment sources.

Figure 6.16 shows a simple three-channel audio mixer that gives

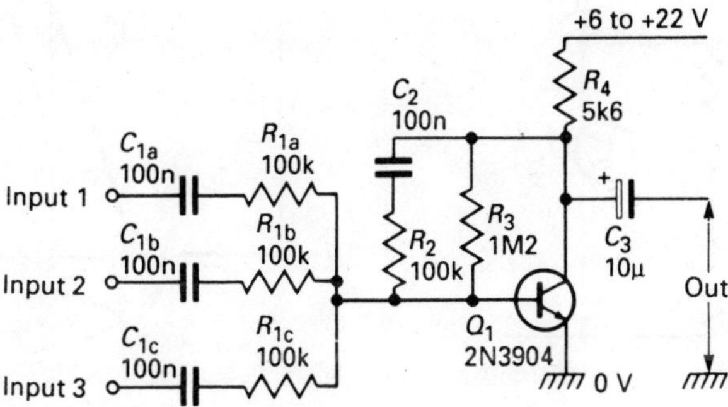

Figure 6.16 *Three-channel audio mixer*

unity gain between the output and each input. Each input channel comprises a single 100n capacitor (C_1) and 100k resistor (R_1), and presents an input impedance of 100k. The circuit can be given any desired number of input channels by simply adding more C_1 and R_1 components. In use, the mixer should be placed between the output of the tone-control circuitry and the input of the main power amplifier, with one input taken from the tone-control output and the others taken from the desired signal sources.

Power amplifiers basics

Basically, a transistor audio power amplifier's job is that of converting the medium-level medium-impedance a.c. output voltage of a pre-amplifier stage into a high-level power-amplified state suitable for driving a low-impedance loudspeaker or pair of headphones, etc., and to do so with the minimum of signal distortion. This action can be achieved by operating the transistor(s) in either of two basic modes, known as the 'class-A' or the 'class-B' modes. *Figures* 6.17 and 6.18 outline the basic principles of these two operating modes.

A basic class-A amplifier normally consists of a single transistor, wired in the common-emitter mode, with the speaker acting as its collector load, as shown in *Figure* 6.17*a*. The essential feature of this type of amplifier is that its input (base) is biased so that the collector current takes up a quiescent value roughly half way between the

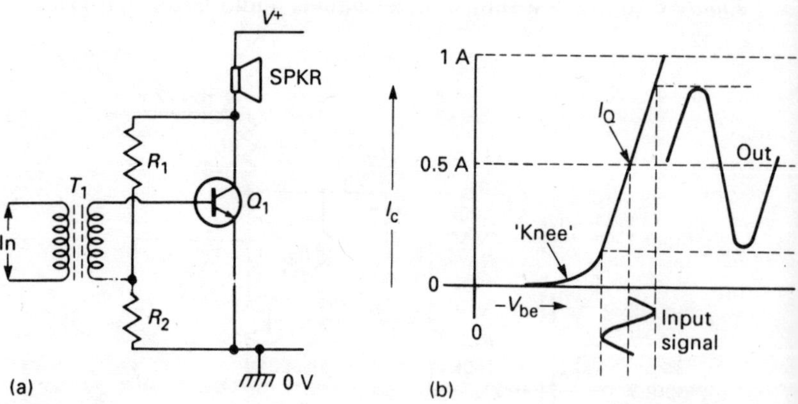

Figure 6.17 *Basic circuit (a) and transfer characteristics (b) of class-A amplifier*

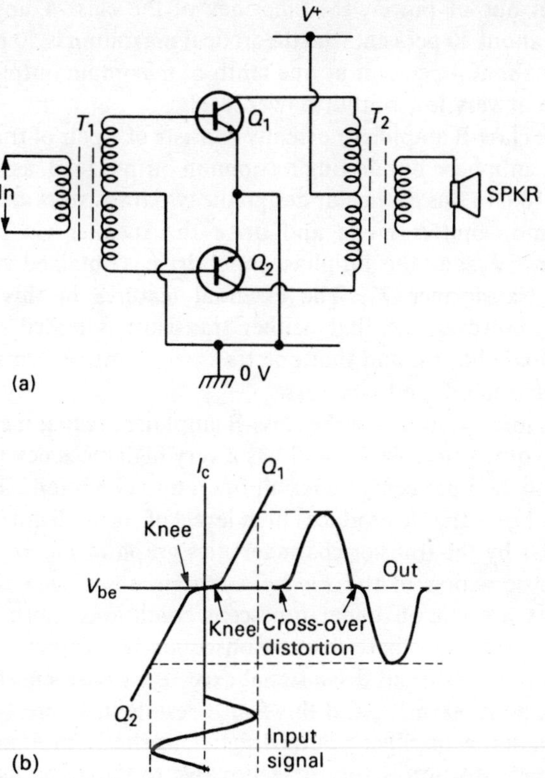

Figure 6.18 *Basic circuit (a) and transfer characteristics (b) of class-B amplifier*

desired maximum and minimum swings of output current, as shown in *Figure* 6.17*b*, so that maximal undistorted output signal swings can be obtained. From this description, it can be seen that if the a.c. and d.c. impedances of the speaker load are the same, the transistor collector voltage takes up a quiescent value of roughly half of the supply voltage.

The class-A amplifier is simple and produces excellent low-distortion audio signals. Its major disadvantages are that it consumes a high quiescent current, and is relatively inefficient. Amplifier 'efficiency' can be regarded as the ratio of a.c. power feeding into the load, compared with the d.c. power consumed by the circuit. At maximum output power, the efficiency of the class-A amplifier is typically about 40 per cent (the theoretical maximum is 50 per cent), falling to about 4 per cent at one tenth of maximum output and to near-zero at very low output power levels.

A basic class-B amplifier normally consists of a pair of transistors, driven in antiphase but driving a common output load, as shown in *Figure* 6.18*a*. In this particular design the two transistors are wired in the common-emitter mode and drive the speaker via push-pull transformer T_2, and the antiphase input drive is obtained via phase-splitting transformer T_1. The essential features of this type of amplifier, however, are that neither transistor is biased on under quiescent conditions, and that one transistor is driven on when the other is driven off, and vice versa.

The major advantages of the class-B amplifier are that it consumes near-zero quiescent current, and has a very high efficiency (theoretically up to 78.5 per cent) under all operating conditions. Its major disadvantage is that it produces high levels of signal distortion, as is made clear by the transfer characteristics graph of *Figure* 6.18*b*.

The basic action of the *Figure* 6.18*a* circuit is such that both transistors are cut off under quiescent conditions, since they are operated with zero base bias. Consequently, neither transistor conducts until the input drive signal exceeds its base–emitter 'knee' voltage (about 600 mV), and this factor results in severe cross-over distortion in the amplifier's output signal, as shown in *Figure* 6.18*b*. Cross-over distortion is very objectionable to the audio listener, so the basic class-B circuit must be modified if it is to be used as a practical audio power amplifier; the modified circuit is known as a 'class-AB' amplifier.

Class-AB basics

The cross-over distortion of the class-B amplifier can be virtually eliminated by applying slight forward bias to the base of each transistor, as shown in *Figure* 6.19, so that each transistor passes a modest quiescent current. Such a circuit is known as a class-AB amplifier. Circuits of this type were widely used in early transistor power amplifier systems but are now virtually obsolete, since they require the use of transformers for input phase-splitting and output speaker driving, and must have closely matched transistor characteristics if a good low-distortion performance is to be obtained.

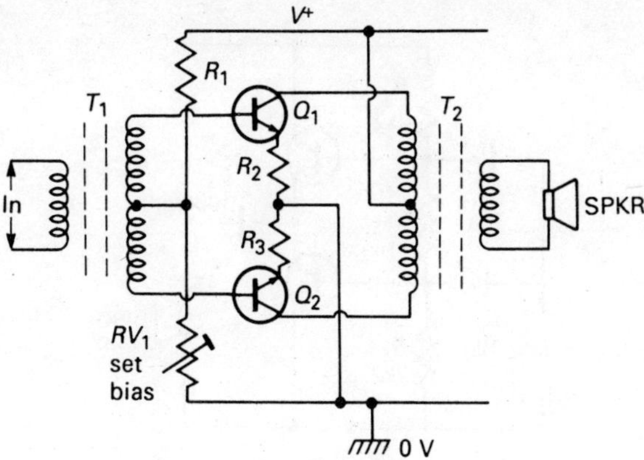

Figure 6.19 *Basic circuit of class-AB amplifier*

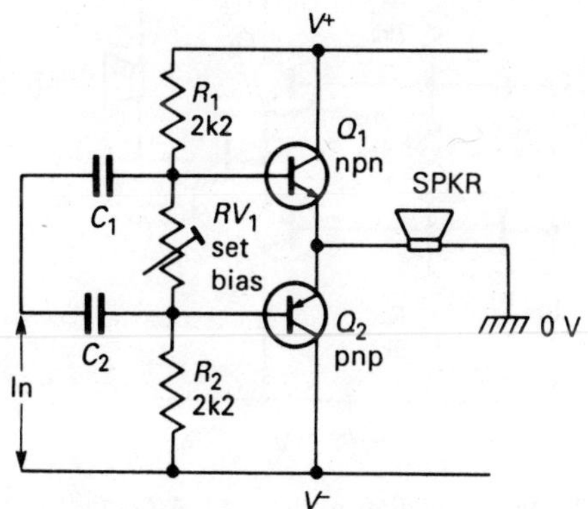

Figure 6.20 *Basic class-AB amplifier with complementary emitter follower output and dual power supply*

Figure 6.20 shows the basic circuit of a class-AB amplifier that suffers from none of the snags mentioned above. It uses a complementary pair of transistors (one pnp and one npn) wired in the emitter follower mode, and uses a split (dual) power supply. The two emitter followers are biased (via R_1–RV_1–R_2) so that their outputs are at zero volts and zero current flows in the speaker load under quiescent conditions, but have slight forward bias applied (via RV_1), so that they pass modest quiescent currents and thus do not suffer from cross-over distortion problems. Identical input signals are applied (via C_1

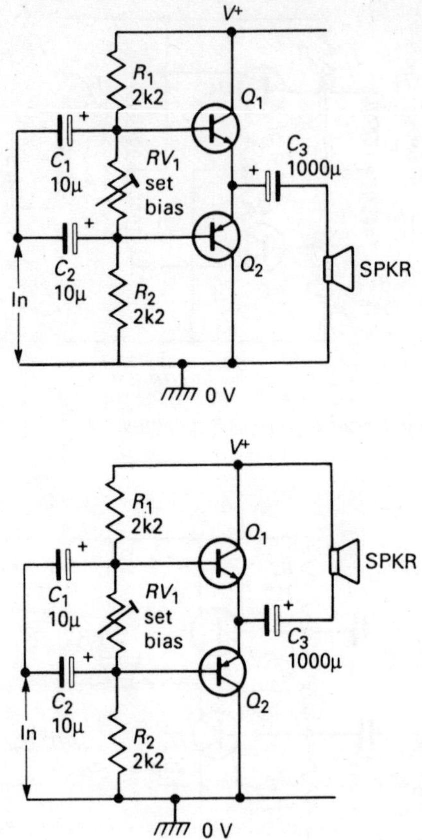

Figure 6.21 *Alternative versions of the class-AB amplifier with single-ended power supply*

and C_2) to the bases of both emitter followers; the circuit operates as follows.

When an input signal is applied to the *Figure* 6.20 circuit the positive parts drive Q_2 off and Q_1 on. Q_1 is an npn transistor and acts as a current source with a very low output (emitter) impedance; it feeds a faithful unity-voltage-gain copy of the signal directly to the speaker under this condition, almost irrespective of Q_1's actual parameter values. Similarly the negative parts of the input signal drive Q_1 off and drive Q_2 on. Q_2 is a pnp device and acts as a current sink with a very low input (emitter) impedance; it sinks a faithful unity-voltage-gain copy of the signal from the speaker under this condition, almost irrespective of Q_2's actual parameter values.

Thus, the basic *Figure* 6.20 circuit does not require the use of transistors with closely matched electrical characteristics, and does not call for the use of input or output transformers. The design can be modified for use with a single-ended power supply by simply connecting one end of the speaker to either the zero or the positive supply rail, and connecting the other end to the amplifier output via a high-value blocking capacitor, as shown in *Figure* 6.21.

The basic *Figure* 6.20 and 6.21 circuit forms the basis of virtually all modern audio power amplifier designs, including those in IC form. Many modifications and variations can be made to the basic circuit.

Circuit variations

The basic *Figure* 6.20 circuit gives zero overall voltage gain, so the most obvious circuit modification is to provide it with a voltage-amplifying driver stage, as in *Figure* 6.22. Here, Q_1 is wired as a common-emitter amplifier, and drives the complementary pair of emitter followers via collector load resistor R_1. Note that Q_1 base bias is derived from the circuit's output via R_2–R_3, thus providing d.c.

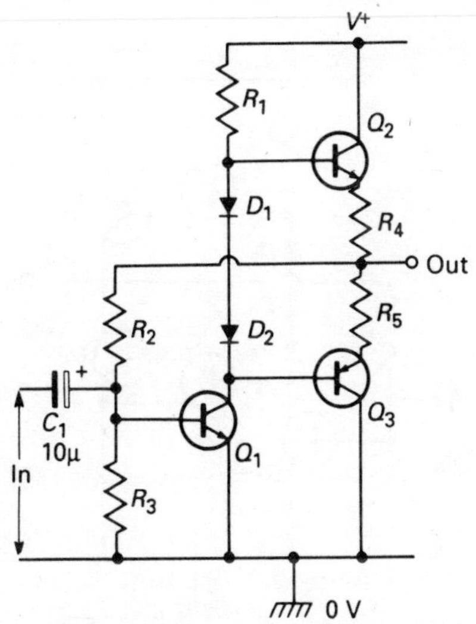

Figure 6.22 *Complementary amplifier with driver and auto-bias*

feedback to stabilize the circuit's operating points and a.c. feedback to minimize signal distortion.

Figure 6.22 also shows how auto-bias can be applied to Q_2 and Q_3 via silicon diodes D_1 and D_2. If simple potential-divider biasing is applied to the circuit (as in *Figure* 6.20) its quiescent current will (because of the thermal characteristics of the transistor base–emitter junctions) increase when the ambient temperature rises, and decrease as it falls. In *Figure* 6.22 the biasing is derived via the forward volt drops of the D_1–D_2 silicon diodes, which inherently have thermal characteristics almost identical to those of the Q_2–Q_3 base–emitter junctions, thus giving the circuit near-perfect thermal compensation. In practice, a small pre-set pot is usually wired in series with D_1–D_2, to enable the bias voltage to be adjusted over a limited range, and low-value resistors R_4 and R_5 are wired in series with Q_2 and Q_3 emitters to provide a degree of d.c. negative feedback.

The input impedance of the basic *Figure* 6.20 circuit equals the product of the speaker load impedance and the h_{fe} of Q_1 or Q_2. An obvious circuit improvement is to replace the individual Q_1 and Q_2 transistors with Darlington or Super-Alpha pairs of transistors, thereby greatly increasing the circuit's input impedance and enabling it to be used with a driver with a high-value collector load. *Figures* 6.23–5 show three alternative ways of modifying the *Figure* 6.22 circuit in this way.

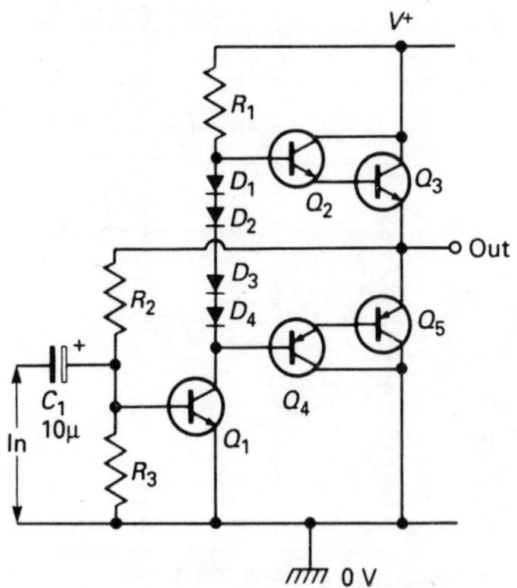

Figure 6.23 *Amplifier with Darlington output stages*

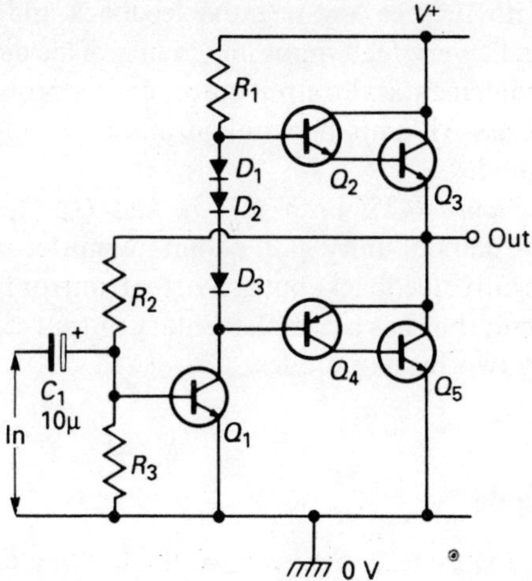

Figure 6.24 *Amplifier with quasi-complementary output stages*

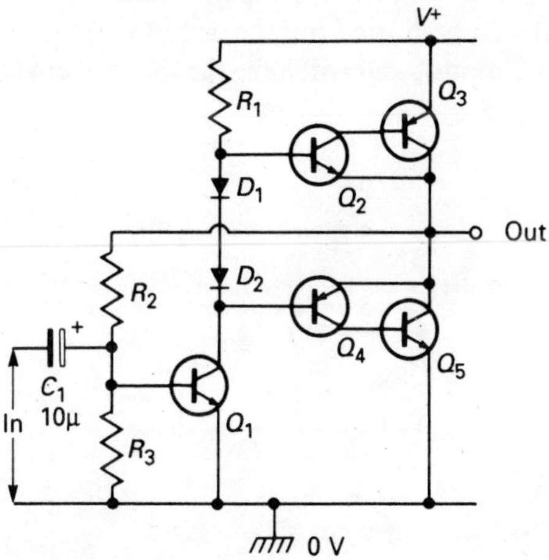

Figure 6.25 *Amplifier with complementary output stages*

In *Figure* 6.23, Q_2–Q_3 are wired as a Darlington npn pair, and Q_3–Q_4 as a Darlington pnp pair; note that four base–emitter junctions exist between Q_2 base and Q_4 base, so this output circuit must be biased via a chain of four silicon diodes.

In *Figure* 6.24, Q_2–Q_3 are wired as a Darlington npn pair, but Q_3–Q_4 are wired as a complementary pair of common-emitter amplifiers that operate with 100 per cent negative feedback and provide unity voltage gain and a very high input impedance. This design is known as a 'quasi-complementary' output stage, and is probably the most popular of all class-AB amplifier configurations; it calls for the use of three biasing diodes.

Finally, in *Figure* 6.25, both Q_2–Q_3 and Q_4–Q_5 are wired as complementary pairs of unity-gain common-emitter amplifiers with 100 per cent negative feedback, but are virtual 'mirror images' of each other. This circuit thus has a complementary output stage; it calls for the use of only two biasing diodes.

Amplified diode

The circuits of *Figure* 6.22–5 all call for the use of a chain of silicon biasing diodes. If desired, each of these chains can be replaced by a single transistor and two resistors, wired in the 'amplified diode' configuration first described in Chapter 4 and shown here in *Figure* 6.26. Note that if R_1 is shorted out the circuit will equal a single base–emitter junction 'diode', and will have the thermal characteristics of a

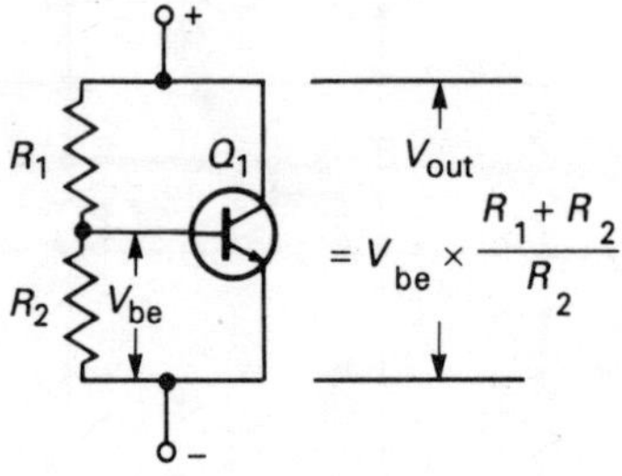

Figure 6.26 *Fixed-gain 'amplified diode' circuit*

single diode. If R_1 equals R_2, the circuit will act like two series-connected diodes, and if R_1 equals $3 \times R_2$ it will act like four series-connected diodes, and so on. Thus, the circuit can, by adjusting the R_1/R_2 ratios, be made to simulate any desired number of series-connected diodes. *Figure* 6.27 shows how the circuit can be modified so that it acts as a fully adjustable 'amplified diode', with an output variable from 1 to 5.7 base–emitter junction voltages.

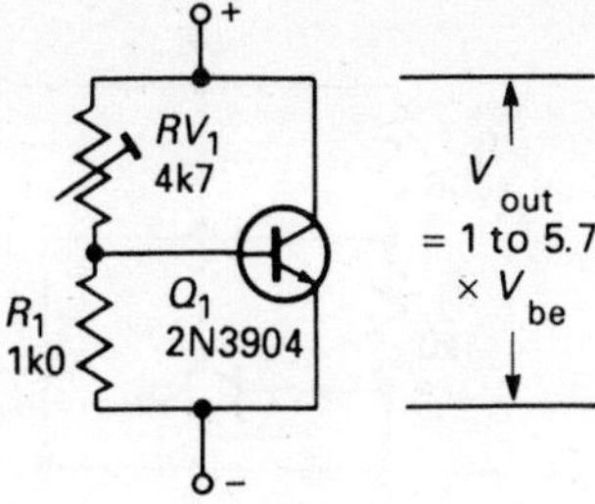

Figure 6.27 *Adjustable 'amplified diode' circuit*

Bootstrapping

In the basic complementary amplifier circuit of *Figure* 6.22, the main purpose of the Q_1 driver stage is to provide significant overall voltage gain. At any given Q_1 collector current value, this voltage gain is directly proportional to the effective Q_1 collector load (R_1) impedance value. A snag here, however, is that the R_1 value is severely limited by the need to meet d.c. biasing requirements. So how can high voltage gain be obtained when using a low-value load resistor? The answer to that question has already been described in Chapter 4; it is 'bootstrapping', that technique that enables a resistor to present a greater a.c. impedance than its true d.c. value. *Figures* 6.28 and 6.29 show examples of bootstrapped class-AB power amplifier circuits.

Note in *Figure* 6.28 that Q_1 collector load comprises R_1 and R_2 in series, and that the circuit's output signal (which also appears across SPKR) is fed back to the R_1–R_2 junction via C_2. This output signal is a near-unity-voltage-gain copy of that appearing on Q_1 collector. Suppose that R_1 has an actual value of 1k0 and that the Q_2–Q_3 stage gives a voltage gain of 0.9. It can be seen that, under actual amplifying conditions, X signal volts appear on the low end of R_2 and $0.9X$ volts appear at the top end of R_2, i.e. only one tenth of X signal volts are developed across R_2, which thus passes only one tenth of the signal current that would be expected from a 1k0 resistor. In other words, R_2's a.c. impedance is ten times greater (10k) than its d.c. value, and the signal voltage gain is similarly increased.

In practice, the bootstrapping technique enables the effective voltage gain and collector load impedance of Q_1 to be increased by a factor of about $\times 20$. *Figure* 6.29 shows an alternative version of the circuit, which saves two components; the SPKR forms part of Q_1's collector load, and is bootstrapped via C_2.

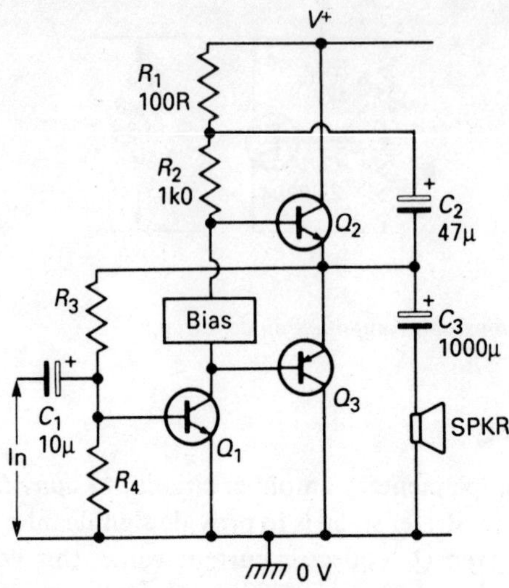

Figure 6.28 *Amplifier with bootstrapped driver stage*

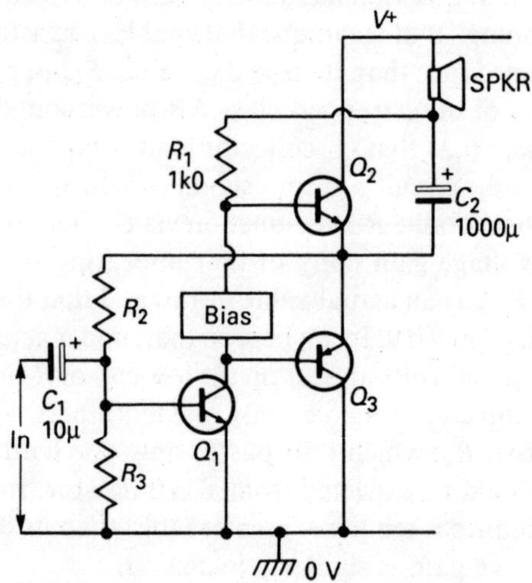

Figure 6.29 *Alternative amplifier with bootstrapped driver stage*

An alternative to the bootstrapping technique is that of replacing the load resistor with a simple constant-current generator; this technique is used in many integrated circuit (IC) types of power amplifier.

Alternative drivers

In the basic *Figure* 6.22 circuit the Q_1 driver stage uses parallel d.c. and a.c. voltage feedback via potential divider network R_2–R_3. This circuit is simple and stable, but suffers from fairly low gain and very low input resistance, and can be used over only a very limited range of power-supply voltages. A simple variation of this circuit is shown in *Figure* 6.30. It uses current feedback via series resistors R_1–R_2, thus enabling the circuit to be used over a wide range of supply voltages. The feedback resistors can be a.c. decoupled (as shown) via C_2 to give increased gain and input impedance, at the expense of increased signal distortion. Q_1 can be a Darlington type, if a very high input impedance is required.

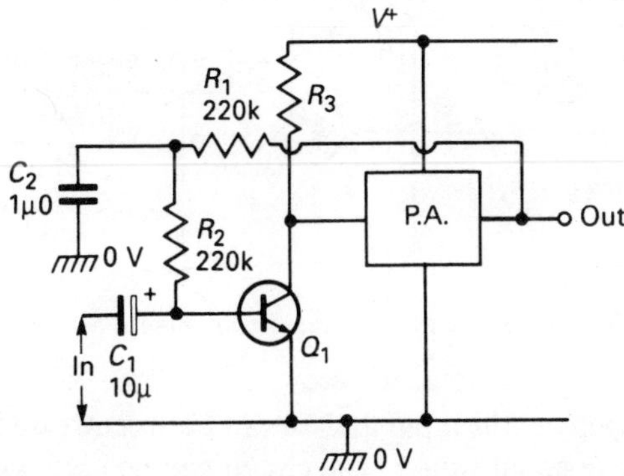

Figure 6.30 *Driver stage with decoupled parallel d.c. feedback*

Figure 6.31 shows an alternative configuration of driver stage. This design uses series d.c. and a.c. feedback, and gives greater gain and input impedance than the basic *Figure* 6.22 circuit, but uses two transistors of opposite polarities.

Finally, *Figures* 6.32 shows a driver circuit meant for use in amplifiers that use dual (split) power supplies and have direct-coupled ground-referenced inputs and outputs. It uses a long-tailed

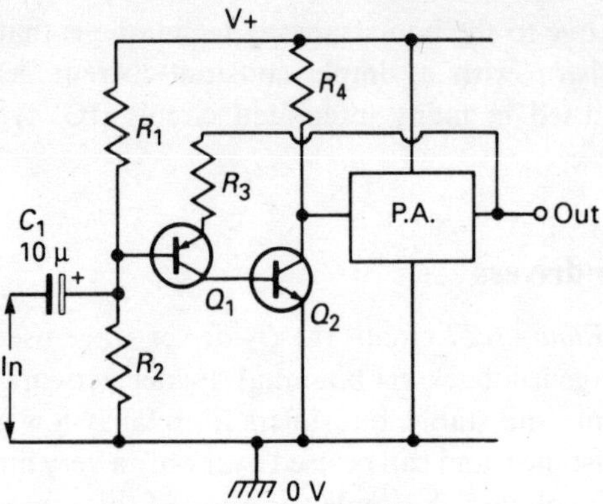

Figure 6.31 *Driver stage with series d.c. feedback*

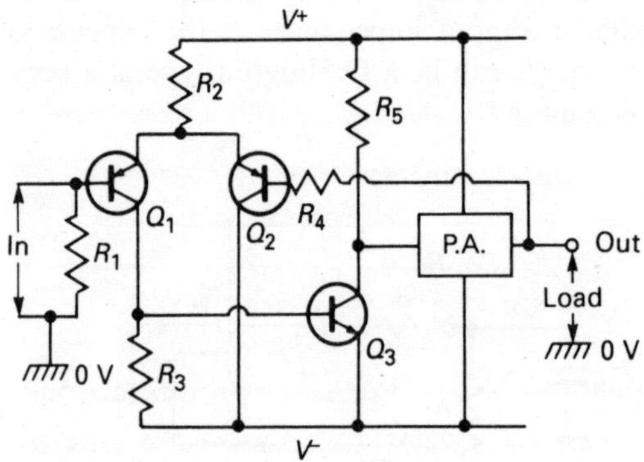

Figure 6.32 *Driver stage with long-tailed pair input*

pair input stage, and the input and output both centre on zero volts if R_1 and R_4 have equal values. The circuit can be used with a single-ended power supply by simply grounding one supply line and using a.c. coupling of the input and the output signals. This basic circuit forms the basis of many IC power amplifier designs.

An IC power amplifier

An integrated circuit consists, in essence, of a group of transistors and resistors all formed (integrated) on the same silicon chip. The techniques used in designing the actual circuit are similar to those used for ordinary transistor ones; this is particularly true of IC power amplifier designs, and to illustrate this point *Figure* 6.33 shows (in basic form) the internal circuit of the popular LM380 2 W audio power amplifier IC, which can be used with single-ended power supplies.

In the LM380, Q_1 and Q_2 are pnp emitter followers that drive the Q_3–Q_4 differential amplifier and enable inputs to be d.c. referenced to the ground line, or to be direct-coupled between ground and input lines. The output of the differential amplifier is direct coupled into the base of Q_{12}, which is wired as a simple common emitter amplifier with Q_{11} acting as its high-impedance (constant-current) collector load, and the collector signal of Q_{12} is fed to the IC's output pin via the Q_7–Q_8–Q_9 quasi-complementary emitter follower set of output transistors. The output currents of Q_7 and Q_9 are rated at 1.3 A peak.

Bias-determining and gain-controlling resistor networks are built into the LM380. Feedback resistor R_2 has half the value of R_1, and these two resistors cause the amplifier's output to balance at a quiescent value of about half supply-line voltage. The IC's voltage gain is internally fixed at × 50 (34 dB) by the ratios of R_2 and R_3, but can easily be altered by using external feedback or decoupling networks. The LM380 is a very versatile and easy-to-use IC.

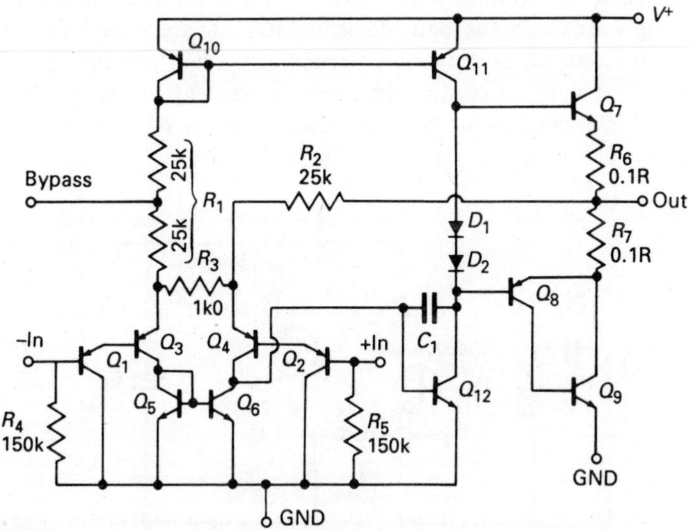

Figure 6.33 *Basic internal circuit of the LM380 2 W audio power amplifier IC*

7 Transistor circuit miscellany

The last four chapters have been devoted to looking at the operating principles and practical examples of a variety of bipolar transistor circuits. This present chapter rounds off this 'transistor' section of the book by looking at a variety of practical power amplifiers, gadgets, and miscellaneous transistor circuits.

Power amplifiers

The easiest way to build a low- to medium-power audio-amplifier is to simply use one of the many dedicated ICs that are available for this task. In some cases, however, particularly when making 'one-off' projects, it may be cheaper or more convenient to use a discrete transistor design, such as one of those shown in *Figures* 7.1–3.

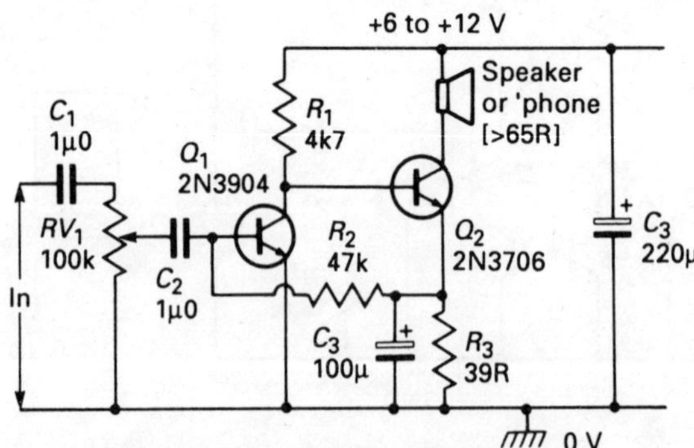

Figure 7.1 *General-purpose high-gain low-power audio amplifier*

The *Figure* 7.1 design is that of a general-purpose low-power high-gain amplifier with a class-A output suitable for driving a medium impedance (greater than 65 ohms) speaker or headset. The circuit draws a quiescent current of about 20 mA (this can be reduced by increasing the R_3 value), and operates as follows.

Q_1 and Q_2 are each wired as common-emitter amplifiers, with the output of Q_1 direct-coupled to the input of Q_2, and give a typical overall voltage gain of about 80 dB. Note that Q_2's emitter load (R_3) is decoupled via C_3, and Q_2 emitter thus 'follows' the mean collector voltage of Q_1, and that Q_1's base bias is derived from Q_2 emitter via R_2; the bias is thus stabilized by d.c. negative feedback. Input pot RV_1 acts as the circuit's volume control.

Figure 7.2 shows a simple three-transistor class-AB complementary amplifier which can typically drive about 1 W into a 3 ohm speaker. Here, Q_1 is wired as a common-emitter amplifier, driving collector load LS_1–R_1–RV_2, and has its output voltage followed and power-boosted by the Q_2–Q_3 complementary emitter follower stage. The output of the amplifier is fed (via C_2) to the LS_1–R_1 junction, thus providing a low impedance drive to the speaker and simultaneously bootstrapping the R_1 value so that the circuit gives a high value of voltage gain. The output is also fed back to Q_1 base via R_4, thus

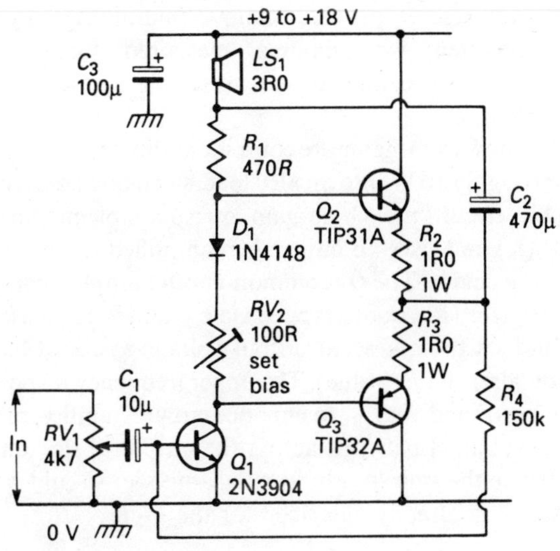

Figure 7.2 *Simple 1 W amplifier*

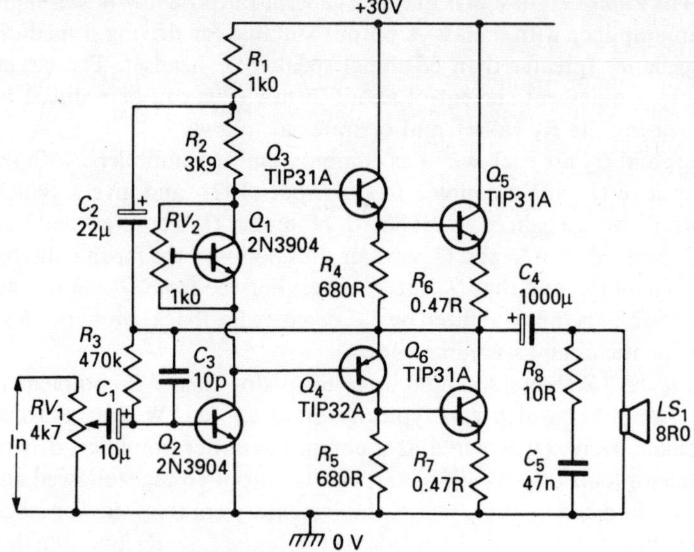

Figure 7.3 *10 W audio amplifier*

providing base bias via a negative feedback loop. In use, RV_2 should be carefully adjusted to provide minimal audible signal cross-over distortion consistent with minimal measured quiescent current consumption; a good compromise is to set the quiescent current at about 10–15 mA.

Figure 7.3 shows a rather more complex audio power amplifier that can deliver roughly 10 W into an 8R0 load when powered from a 30 V supply. This circuit uses high-gain quasi-complementary output stages (Q_3–Q_6) and uses an adjustable 'amplified diode' (Q_1) as an output biasing device. The Q_2 common-emitter amplifier stage has its main load resistor (R_2) bootstrapped via C_2, and is d.c. biased via R_3, which should set the quiescent output voltage at about half-supply value (if not, alter the R_3 value). The upper frequency response of the amplifier is restricted via C_3, to enhance circuit stability, and C_5–R_8 are wired as a Zobel network across the output of the amplifier to further enhance the stability. In use, the amplifier should be initially set up in the way already described for the *Figure* 7.2.

Scratch/rumble filters

A common annoyance when playing old records is that of 'scratch' and/or 'rumble' sounds. The 'scratch' noises are mainly high-frequency sounds (usually greater than 10 kHz) picked up from the disc surface, and the 'rumbles' are low-frequency sounds (usually less than 50 Hz) that are mostly caused by slow variations in motor-drive speed. Each of these noises can be effectively eliminated (or greatly reduced) by passing the record player audio signals through a frequency filter that rejects the troublesome part of the audio spectrum. *Figures* 7.4 and 7.5 show suitable circuits.

The rumble filter of *Figure* 7.4 acts as a high-pass filter that gives unity voltage gain to all signal frequencies above 50 Hz, but gives

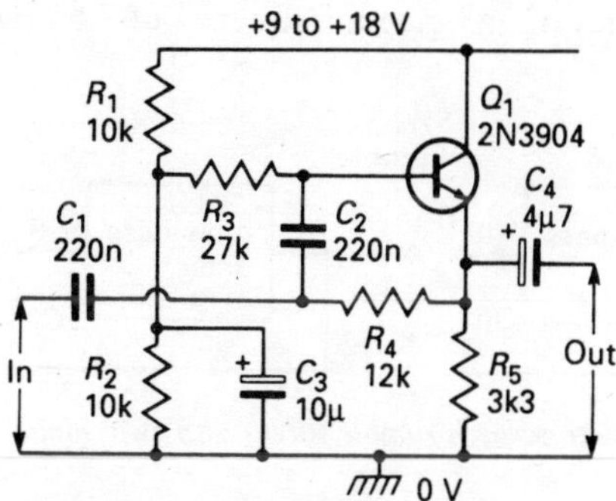

Figure 7.4 *50 Hz 'rumble' or hi-pass filter*

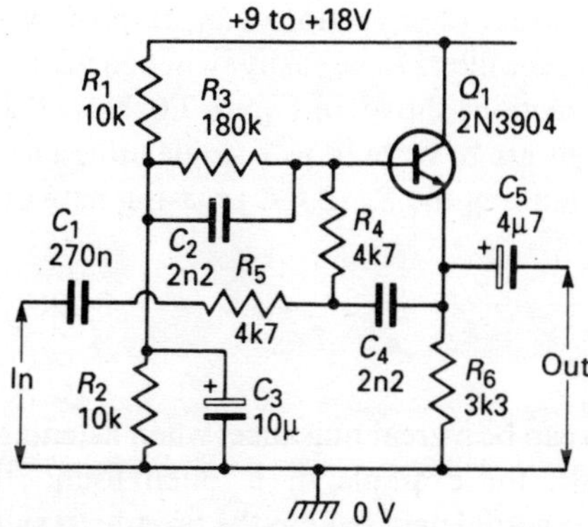

Figure 7.5 *10 kHz 'scratch' or low-pass filter*

12 dB/octave rejection to those below this value, i.e., it gives 40 dB of attenuation at 5 Hz, etc. Q_1 is wired as an emitter follower and is biased at half-supply volts from the low-impedance point formed by R_1–R_2–C_3, but has negative feedback applied via the R_3–C_2–C_1–R_4 filter network, which gives the filter response mentioned above. The circuit's frequency turn-over point can be altered by changing the C_1–C_2 values (which must be equal); thus, if the C_1–C_2 values are halved (to 110n), the turn-over frequency will double (to 100 Hz), etc.

The scratch filter of *Figure* 7.5 acts as a low-pass filter that gives unity voltage gain to all signal frequencies below 10 kHz, but gives 12 dB/octave rejection to those above this value. This circuit is similar to that of *Figure* 7.4, except that the positions of the resistors and capacitors are transposed in the C_2–R_4–C_4–R_5 filter network. The circuit's turn-over frequency can be altered by changing the C_2–C_4 values; e.g., values of 3n3 give a frequency of 7.5 kHz.

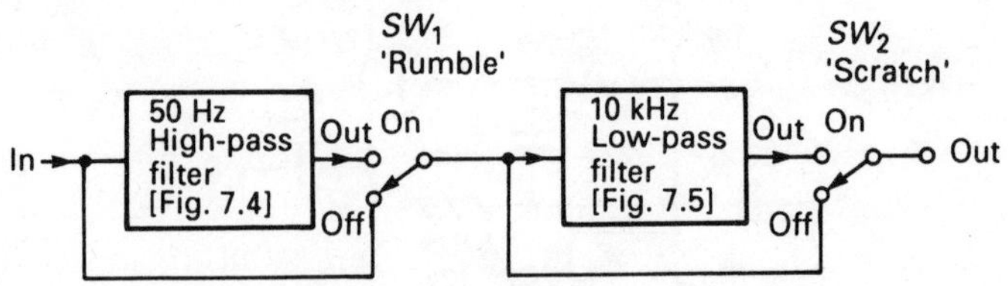

Figure 7.6 *Complete scratch/rumble filter, with switching*

The circuits of *Figures* 7.4 and 7.5 can be combined, to make a composite 'scratch and rumble' filter, by simply connecting the output of the high-pass filter to the input of the low-pass filter; if desired, the individual filter sections can be provided with bypass switches, enabling the filters to be easily switched in and out of circuit, by using the connections shown in *Figure* 7.6. Note that if the *Figure* 7.4 and 7.5 designs are to be built as a single unit, a few components can be saved by making the R_1–R_2–C_3 biasing network common to both circuits.

A noise limiter

Unwanted noise can be a great nuisance; when listening to very weak broadcast signals, for example, it is often found that peaks of background noise completely swamp the broadcast signal, making it unintelligible. This problem can often be overcome by using the 'noise

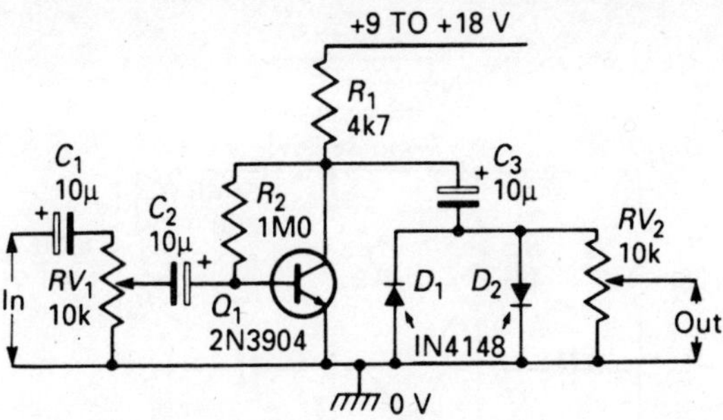

Figure 7.7 *Noise limiter*

limiter' circuit of *Figure* 7.7. Here, the signal-plus-noise waveform is fed to amplifier Q_1 via RV_1. Q_1 amplifies both waveforms equally, but diodes D_1 and D_2 automatically limit the peak-to-peak output swing of Q_1 to about 1.2 V. Thus, if RV_1 is adjusted so that the 'signal' output is amplified to this peak level, the 'noise' peaks will not be able to greatly exceed the signal output, and intelligibility is greatly improved.

Astable multivibrators

The astable multivibrator or 'square-wave generator' circuit has many uses. *Figure* 7.8, for example, shows how it can be used as a two-LED 'flasher' that operates at about 1 flash/second. The rate is controlled by the time-constant values of C_1–R_4 and C_2–R_3. The

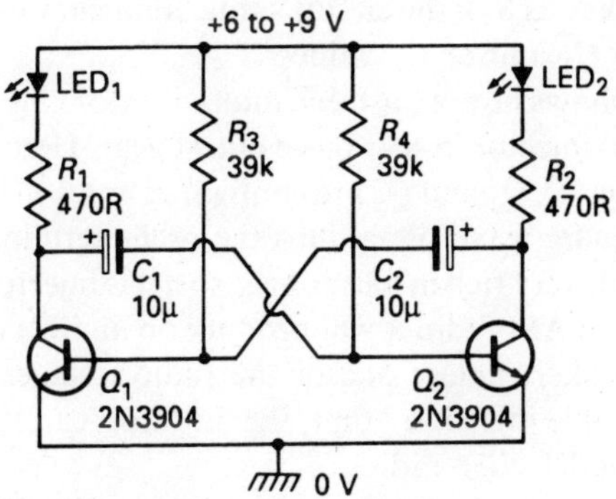

Figure 7.8 *Two-LED 'flasher' circuit*

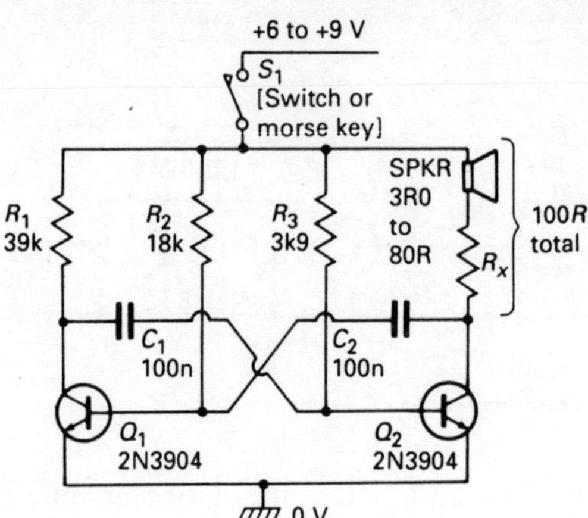

Figure 7.9 *Morse-code practice oscillator*

LEDs are wired in series with the transistor collectors and flash on and off in opposition to one another, with even symmetry. The flash rate can be changed by altering the values of either C_1/C_2 or R_3/R_4. If desired, one of the LEDs can be replaced by a short circuit, to make a '1-LED' flasher.

A simple variation of the astable circuit is shown in *Figure* 7.9. Here, a non-symmetrical waveform of about 800 Hz is generated and is fed to a speaker and limiting resistor in the collector of Q_2, thus producing a monotone audio signal when S_1 is closed. The circuit can thus be used as either a simple sound generator (by using an ordinary switch in the S_1 position) or as a 'Morse code practice oscillator' (by using a Morse key as S_1); the circuit's tone frequency can be changed by altering the C_1 and/or C_2 values.

Figure 7.10 shows how an astable multivibrator can be used as the basis of a signal injector–tracer piece of test gear. Here, when SW_1 is in *inject* position '1', Q_1 and Q_2 are configured as a 1 kHz astable, and feed a good square-wave signal into the *probe* terminal via R_1–C_1. This waveform is very rich in harmonics, so if it is injected into any AF or RF stage of an AM radio it will produce an audible output via the radio's loudspeaker, unless one of the radio's stages is faulty. By choosing a suitable injection point, the 'injector' can thus be used to trouble-shoot a defective radio.

When SW_1 is switched to *trace* position '2', the *Figure* 7.10 circuit is configured as a cascaded pair of common-emitter amplifiers,

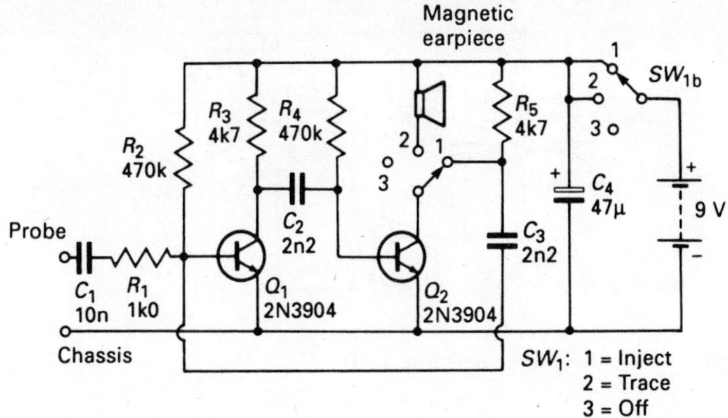

Figure 7.10 *Signal injector–tracer*

with the probe input feeding to Q_1 base, and Q_2 output feeding into a magnetic earpiece or headset. Thus, any weak audio signal fed to the probe will be directly amplified and heard in the earpiece. Similarly, any amplitude-modulated RF signals that are fed to the probe will be demodulated by the non-linear action of Q_1 and the resulting audio signals will then be amplified and heard in the earpiece. By connecting the probe to suitable points in a radio, the 'tracer' can thus be used to trouble-shoot a faulty radio, etc.

L–C oscillators

L–C oscillators have lots of applications in test gear and gadgets of various sorts. *Figures* 7.11–13 show some simple examples.

The *Figure* 7.11 circuit is that of a medium-wave (MW) signal generator or beat-frequency oscillator (BFO). Here, Q_1 is wired as a straightforward Hartley oscillator, but uses a modified 465 kHz IF transformer as its collector load. The internal tuning capacitor of the IF transformer should be removed; variable oscillator tuning is then available via VC_1, which enables the output frequency (on either fundamentals or harmonics), to be varied from well below 465 kHz to well above 1.7 MHz. Any MW radio will detect the oscillation frequency if simply placed near the circuit; if the unit is tuned to the IF frequency of a radio, a beat note will be heard, enabling c.w. and s.s.b. transmissions to be clearly detected.

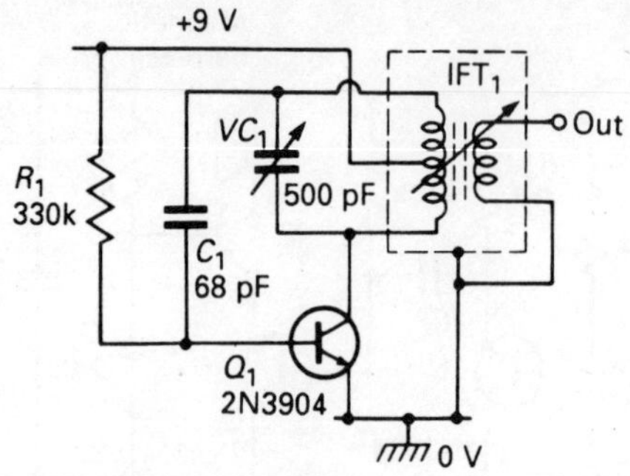

Figure 7.11 *MW signal generator/BFO*

Figure 7.12 shows how the above oscillator can be modified so that, when used in conjunction with an MW radio, it functions as a simple 'metal/pipe locator'. In this case oscillator coil L_1 is hand-wound and comprises 30 centre-tapped turns of wire, firmly wound over about 25 mm length of a 75–100 mm diameter non-metallic former or 'search head' and connected to the main circuit via three-core cable. The search head can be fixed to the end of a long non-metallic handle if the circuit is to be used in the classic 'metal detector' mode, or can be hand-held if it is to be used to locate metal pipes or wiring that are hidden behind brickwork or plaster, etc.

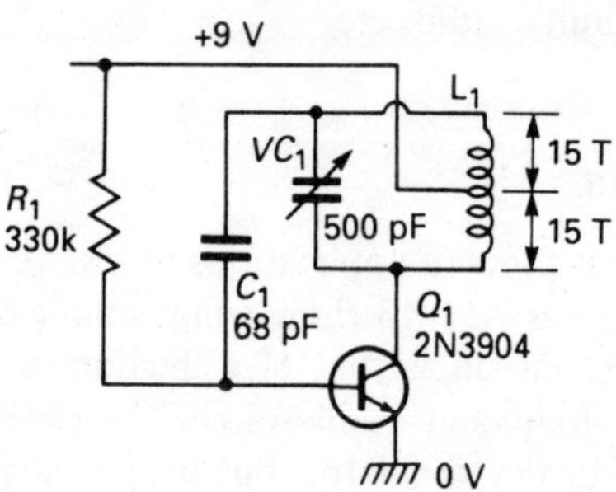

Figure 7.12 *Metal/pipe locator*

Operation of the *Figure* 7.12 circuit relies on the fact that the electromagnetic field of L_1 is disturbed by the presence of metal, causing the inductance of L_1 and the frequency of the oscillator to alter. This frequency shift (and thus the presence of metal) can be detected on a portable MW radio placed close to the search head by

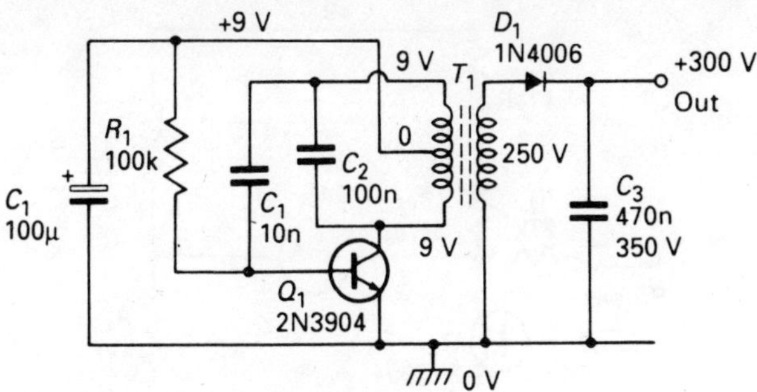

Figure 7.13 *9 V-to-300 V d.c.-to-d.c. converter*

tuning the radio to a local station and then adjusting VC_1 so that a low-frequency 'beat' or 'whistle' note is heard from the radio's loudspeaker. This beat note will change significantly if the head is placed near metal, and the circuit thus functions as a simple metal detector.

Figure 7.13 shows another application of the Hartley oscillator. In this case the circuit functions as a D.C.-to-D.C. converter, which converts a 9 V battery supply into a 300 V D.C. output. T_1 is a 9 V–0–9 V to 250 V mains transformer, with its primary forming the L part of the oscillator. The supply voltage is stepped up to about 350 V peak at T_1 secondary, and is half-wave rectified by D_1 and used to charge C_3. With no permanent load on C_3, the capacitor can deliver a powerful but non-lethal 'belt'. With a permanent load on the output, the output falls to about 300 V at a load current of a few milliamperes.

Lie detector

The 'lie detector' of *Figure* 7.14 is an 'experimenter's' circuit, in which the victim is connected (via a pair of substantial metal probes) into a Wheatstone bridge circuit formed by R_1–RV_1–Q_1 and R_3–R_4; the 1 mA centre-zero meter is used as a bridge-balance detector. In use, the victim makes firm contact with the probes and, once he or she has attained a relaxed state (in which the skin resistance reaches a stable value), RV_1 is adjusted to obtain a null on the meter. The victim is then cross-questioned. According to theory, the victim's skin resistance will then change and the bridge will go out of balance if he/she lies or shows any signs of emotional upset (embarassment, etc.) when being questioned.

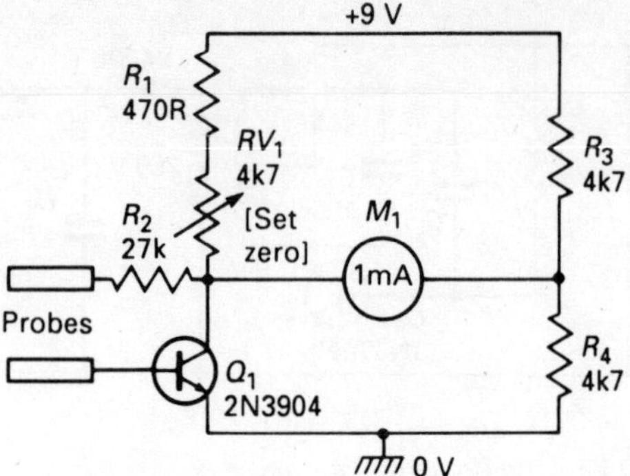

Figure 7.14 *Simple 'lie detector'*

Current mirrors

A current mirror is a circuit which when fed with an input current sinks an identical current into its output; i.e. its output acts as a constant current sink with a magnitude controlled by an independent input current. This type of circuit is widely used in modern linear IC design. *Figure* 7.15 shows a simple current mirror using ordinary npn transistors; Q_1 and Q_2 are a matched pair and share a common thermal environment. When an input current (I_{in}) is fed into diode-connected Q_1 it makes Q_1 generate a proportionate forward base–emitter voltage, which is applied directly to the base–emitter junction

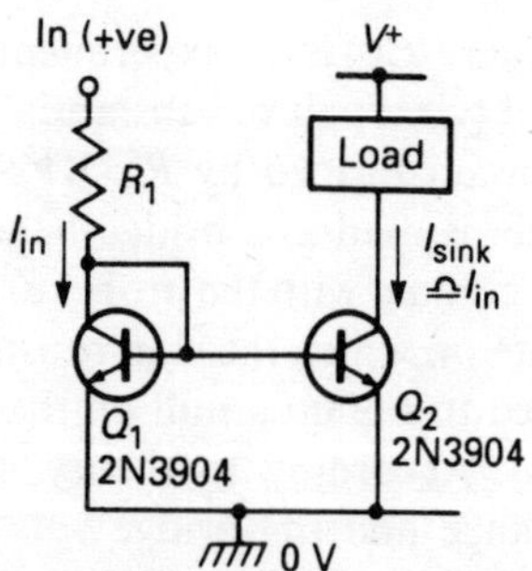

Figure 7.15 *An npn current mirror*

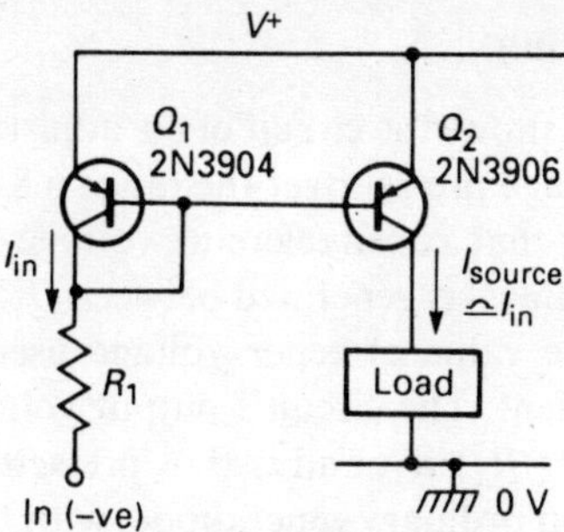

Figure 7.16 *A pnp current mirror*

of matched transistor Q_2, causing it to sink an almost identical ('mirror') value of collector current (I_{sink}). Q_2 thus acts as a constant current sink that is controlled by I_{in}, but has the outstanding advantage of acting as such even at collector voltages as low as a few hundred millivolts.

Figure 7.16 shows a pnp version of the simple current mirror circuit. This works in the same basic way as already described, except that Q_2's collector acts as a constant current *source* that has its amplitude controlled by I_{in}. Note that both of these circuits will still work quite well as current-controlled constant current sinks or sources even if Q_1 and Q_2 have badly matched characteristics, but in this case may not act as true current mirrors, since their I_{sink} and I_{in} values may be very different.

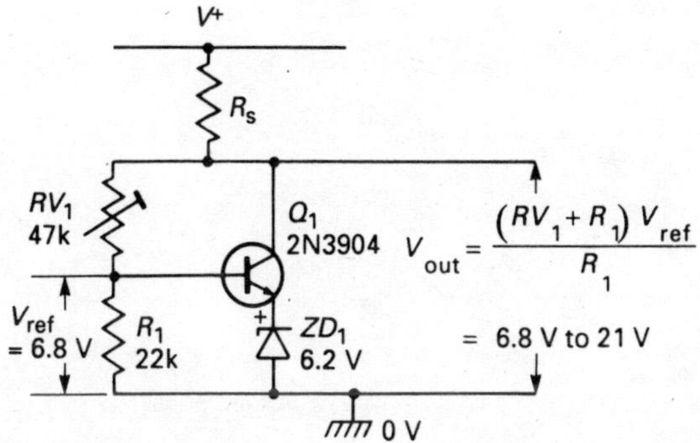

Figure 7.17 *Adjustable zener*

An adjustable zener

Finally, *Figure* 7.17 shows the circuit of an 'adjustable zener' that can have its output voltage pre-set over the range 6.8–21 V via RV_1. The circuit action is such that a fixed reference voltage (equal to the sum of the zener and V_{be} values) is generated between Q_1's base and ground, and (because of the value of zener voltage used) has a near-zero temperature coefficient. The circuit's output voltage is equal to V_{ref} multiplied by $(RV_1 + R_1)/R_1$, and is thus pre-settable via RV_1. This circuit is used like an ordinary zener diode, with the R_s value chosen to set its operating current at a nominal value in the range 5–20 mA.

8 FET principles

Field-effect transistors (FETs) are unipolar devices, and have some important advantages over conventional bipolar transistors. They have a near-infinite input impedance and thus offer near-infinite current and power gain; their operating speeds are not limited by charge-storage problems, and they can thus outperform most bipolars in terms of cut-off frequency and switching speeds; their operating currents are inversely proportional to temperature, and they are thus immune to thermal runaway problems.

Several different basic types of field-effect transistor are available, and FET literature abounds with terms such as 'depletion-type', 'enhancement-type', JFET, IGFET, MOSFET and VFET, etc. This chapter looks at the basic operating principles of the various FET types, and shows basic ways of using them; Chapters 9–11 take detailed looks at specific types of FET.

FET basics

A FET is essentially a three-terminal amplifying device. Its terminals are known as the *source*, *gate*, and *drain*, and correspond respectively to the emitter, base, and collector of a conventional bipolar transistor. Both 'n-channel' and 'p-channel' versions of the FET are available, just as normal transistors are available in either npn or pnp versions, and *Figure* 8.1 shows the symbols and supply polarities of both types of bipolar transistor and compares them with the two FET versions. Note that the specific FET symbols shown in fact apply to a 'junction-type field-effect transistor' or JFET, which will be described shortly.

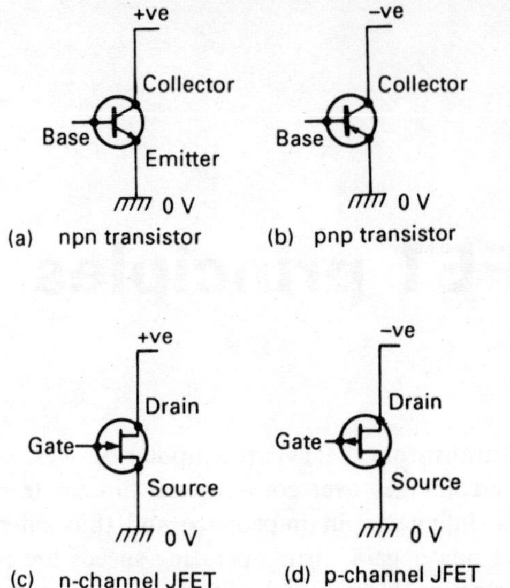

Figure 8.1 *Comparison of transistor and JFET symbols, notations, and supply polarities*

Figure 8.2 illustrates the basic construction and operating principle of a simple n-channel FET. The device consists essentially of a bar or channel of n-type semiconductor material with a *drain* terminal at one end and a *source* terminal at the other: a p-type control electrode or *gate* surrounds (and is joined to the surface of) the middle section of the n-type bar, thus forming a p–n semiconductor junction.

In normal use the drain terminal is connected to a positive supply and the gate is biased at a value that is negative (or equal) to the source voltage, thus reverse biasing the FET's internal p–n junction and accounting for its very high input impedance. With zero gate bias applied, a current flows from drain to source via the n-type 'channel', its magnitude being limited by the characteristics of the n-type material.

When a negative gate bias is applied to the FET a region that is depleted of charge current is formed within the junction, and acts like an insulating or high-resistance region that reduces the effective width of the n-type conduction channel and thus reduces the magnitude of the drain-to-source current. As the gate bias is increased, the 'depletion' region spreads deeper into the n-type channel, until

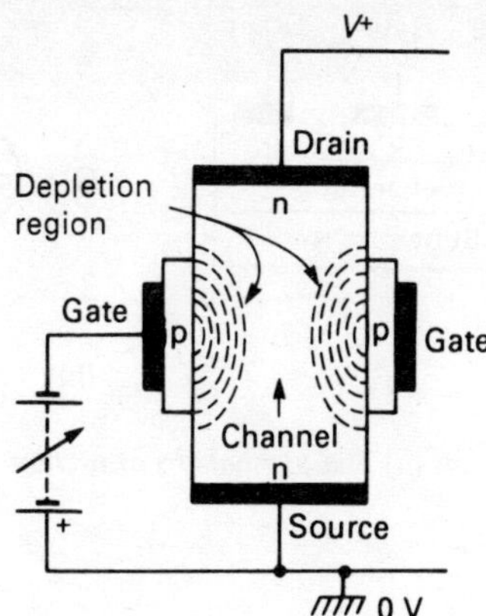

Figure 8.2 *Basic structure of a simple n-channel FET, showing how channel width is controlled via the gate bias*

eventually, at some 'pinch-off' voltage value, the depletion layer becomes so deep that conduction ceases completely.

Thus, the basic FET of *Figure* 8.2 passes maximum current when its gate bias is zero, and its current is reduced or 'depleted' when the gate bias is increased. It is thus known as a 'depletion-type' n-channel FET. A p-channel version of the device can be made by simply transposing the p and n materials.

The JFET

Two distinct families of FET are in general use. The first of these is known as the 'junction-gate' type of FET, this term generally being abbreviated to either JUGFET or (more usually) JFET. The second type is known as either the 'insulated-gate' FET or 'metal oxide semiconductor' FET, and these terms are generally abbreviated to IGFET or MOSFET respectively.

Figure 8.3*a* shows the basic form of construction of an n-channel JFET, and *Figure* 8.3*b* shows the device's conventional symbol. A p-channel JFET can be made by simply transposing the p and n materials in *Figure* 8.3*a*, in which case the symbol should be changed by reversing the arrow in *Figure* 8.3*b*.

All JFETs operate in the depletion mode and work in the way already explained for the *Figure* 8.2 device. *Figure* 8.4 shows, in

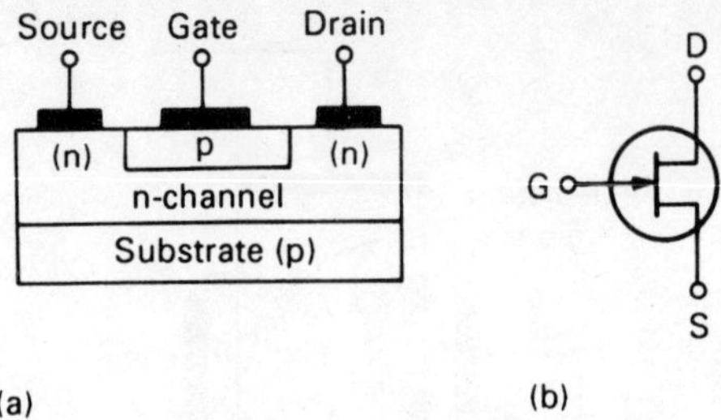

Figure 8.3 *Construction (a) and symbol (b) of n-channel JFET*

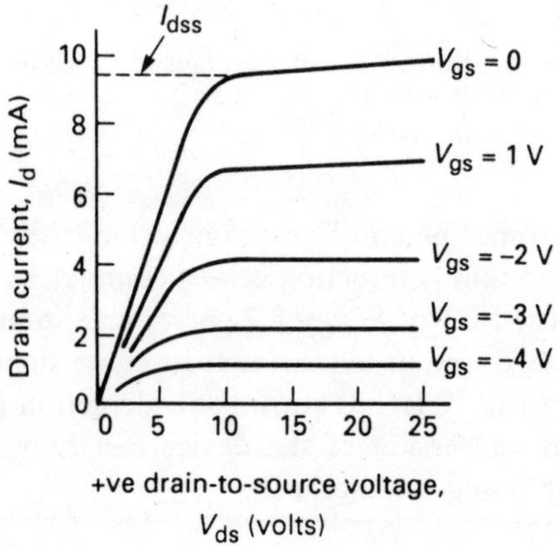

Figure 8.4 *Idealized transfer characteristics of n-channel JFET*

idealized form, the typical transfer characteristics of a low-power n-channel JFET, and illustrates some important features of this type of device. The most important characteristics of the JFET are as follows.

(1) When a JFET is connected to a supply with the polarity shown in *Figure* 8.1 (drain +ve for an n-channel FET, −ve for a p-channel FET), a drain current (I_d) flows in the device and can be controlled via gate-to-source bias voltage V_{gs}.

(2) I_d is greatest when $V_{gs}=0$, and is reduced (to bring the device into a linear operating region) by applying a reverse bias to the gate (negative bias in a n-channel device, positive bias in a p-type). The magnitude of V_{gs} needed to reduce I_d to zero is called the 'pinch-off' voltage, V_p, and typically has a value between 2

and 10 V. The magnitude of I_d when $V_{gs}=0$ is denoted I_{dss}, and typically has a value in the range 2–20 mA.

(3) The JFET's gate-to-source junction has the characteristics of a silicon diode. When reverse biased (to bring it into the linear operating region), gate leakage currents (I_{gss}) are only a couple of nanoamperes (1 nA = 0.001 μA) at room temperature. Actual gate signal currents are only a fraction of a nanoampere, and the input impedance of the gate is typically thousands of megohms at low frequencies. The gate junction is effectively shunted by a few picofarads, so the input impedance falls as frequency is increased.

If the JFET's gate-to-source junction is forward biased, it conducts like a normal silicon diode, and if excessively reverse-biased avalanches like a zener diode; in either case, the JFET suffers no damage if gate currents are limited to a few milliamperes.

(4) Referring to *Figure* 8.4's n-channel JFET transfer characteristics, note that, for each V_{gs} value, drain current I_d rises linearly from zero as the drain-to-source voltage (V_{ds}) is increased from zero up to some value at which a 'knee' occurs on each curve, and that I_d then remains virtually constant as V_{ds} is increased beyond this knee value.

Thus, when V_{ds} is below the JFET's knee value the drain-to-source terminals act as a resistor, R_{ds}, with a value dictated by V_{gs}, and can thus be used as a voltage-variable resistor, as in *Figure* 8.5. Typically, R_{ds} can be varied from a few hundred ohms (at $V_{gs}=0$) to thousands of megohms (at $V_{gs}=V_p$), enabling the JFET to be used as a voltage-controlled switch

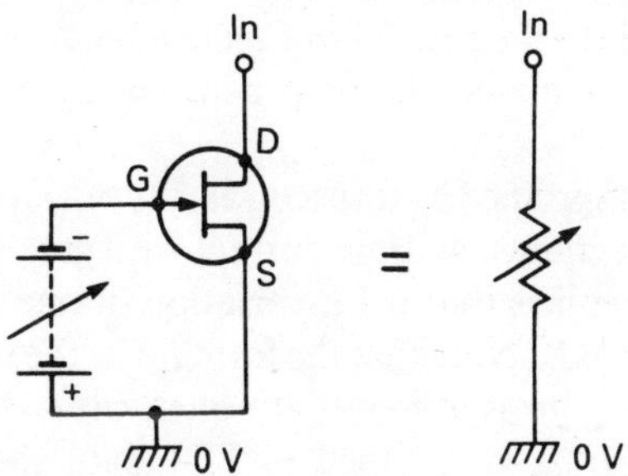

Figure 8.5 *An n-channel JFET can be used as a voltage-controlled resistor*

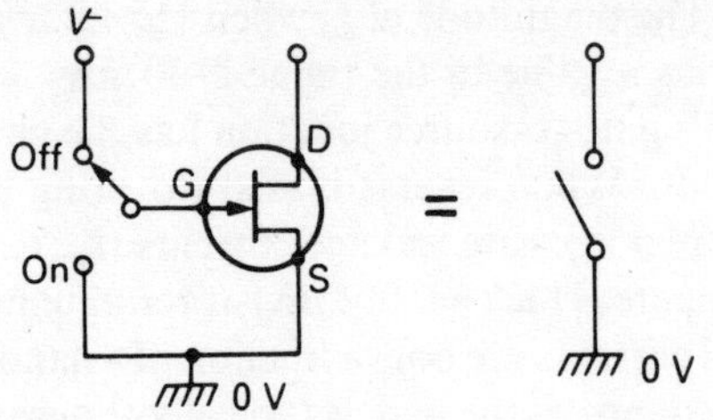

Figure 8.6 *An n-channel JFET can be used as a voltage-controlled switch*

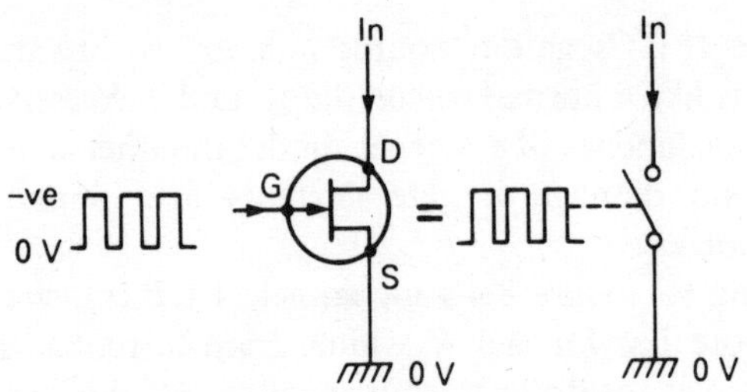

Figure 8.7 *An n-channel JFET can be used as an electronic 'chopper'*

(*Figure* 8.6) or as an efficient 'chopper' (*Figure* 8.7) which does not suffer from the offset-voltage or saturation-voltage problems associated with bipolar versions of such devices.

Returning to *Figure* 8.4, note that when V_{ds} is above the knee value the I_d value is dictated primarily by V_{gs} value and is virtually independent of V_{ds}, i.e. the device functions as a voltage-controlled current generator. Thus, the JFET can be used as a fixed-value constant-current generator by either tying the gate to the source, as in *Figure* 8.8*a*, or by applying a fixed negative basis to the gate, as in *Figure* 8.8*b*. Alternatively, it can (when suitably biased) be used as a voltage-to-current signal amplifier.

(5) FET 'gain' is specified as transconductance, g_m, and denotes the magnitude of change of drain current with gate voltage, i.e. a g_m of 5 mA/V signifies that a V_{gs} variation of one volt produces a 5 mA change in I_d. Note that the form I/V is the inverse of Ohm's formula, so g_m measurements are often expressed in 'mho' (℧) units; usually, g_m is specified in FET data sheets in terms of mmhos (milli-mhos) or μmhos (micro-mhos). Thus, a g_m of 5 mA/V = 5 mmho or 5000 μmho.

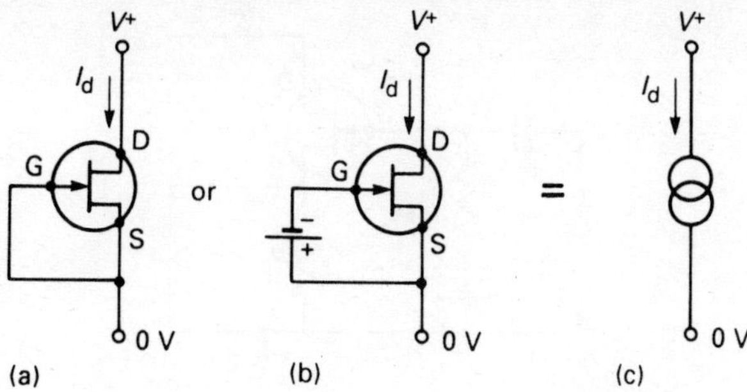

Figure 8.8 *An n-channel JFET can be used as a constant-current generator*

In most practical applications the JFET is biased into the linear region and used as a voltage amplifier by wiring a suitable load resistor in series with its drain-to-source current. Looking at n-channel versions of the JFET, it can be used as a common source amplifier (corresponding to a bipolar npn common emitter amplifier) by using the basic connections of *Figure* 8.9. Alternatively, the common drain or source follower (similar to the bipolar emitter follower) configuration can be obtained by using the connections of *Figure* 8.10 or the common gate (similar to common base) configuration can be obtained by using the basic *Figure* 8.11 circuit. In practice, fairly accurate biasing techniques (discussed in the next chapter) must be used in these circuits.

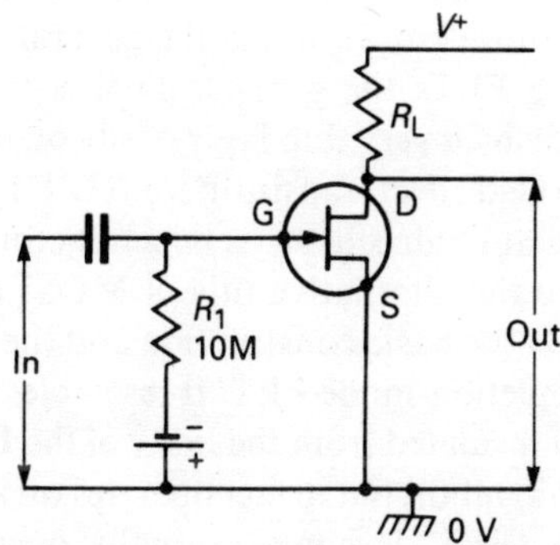

Figure 8.9 *Basic n-channel common-source amplifier JFET circuit*

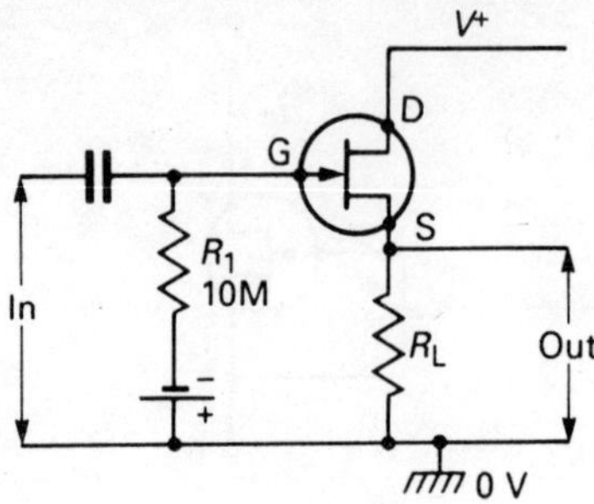

Figure 8.10 *Basic n-channel common-drain (source-follower) JFET circuit*

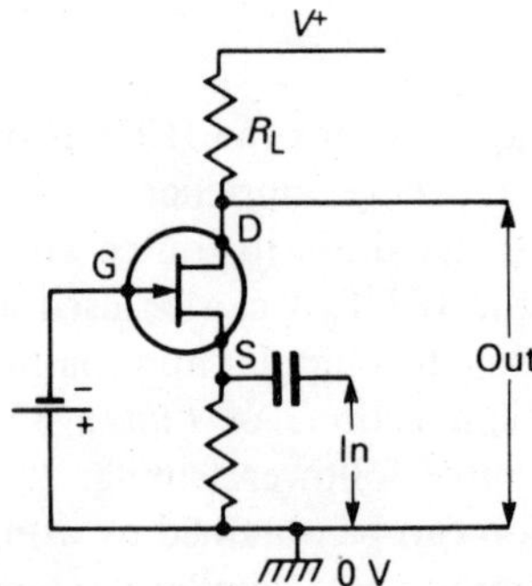

Figure 8.11 *Basic n-channel common-gate JFET circuit*

The IGFET/MOSFET

The second (and by far the largest and most important) family of FET devices consists of those known under the general title of IGFET or MOSFET. In these FETs the gate terminal is insulated from the semiconductor body by a very thin layer of silicon dioxide, hence the title 'insulated gate field effect transistor', or IGFET. Also, the devices generally use a 'metal-oxide silicon' semiconductor material in their construction, hence the alternative title of MOSFET.

Figure 8.12 shows the basic construction and the standard symbol of the n-channel depletion-mode FET. It resembles the JFET, except that its gate is fully insulated from the body of the FET (as indicated by the *Figure* 8.12*b* symbol) but in fact operates on a slightly different principle from the JFET. It has a normally open n-type channel between drain and source, but the channel width is controlled by the

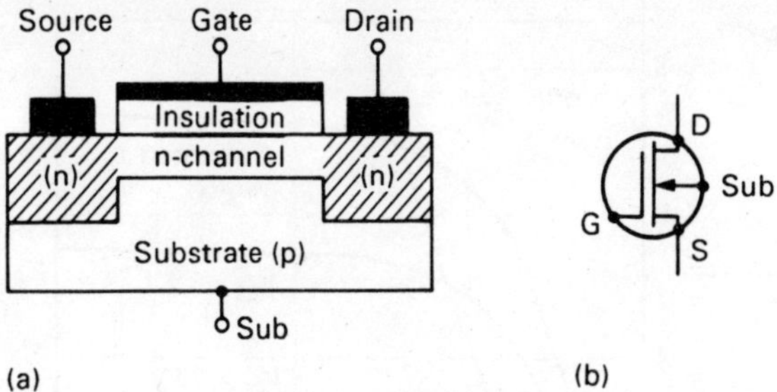

Figure 8.12 *Construction (a) and symbol (b) of n-channel depletion-mode IGFET/MOSFET*

electrostatic field of the gate bias. The channel can be closed by applying suitable negative bias, or can be increased by applying positive bias. In practice, the FET substrate may be externally available, making a four-terminal device, or it may be internally connected to the source, making a three-terminal device.

The most important thing about the IGFET/MOSFET is that it is also available as an enhancement-mode device, in which its conduction channel is normally closed but can be opened by applying forward bias to the gate terminal. *Figure* 8.13 shows the basic construction and the symbol of the n-channel version of such a device.

In the enhancement-mode device, no n-channel drain-to-source conduction path exists through the p-type substrate, so with zero gate bias there is no conduction between drain and source; this feature is indicated in the symbol of *Figure* 8.13*a* by the gaps between source and drain. To turn the device on, significant positive gate bias is needed, and when this is of sufficient magnitude it starts to convert the

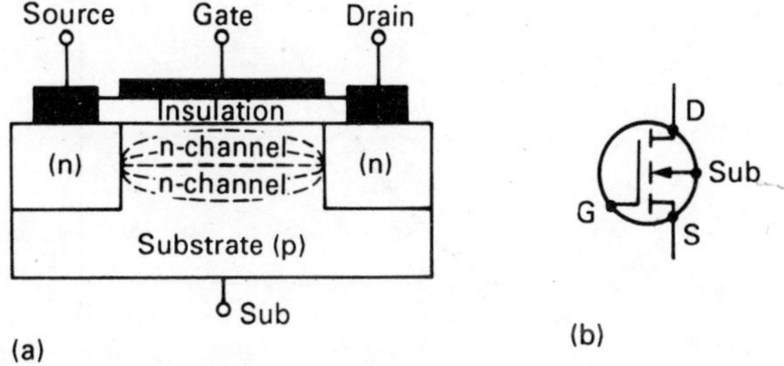

Figure 8.13 *Construction (a) and symbol (b) of n-channel enhancement-mode IGFET/MOSFET*

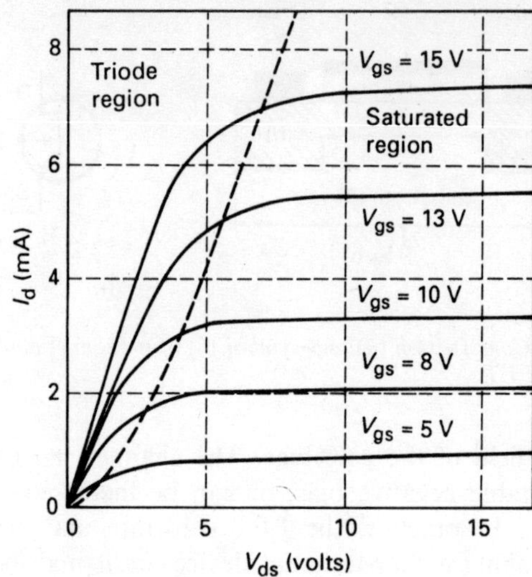

Figure 8.14 *Typical transfer characteristics of n-channel enhancement-mode IGFET/MOSFET*

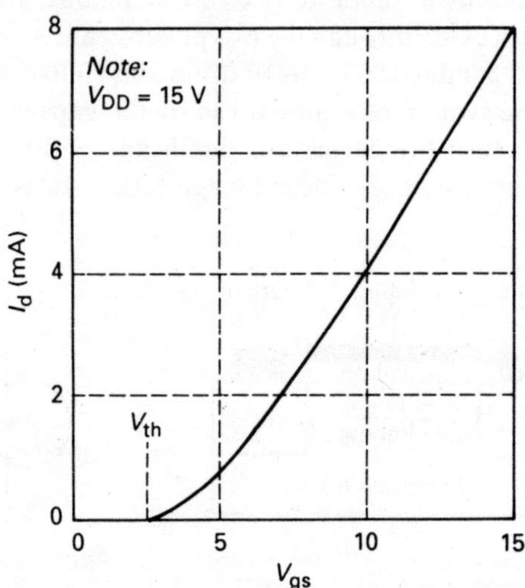

Figure 8.15 *Typical* V_{gs}/I_d *characteristics of n-channel enhancement-mode IGFET/MOSFET*

p-type substrate material under the gate into an n-channel, enabling conduction to take place.

Figure 8.14 shows the typical transfer characteristics of an n-channel enhancement-mode IGFET/MOSFET, and *Figure* 8.15 shows the V_{gs}/I_d curves of the same device when powered from a 15 volt supply. Note that no significant I_d current flows until the gate voltage reaches a 'threshold' (V_{th}) value of a few volts, but that beyond this value the drain current rises in a non-linear fashion.

Also note that the *Figure* 8.14 graph is divided into two characteristic regions, as indicated by the dotted line, these being the 'triode' region and the 'saturated' region. In the triode region, the device acts like a voltage-controlled resistor; in the saturated region it acts like a voltage-controlled constant-current generator.

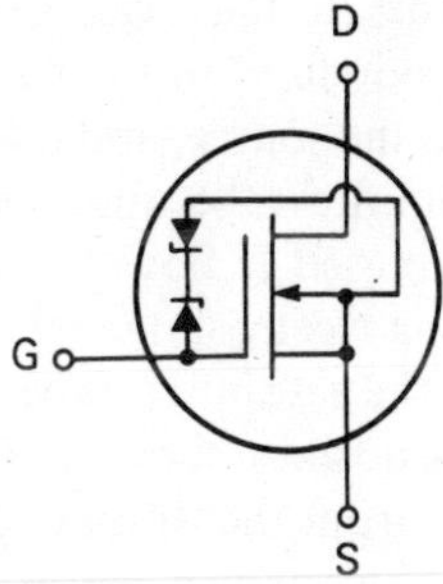

Figure 8.16 *Internally protected n-channel depletion-mode IGFET/MOSFET*

Note that the n-channel IGFETs/MOSFETs of *Figures* 8.12 and 8.13 can be converted to p-channel devices by simply transposing their p and n materials, in which case their symbols must be changed by reversing the directions of the substrate arrows.

The very high gate impedance of IGFET/MOSFET devices makes them liable to damage from electrostatic discharges, and for this reason they are often provided with internal protection via integral diodes or zeners, as shown in the example of *Figure* 8.16.

VFET devices

In a normal small-signal JFET or IGFET/MOSFET, the main signal current flows 'horizontally' (see *Figures* 8.3, 8.12 and 8.13) through the device's conductive channel. This channel is very thin, however, and maximum operating currents are consequently very limited (typically to maximum values in the range 2–40 mA).

In recent years many manufacturers have tried to produce viable high-power/high-current versions of the FET, and the most successful of these have relied on the use of a 'vertical' flow of current through the conductive channel of the device. One of the best known of these devices is the 'VFET', an enhancement-mode power IGFET/MOSFET which was first introduced by Siliconix in 1976.

Figure 8.17 shows the basic structure of the original Siliconix VFET. It has an essentially four-layer structure, with an n-type *source* layer at the top, followed by a p-type *body* layer, an epitaxial n-type layer, and (at the bottom) an n-type *drain* layer. Note that a 'V' groove (hence the 'VFET' title) passes through the first two layers and into the third layer of the device and is electrostatically connected (via an insulating silicon dioxide film) to the gate terminal.

If the gate is shorted to the source, and the drain is made positive, no drain-to-source current flows, because the diode formed by the p and n materials is reverse biased. If, however, the gate is made positive to the source, the resulting electrostatic field converts the area of p-type material adjacent to the gate into n-type material, thus creating a conduction channel in the position shown in *Figure* 8.17 and enabling current to flow *vertically* from the drain to the source. As the gate becomes more positive, the channel width increases, enabling the drain-to-source current to increase as the drain-to-source resistance decreases. This basic VFET can thus pass high currents (typically up

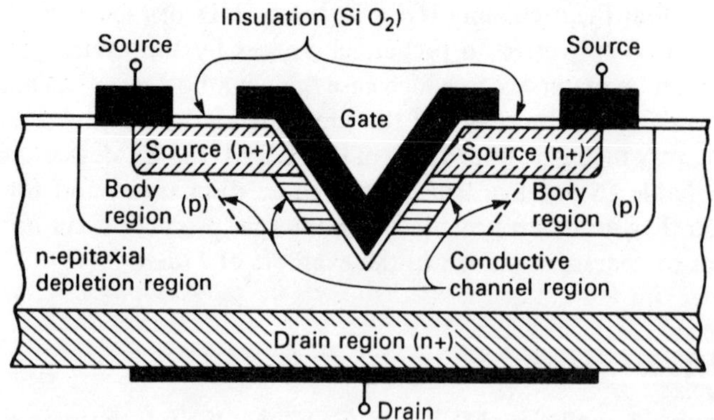

Figure 8.17 *Basic structure of the VFET power device*

to 2 A) without creating excessive current density within its channel regions.

The original Siliconix VMOS design of *Figure* 8.17 was highly successful, but not perfect. The sharp bottom of its V-groove caused an excessive electric field at this point and placed a severe limit on the device's operating voltage. Subsequent to the original introduction of VMOS, Intersil introduced their own version of the basic technique, but with a U-shaped groove (plus other modifications) that improved device reliability and gave higher maximum operating voltages. In 1980, Siliconix added these and other modifications to their own VMOS devices, resulting in further improvements in performance.

Other power FETs

Several manufacturers have produced viable power FETs without using the V- or U-groove technique, but still relying on the vertical flow of current between drain and source. Hitachi produce both p-channel and n-channel power MOSFET devices with ratings up to 8 A and 200 V, but these are suitable for use only in audio and low-RF applications.

Supertex of California and Ferranti of England produce a range of power MOSFETs with the general title of 'vertical DMOS'. These feature high operating voltages (up to 650 V), high current rating (up to 16 A), low *on* resistance (down to 50 milliohms) and very fast operating speeds (up to 2 GHz at 1 A, 500 MHz at 10 A). Siemens of Germany use a modified version of DMOS, known as SIPMOS, to

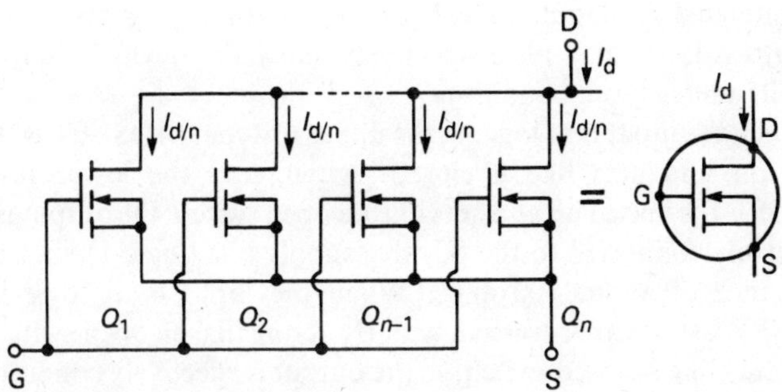

Figure 8.18 *The IR HEXFET comprises a balanced matrix of parallel-connected low-power MOSFETs, which are equivalent to a single high-power MOSFET*

produce a range of n-channel devices with voltage ratings as high as 1 kV and with current ratings as high as 30 A.

The International Rectifier solution to the power FET problem is to produce a device which, in effect, houses a vast array of parallel-connected low-power vertical MOSFETs or 'cells' which share the total current equally between them and thus act like a single power FET, as indicated in *Figure* 8.18. These devices are named HEXFET, after the hexagonal structure of these cells, which have a density of about 100 000 per square centimetre of semiconductor material.

In parallel-connected FETs (as in the HEXFET), equal current sharing is ensured by the conduction channel's positive temperature coefficient; if the current of one FET becomes excessive, the resultant heating of its channel raises its resistance, thus reducing its current flow and tending to equalize it with the other parallel-connected FETs. This feature makes power FETs immune to thermal runaway problems.

CMOS basics

One of the most important applications of FETs is in digital ICs. The best-known range of such devices use the technology known as COSMOS or CMOS, and rely on the use of COmplementary–Symmetry pairs of *MOS*FETs. *Figure* 8.19 illustrates basic CMOS principles.

The basic CMOS device comprises a p-type and n-type symmetrical complementary pair of enhancement-mode MOSFETs, wired in series, with their gates shorted together at the input and their drains tied together at the output, as shown in *Figure* 8.19*a*. The pair are intended to handle logic-0 or logic-1 digital signals only, and *Figures* 8.19*b* and 8.19*c* respectively show the device's equivalent circuits under these conditions.

When the input is at logic-0, the upper (p-type) MOSFET is biased fully on and acts like a closed switch, and the lower (n-type) MOSFET is biased off and acts like an open switch; the output is thus effectively connected to the positive supply line (logic-1) via a series resistance of about 100 ohms. When the input is at logic-1, the MOSFET states are reversed, with Q_1 acting like an open switch and Q_2 acting like a closed switch, so the output is effectively connected to ground (logic-0) via 100 ohms. Note in both cases that the entire signal current is fed to the load, and none is shunted off by the CMOS circuitry; this is a major feature of CMOS technology.

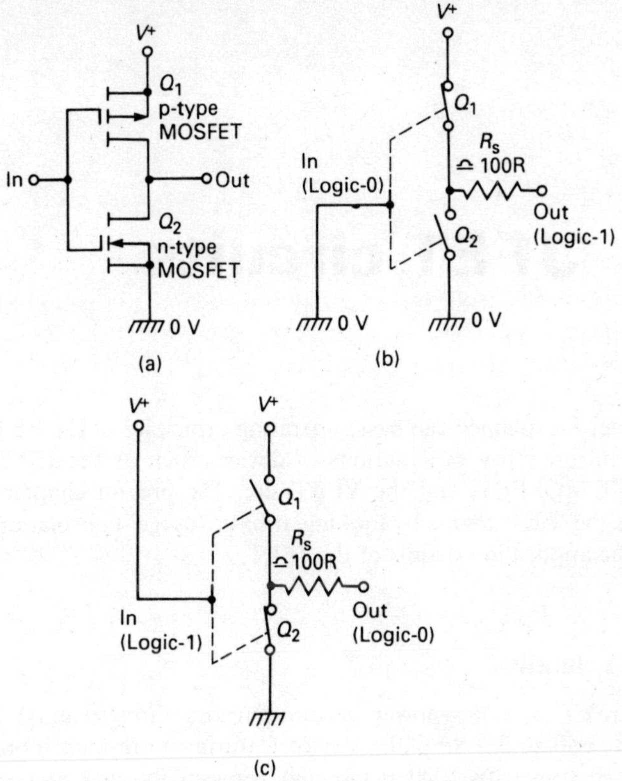

Figure 8.19 *(a) Basic CMOS circuit, and its equivalent with (b) a logic-0 input and (c) a logic-1 input*

9 JFET circuits

Chapter 8 explained the basic operating principles of the FET and gave introductory explanations of devices such as the JFET, the IGFET/MOSFET, and the VFET, etc. The present chapter continues the 'FET' theme by looking at basic 'usage' information and specific application details of the JFET.

JFET details

The JFET is a low-power general-purpose three-terminal (*gate*, *source*, and *drain*) amplifier device featuring ultra-high input impedance (typically 1000 megohms) between its gate and source terminals. Signal voltages applied between the gate and source control the magnitudes of the device's drain current. The JFET thus functions like a voltage-to-current converter; typical conversion or 'transconductance' sensitivity is a few milliamperes of output current per input volt.

JFETs invariably operate in the depletion mode, i.e. the JFET passes maximum current when its gate bias is zero, and its current is reduced or 'depleted' by reverse-biasing its gate terminal, as indicated in the typical n-channel transfer-characteristics graph of *Figure* 8.4 of Chapter 8.

Practical JFETs are available in both n-channel and p-channel forms, just as bipolar transistors are available in npn and pnp versions. *Figure* 8.1 (see Chapter 8) shows the standard symbols of the two basic types of JFET. The two best-known JFETs are the 2N3819 n-channel device and the 2N3820 p-channel device, which are usually housed in T0-92 plastic packages with the connections shown in

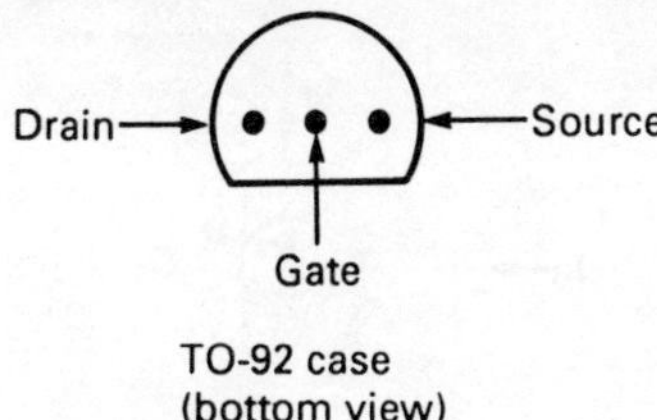

Figure 9.1 *Outline and connections of the 2N3919 and 2N3820 JFETs*

V_{ds} = +25 V (= max. drain-to-source voltage)
V_{dg} = +25 V (= max. drain-to-gate voltage)
V_{gs} = −25 V (= max. gate-to-source voltage)
V_p = −8 Vmax (= gate-to-source voltage needed to cut off I_d)
I_{dss} = 2–20 mA (= drain-to-source current with V_{gs} = 0 V)
I_{gss} = −2 nA max. (= gate leakage current at 25°C)
I_g = 10 mA (= max. gate current)
g_m = 2.0 to 6.5 mmho (= small signal transconductance)
C_{iss} = 8 pf max. (= common source input capacitance)
P_T = 200 mW max. (= power dissipation, in free air)
f_T = 100 MHz (= gain-bandwidth product)

Figure 9.2 *General characteristics of the 2N3819 n-channel JFET*

Figure 9.1. All of the 'application' circuits shown in this chapter are based on the 2N3819 n-channel JFET, and *Figure* 9.2 lists the general characteristics of this device.

JFET biasing

The JFET can be used in both digital and analogue applications. In the latter case it must, if it is to act as a low-distortion amplifier, first be biased into its linear region by reverse biasing its gate relative to its source terminal. Three basic JFET biasing techniques are in common use. The simplest of these is the 'self-biasing' system shown in *Figure* 9.3. Here, the gate is grounded via R_g and R_s is wired from source to ground. Any current flowing in R_s drives the source positive relative to the gate, which is thus reverse biased under this condition. Suppose

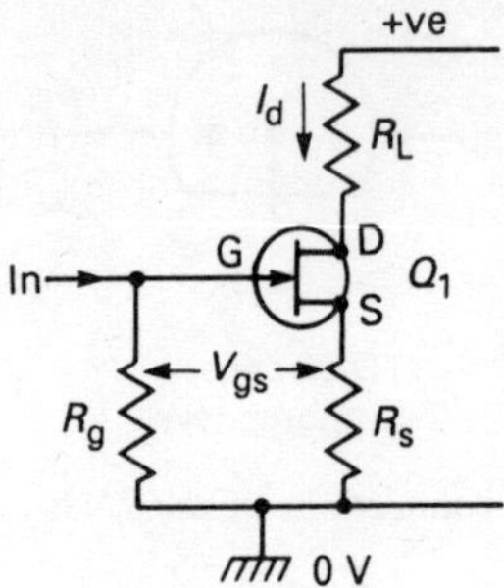

Figure 9.3 *Basic JFET 'self-biasing' system*

that an I_d of 1 mA is wanted, and that a V_{gs} bias of −2V2 is needed to set this condition. The correct bias can be obtained by giving R_s a value of 2k2, since I_d flows in R_s and a current of 1 mA through 2k2 gives the required V_{gs} of −2V2. If I_d tends to fall for some reason, V_{gs} naturally falls as well and thus makes I_d increase and counter the original change; the bias is thus self-regulating via negative feedback.

In practice, the precise V_{gs} value needed to set a given I_d varies widely between individual JFETs of the same type, and the only sure way of getting a precise I_d value in this system is to either select R_s by trial and error or to replace it with a variable resistor. The basic self-biasing system has, however, the advantage of low cost and is accurate enough for most practical applications, and is thus the most widely used of the three biasing systems.

A more accurate way of biasing the JFET is via the 'offset' system shown in *Figure* 9.4*a*. Here, potential divider R_1–R_2 applies a fixed

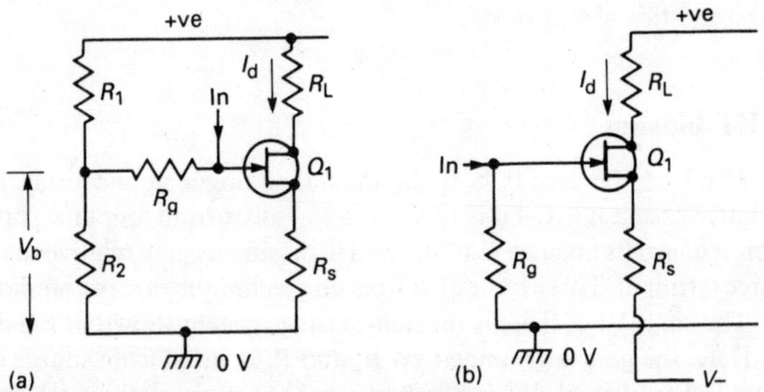

Figure 9.4 *Basic JFET 'offset biasing' system*

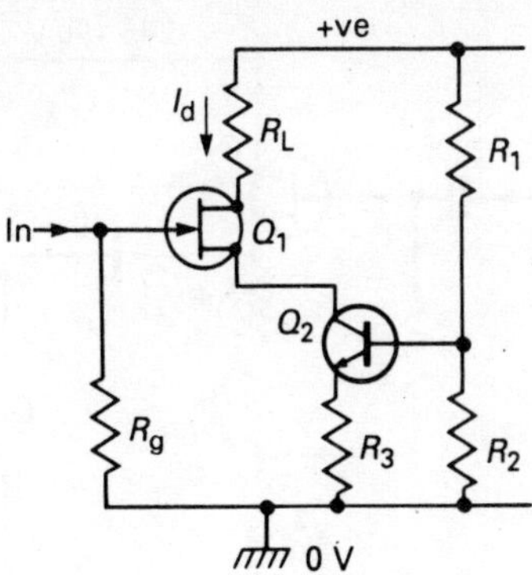

Figure 9.5 *Basic JFET 'constant-current' biasing system*

positive bias to the gate via R_g, and the source voltage thus equals this voltage minus V_{gs}. If the gate voltage is large relative to V_{gs}, I_d is set mainly by the values of R_s and the gate voltage, and is not greatly influenced by V_{gs} variations. This system thus enables I_d values to be set with good accuracy and without need for individual component selection. Similar results can also be obtained by grounding the gate and taking the bottom end of R_s to a large negative voltage, as shown in *Figure* 9.4*b*.

The third type of biasing system is shown in *Figure* 9.5. Here, the normal source resistor is replaced by npn transistor Q_2, which is wired as a constant-current generator and sets the I_d value; this value is determined by the values of Q_2's base voltage (set by potential-divider R_1–R_2) and R_3. This system gives excellent biasing stability, since I_d is independent of the JFET characteristics, but at the expense of increased circuit complexity and cost.

In the three biasing systems described, R_g can have any value up to 10 megohms, the maximum limit being imposed by the volt drop across this resistor caused by gate leakage currents, which may upset the biasing conditions.

Source follower circuits

When used as linear amplifiers, JFETs are usually used in either the source follower (common-drain) or the common-source modes. The source follower offers a very high input impedance, and gives near-unity overall voltage gain (hence the alternative title of 'voltage

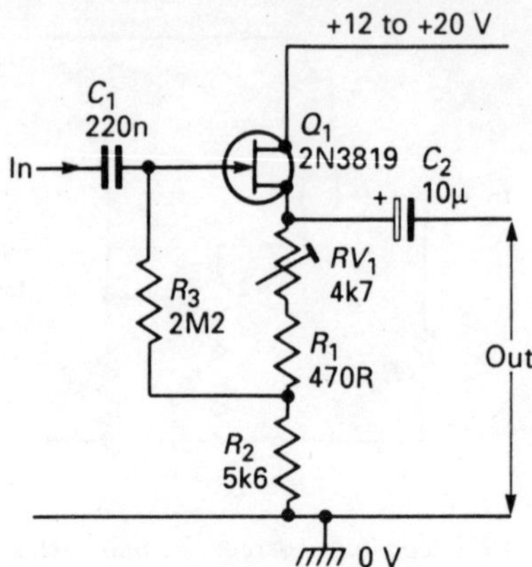

Figure 9.6 *Self-biasing source follower.* $Z_{in} = 10\ M\Omega$

follower'). *Figure* 9.6 shows a practical example of a simple JFET source follower circuit.

Here, a self-biasing system is used, and the drain current can be varied via RV_1. The circuit can be used with any supply in the 12–20 V range, and RV_1 should be adjusted to set a quiescent R_2 volt-drop of 5V6, giving a drain current of 1 mA. The circuit gives an actual input–output voltage gain of 0.95. A degree of 'bootstrapping' is applied to R_3 via the RV_1–R_1 and R_2 divider, increasing its effective impedance by about five times; the circuit's actual input impedance is thus about 10 megohms shunted by 10 pF, i.e. it is 10 megohms at very low frequencies, falling to 1 megohm at about 16 kHz and 100k at 160 kHz, etc.

Figure 9.7 shows an alternative version of the source follower. In this case gate-offset biasing is used and individual component adjustment is not needed. Overall voltage gain is about 0.95. C_2 is an optional bootstrapping capacitor and raises R_3's impedance by about 20 times. Without C_2, the circuit's input impedance is about 2M2 shunted by 10 pF; with C_2, the input impedance is 44 megohms shunted by 10 pF. Alternative impedance values can be obtained by altering the R_3 value, up to a maximum of 10M.

Finally, *Figure* 9.8 shows a hybrid (JFET plus bipolar) version of the source follower, which gives an input impedance of about 500 megohms shunted by 10 pF. Here, offset biasing is applied via the R_1–R_2 potential divider, as in *Figure* 9.7, but the R_4 source resistor of *Figure* 9.7 is replaced by the Q_2–R_4 (etc.) network, which makes Q_2

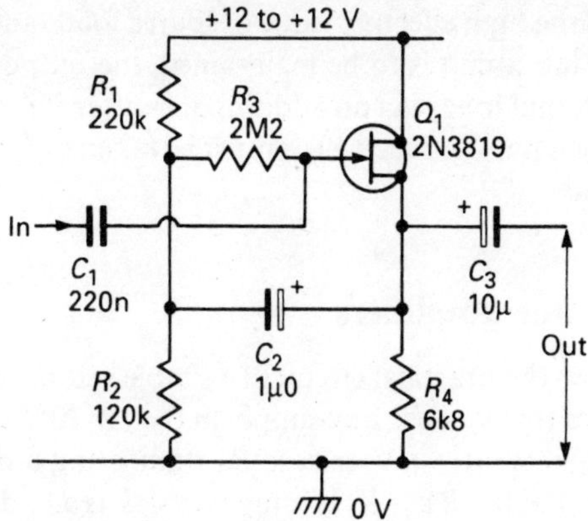

Figure 9.7 *Source follower with offset biasing. Z_{in} = 44 MΩ*

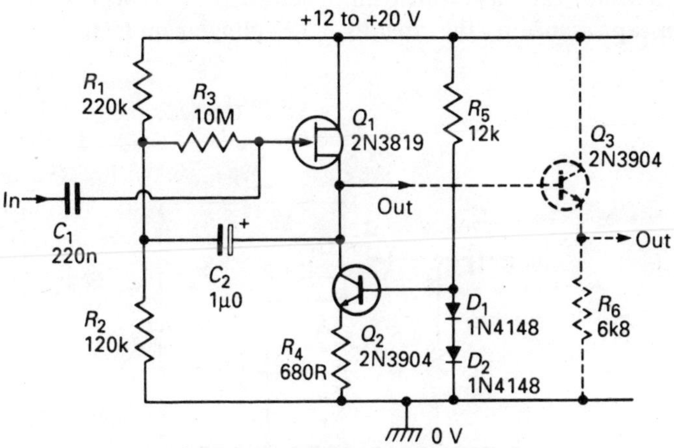

Figure 9.8 *Hybrid sources follower. Z_{in} = 500 MΩ*

act as a very high-impedance source load and as a constant-current generator that sets Q_1's drain–source current at about 1 mA and gives it an overall voltage gain of about 0.99. C_2 is a bootstrapping capacitor that, because of the circuit's excellent voltage gain, raises R_3's impedance by about 100 times, to 1000 megohms; this impedance is shunted by the JFET's gate impedance of about 1000 megohms, so the input impedance of the complete circuit works out at about 500 megohms shunted by 10 pF.

Note that, if the high effective value of source load (and thus input) impedance of this circuit is to be maintained, the output must either be taken to external loads via an additional emitter follower stage (as shown by dashed lines in Fig. 9.8) or must be taken only to fairly high impedance loads.

Common source amplifiers

Figure 9.9 shows the practical circuit of a simple self-biasing common source amplifier that can use any supply in the 12–20 V range; RV_1 is used to set a quiescent 5.6 V across R_3 (indicating a drain current of 1 mA). Note that the RV_1–R_2 biasing network is a.c.-decoupled via C_2. The circuit gives a voltage gain of about 21 dB (= × 12), has a ±3 dB frequency response that spans 15 Hz to 250 kHz, and has an input impedance of 2M2 shunted by 50 pF (this high shunt value is due to Miller feedback, which multiplies the JFET's effective gate-to-drain capacitance by the circuit's × 12 voltage gain factor.

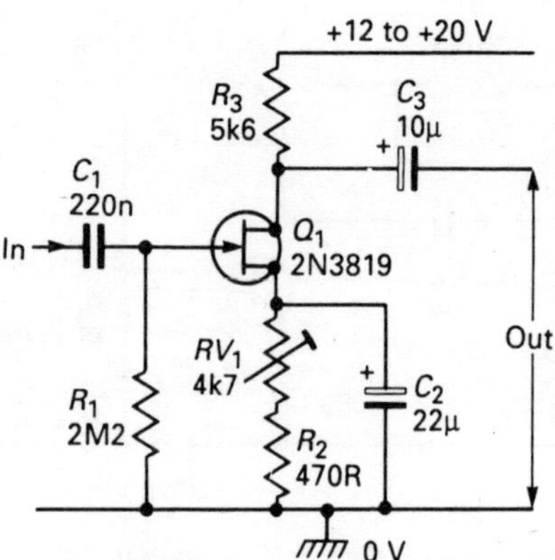

Figure 9.9 *Simple self-biasing common-source amplifier*

The *Figure* 9.9 circuit uses a variable biasing component (RV_1) that can be adjusted to enable the circuit to accept, with minimal distortion, strong input signals that generate large output-voltage swings. In cases where only low-level input signals are to be handled (as in pre-amplifiers, etc), this 'adjustable bias' facility can be eliminated and a fixed-bias network used in its place. *Figures* 9.10 and 9.11 show examples of circuits of this type.

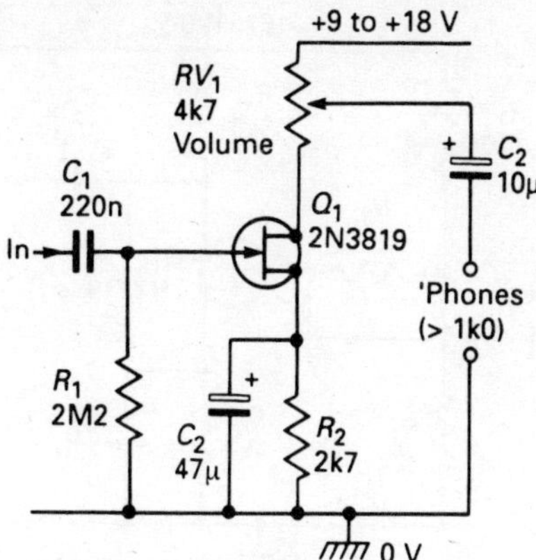

Figure 9.10 *Simple headphone amplifier*

The *Figure* 9.10 circuit is a simple headphone amplifier for use with 'phone impedances of 1k0 or greater. It has a built-in volume control (RV_1), has an imput impedance of 2M2, and can use any supply in the 9–18 V range.

The *Figure* 9.11 design is an add-on pre-amplifier that gives a voltage gain in excess of 20 dB, has a bandwidth that extends beyond 100 kHz, and has an input impedance of 2.2 megohms. It can be used with any existing amplifier that can provide a 9–18 V power source.

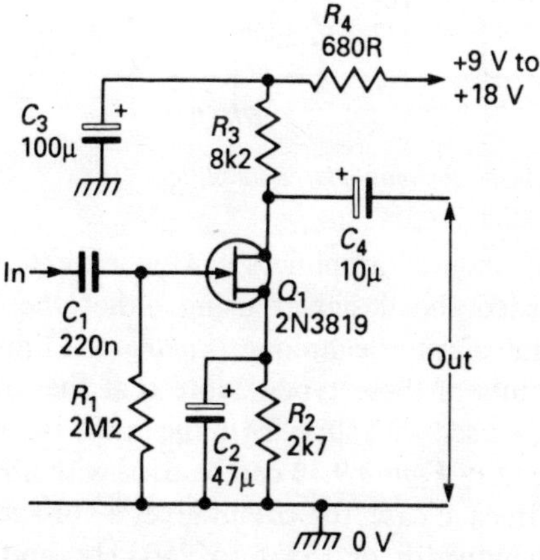

Figure 9.11 *General-purpose add-on pre-amplifier*

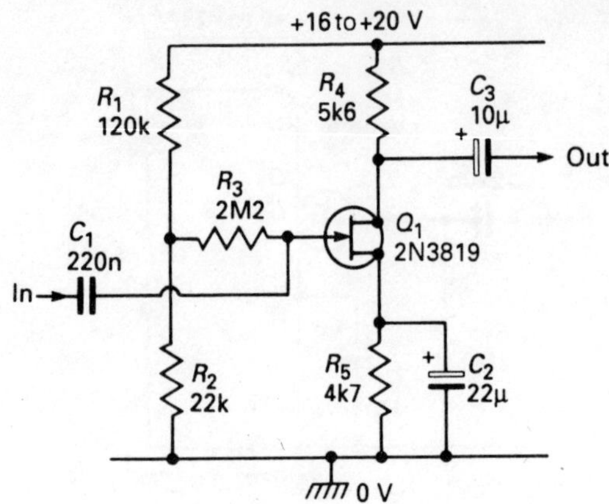

Figure 9.12 *Common-source amplifier with offset gate biasing*

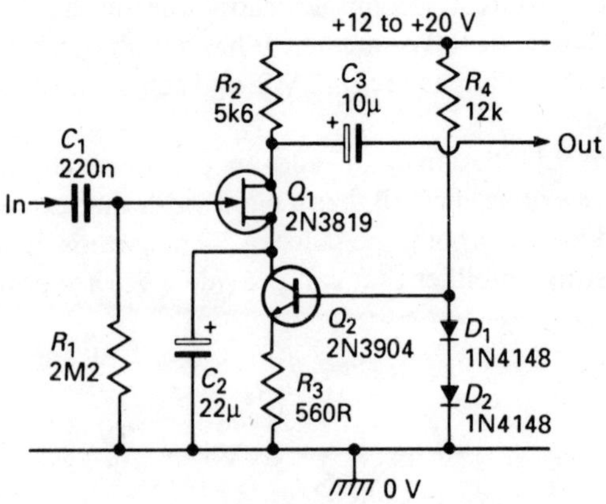

Figure 9.13 *'Hybrid' common-source amplifier*

JFET common source amplifiers can, when exceptional biasing accuracy is needed, be designed using either the 'offset' or the 'constant-current' biasing technique. *Figures* 9.12 and 9.13 respectively show circuits of these types. Note that the 'offset' circuit of *Figure* 9.12 can be used with supplies in the range 16–20 V only, while the 'hybrid' circuit of *Figure* 9.13 can be used with any supply in the 12–20 V range. In each case, the circuit gives a voltage gain of 21 dB, has a ±3 dB bandwidth of 15 Hz to 250 kHz, and has an input impedance of 2M2.

D.C. voltmeters

Figure 9.14 shows how a JFET can be used as the basis of a simple three-range analogue voltmeter with a maximum f.s.d. sensitivity of 0.5 V and an input resistance of 11.1 megohms on all ranges. Here, R_6–RV_2 and R_7 form a potential divider across the 12 V supply and, if the R_7–RV_2 junction is regarded as the circuit's zero-voltage 'ground' point, sets the top of R_6 at +8 V and the bottom of R_7 at −4 V. Q_1 is wired as a source follower, with its gate grounded via the R_1 to R_4 network and its source taken to the −4 V line via source load resistor R_5; the JFET is thus offset biased and its drain current is set at about 1 mA.

In the circuit, R_6–RV_2 and Q_1–R_5 act as a Wheatstone bridge network, and RV_2 is adjusted so that the bridge is balanced and zero current flows in the meter in the absence of an input voltage at Q_1 gate. Any voltage applied to Q_1 gate then drives the bridge out of balance by a proportional amount, which can be read directly on the meter. R_1–R_3 form a range multiplier network which, when RV_1 is correctly adjusted, gives f.s.d. ranges of 0.5, 5.0, and 50 V. R_4 is used to protect Q_1 gate against damage if excessive input voltage is applied to the circuit.

To use the *Figure* 9.14 circuit, first adjust RV_2 to give zero meter reading in the absence of an input voltage, and then connect an accurate 0.5 V d.c. to the input and adjust RV_1 to give a precise full-

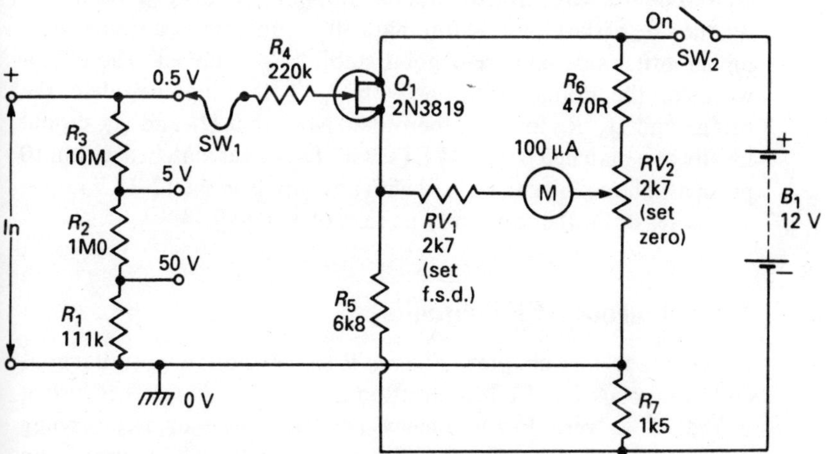

Figure 9.14 *Simple three-range d.c. voltmeter*

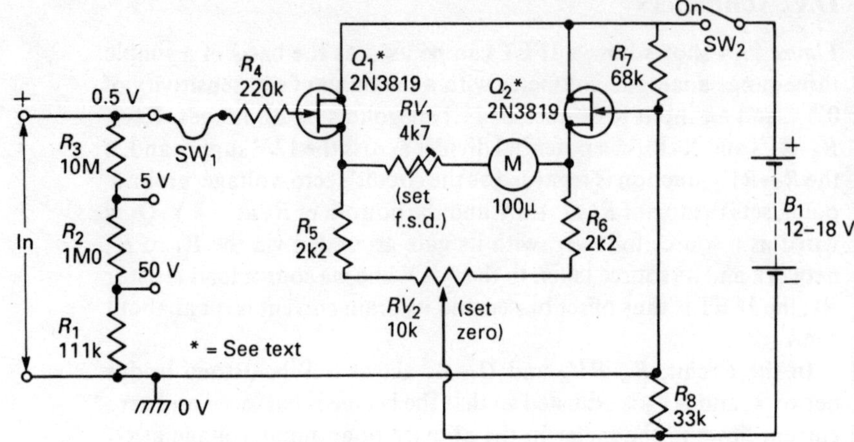

Figure 9.15 *Low-drift three-range d.c. voltmeter*

scale meter reading. Repeat these adjustments until consistent zero and full-scale readings are obtained; the unit is then ready for use. In practice, this simple circuit tends to drift with variations in supply voltage and temperature, and fairly frequent trimming of the zero control is needed. Drift can be greatly reduced by using a zener-stabilized 12 V supply.

Figure 9.15 shows a low-drift version of the JFET voltmeter. Here, Q_1 and Q_2 are wired as a differential amplifier, so any drift occurring on one side of the circuit is automatically countered by a similar drift on the other side, and very good stability is obtained. The circuit works on the 'bridge' principle, with Q_2–R_5 forming one side of the bridge and Q_2–R_6 forming the other. Note that Q_1 and Q_2 should ideally be a matched pair of JFETs, with I_{dss} values matched within 10 per cent. The circuit can be used with any supply in the 12–18 V range, and is set up in the same way as that of *Figure* 9.14.

Miscellaneous JFET circuits

To conclude this chapter, *Figures* 9.16–19 show a miscellaneous collection of useful JFET application circuits. The *Figure* 9.16 circuit is that of a very low-frequency (VLF) astable or free-running multivibrator that generates a square-wave output. The circuit's on and off periods are controlled by C_1–R_4 and C_2–R_3, and R_3 and R_4

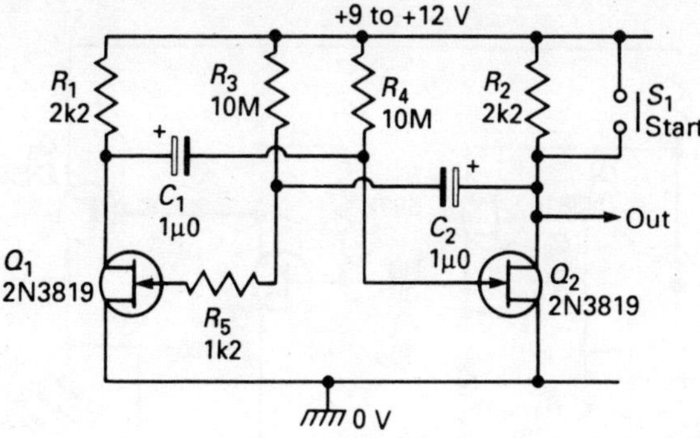

Figure 9.16 *VLF astable multivibrator*

can (because of the high input impedances of the JFETs) be given very large values. With the component values shown, the circuit cycles at a rate of once per 20 s, i.e. at a frequency of 0.05 Hz. Note that *start* button S_1 must be held closed for at least one second to initiate the astable action, so this circuit should be regarded as an 'experimental' design.

Figure 9.17 shows, in basic form, how a JFET and a 741 op-amp can be used to make a voltage-controlled amplifier/attenuator. Here, the op-amp is wired as an inverting amplifier with its voltage gain determined mainly by the R_2/R_3 ratio, and the JFET is used as a voltage-controlled resistor that (in conjunction with R_1) can attenuate the amplifier's input signal. When a large negative control voltage

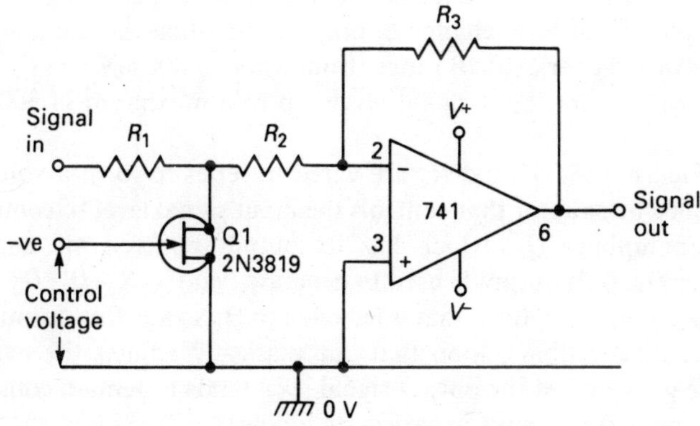

Figure 9.17 *Voltage-controlled amplifier/attenuator*

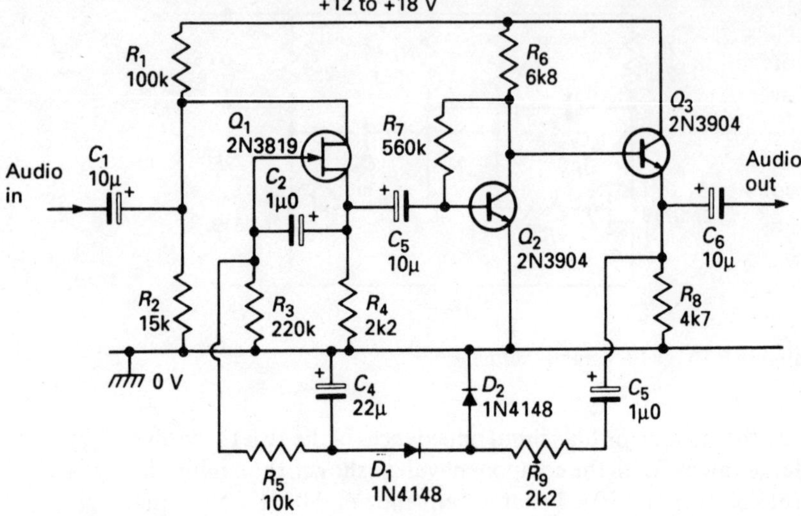

Figure 9.18 *Constant-volume amplifier*

is fed to Q_1 gate the JFET acts like a near-infinite resistance and causes no signal attenuation, so the circuit gives high overall gain, but when the gate bias is zero the JFET acts like a low resistance and causes heavy signal attenuation, so the circuit gives an overall signal loss. Intermediate values of signal attenuation and overall gain or loss can be obtained by varying the control voltage value.

Figure 9.18 shows how this 'voltage-controlled attenuator' technique can be used to make a 'constant volume' amplifier that produces an output signal level change of only 7.5 dB when the input signal level is varied over a 40 dB range (from 3 mV to 300 mV r.m.s.). The circuit can accept input signal levels up to a maximum of 500 mV r.m.s.

In *Figure* 9.18, Q_1 and R_4 are wired in series to form a voltage-controlled attenuator that controls the input signal level to common emitter amplifier Q_2, which has its output buffered via emitter follower Q_3. Q_3's output is used to generate (via C_5–R_9–D_1–D_2–C_4–R_5) a d.c. control voltage that is fed back to Q_1's gate, thus forming a d.c. negative-feedback loop that automatically adjusts the overall voltage gain so that the output signal level tends to remain constant as the input signal level is varied, as follows.

When a very small input signal is applied to the circuit, Q_3's output signal is also small, so negligible d.c. control voltage is fed to Q_1's gate; Q_1 thus acts as a low resistance under this condition, so almost the full input signal is applied to Q_2 base, and the circuit gives high overall gain. When a large input signal is applied to the circuit, Q_3's output signal tends to be large, so a large d.c. negative control voltage is fed to Q_1's gate; Q_1 thus acts as a high resistance under this condition, so only a small part of the input signal is fed to Q_2's base, and the circuit gives low overall gain. Thus, the output level stays fairly constant over a wide range of input signal levels; this characteristic is useful in cassette recorders, intercoms, and telephone amplifiers, etc.

Finally, *Figure* 9.19 shows how a JFET can be used to make a d.c.-to-a.c. converter or 'chopper' that produces a square-wave output with a peak amplitude equal to that of the d.c. input voltage. In this case Q_1 acts like an electronic switch that is wired in series with R_1 and is gated on and off at a 1 kHz rate via the Q_2–Q_3 astable circuit, thus giving the d.c.-to-a.c. conversion.

Note that Q_1's gate-drive signal amplitude can be varied via RV_1; if too large a drive is used, Q_1's gate-to-source junction starts to avalanche, causing a small spike voltage to break through the drain and give an output even when no d.c. input is present. To prevent this, connect a d.c. input and then trim RV_1 until the output is just on the verge of decreasing; once set up in this way, the circuit can be reliably used to chop voltages as small as a fraction of a millivolt.

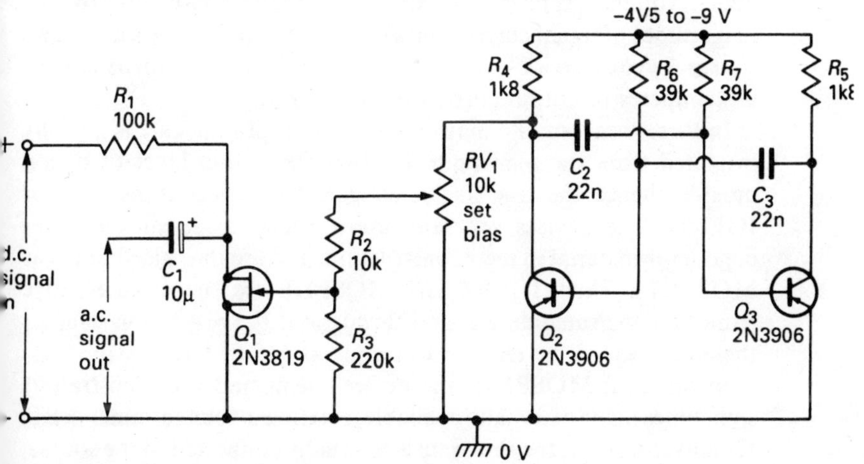

Figure 9.19 *D.c.-to-a.c. converter or 'chopper' circuit*

10 MOSFET and CMOS circuits

Chapter 8 explained the basic operating principles of the FET and, amongst other things, gave an introductory explanation of those devices known as MOSFETs or IGFETs. The present chapter continues this theme by taking an in-depth look at these low-power devices.

MOSFET basics

The MOSFET (or IGFET) is basically a low-power general-purpose three-terminal (*gate*, *source*, and *drain*) amplifier device featuring a near-infinite input impedance between its gate and source terminals. Signal voltages applied between the gate and source control the magnitudes of signal currents flowing between the device's drain and source. Typical device 'gain' or 'transconductance' sensitivity is a few milliamperes of output current per input volt.

In these 'near-infinite input impedance' FETs the gate is actually insulated from the semiconductor body by a thin layer of silicon dioxide (hence the title 'insulated gate field effect transistor', or IGFET). The devices generally use a 'metal oxide silicon' semiconductor material in their construction, and are thus also known as MOSFETs. Thus, IGFET and MOSFET are simply alternative names for the same device, and throughout the rest of this chapter these devices will be referred to simply as MOSFETs.

In practical MOSFETs, the device's semiconductor substrate is sometimes made externally available, creating a 'four-terminal' FET. Usually, however, the substrate is internally connected to the source, and the device is thus manufactured as a three-terminal MOSFET.

Figure 10.1 *Standard symbols of (a) three-pin and (b) four-pin n-channel depletion-mode MOSFETs*

Many early types of MOSFET operated in the depletion mode, like a JFET, and *Figure* 10.1 shows the symbols used to represent the 3- and 4-pin n-channel versions of these devices (arrowhead directions are reversed to represent p-channel types). Depletion-mode MOSFETs are used in the same way as the JFET devices described in the last chapter and, with one exception, offer no significant advantages over the JFET. The one exception is the dual-gate or tetrode MOSFET, in which the drain-to-source currents can be controlled via either or both of a pair of input terminals. The best-known examples of these devices are the 3N140 and 40673 n-channel types, which use the symbols and T0-72 outline shown in *Figure* 10.2.

Figure 10.2 *Symbol (a) and TO72 outline (b) of the 3N140 and 40673 dual-gate or 'tetrode' MOSFET*

Most modern MOSFETs are enhancement-mode devices, in which the drain-to-source conduction channel is normally (with zero gate bias) closed, but can be opened by applying forward gate bias. This 'normally open-circuit' action of the enhancement-mode MOSFET is implied by the gaps between source and drain in the device's standard symbol, shown in *Figure* 10.3, which depicts the n-channel device (the arrowheads are reversed to indicate a p-channel device).

Figure 10.3 *Standard symbols of (a) three-pin and (b) four-pin n-channel enhancement-mode MOSFETs*

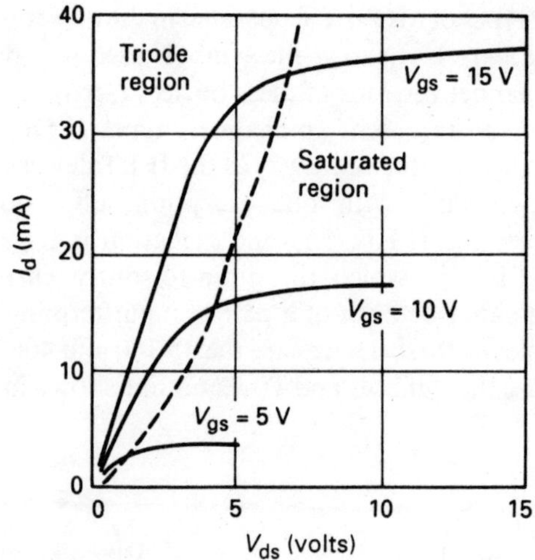

Figure 10.4 *Typical transfer characteristics of 4007UB n-channel enhancement-mode MOSFETs*

Figure 10.4 shows the typical transfer characteristics of an n-channel enhancement-mode MOSFET, and *Figure* 10.5 shows the V_{gs}/I_d curves of the same device when powered from a 15 V supply. Note that no significant I_d current flows until the gate voltage rises to a threshold (V_{th}) value of a few volts, but that beyond this value the drain current rises in a non-linear fashion. Also note that the graph is divided into two characteristic regions, as indicated by the dotted line, these being the 'triode' region and the 'saturated' region. In the triode region the MOSFET acts like a voltage-controlled resistor; in the saturated region it acts like a voltage-controlled constant-current generator.

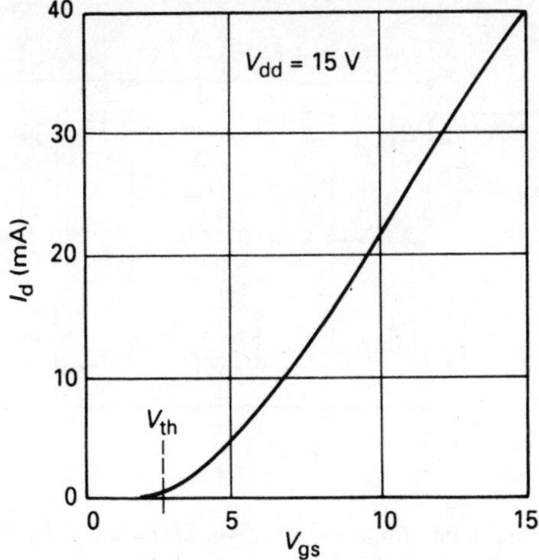

Figure 10.5 *Typical* V_{gs}/I_d *characteristics of 4007UB n-channel enhancement-mode MOSFET*

One very important point about MOSFET devices is that, because of their very high input impedances, they are very vulnerable to damage via electrostatic discharges; for this reason, MOSFETs are often (but not always) provided with integral protection via diodes or zeners.

The 4007UB

The easiest and cheapest practical way of learning about enhancement-mode MOSFETs is via a 4007UB chip, which is the simplest member of the popular CMOS digital IC range and actually houses six useful MOSFETs in a single 14-pin dil package.

Figure 10.6 shows the functional diagram and pin numbering of the 4007UB, which contains two complementary pairs of independently accessible MOSFETs and a third complementary MOSFET pair that are connected as a standard CMOS inverter stage. Each of the IC's three independent input terminals is internally connected to the standard CMOS protection networks shown in *Figure* 10.7. Within the IC, Q_1, Q_3 and Q_5 are p-channel MOSFETs, and Q_2, Q_4 and Q_6 are n-channel types. Note that the performance graphs of *Figures* 10.4 and 10.5 actually apply to the individual n-channel devices within this CMOS IC.

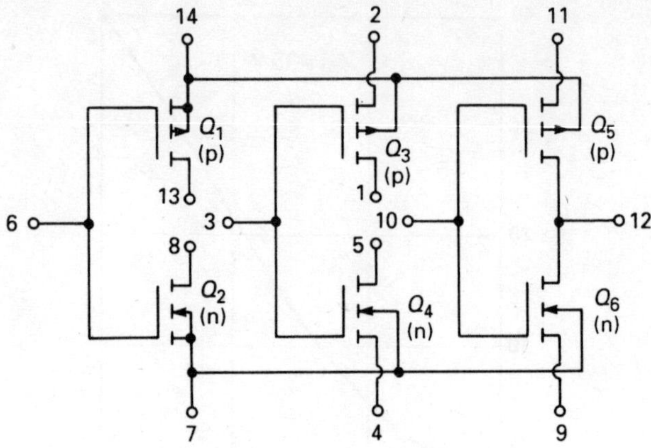

Figure 10.6 *Functional diagram of the 4007UB dual CMOS pair plus inverter*

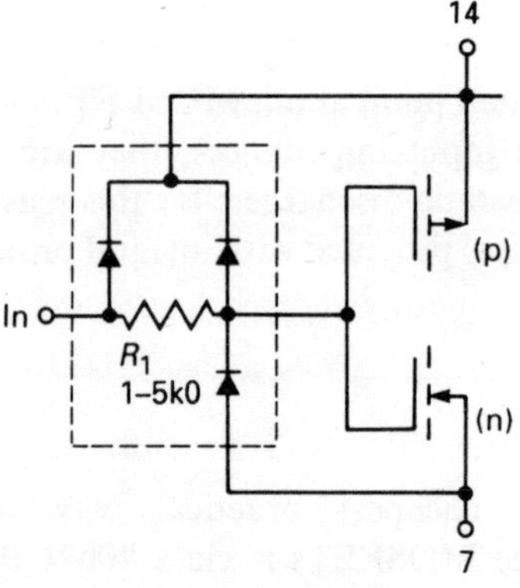

Figure 10.7 *Internal input-protection network (within dotted lines) on each input of the 4007UB*

The term 'CMOS' actually stands for 'complementary metal oxide silicon field-effect transistors', and all CMOS ICs are in fact designed around the simple basic elements shown in *Figure* 10.6. The reader will thus find it rewarding to have a good understanding of these elements, and this subject will be discussed in depth after first looking at the 4007UB's basic usage rules.

The 4007UB usage rules are simple. In any given application, all unused IC elements must be disabled. Complementary pairs of

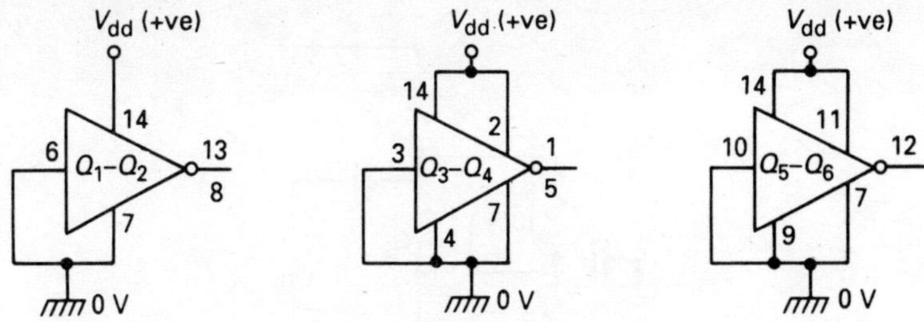

Figure 10.8 *Individual 4007UB complementary pairs can be disabled by connecting them as CMOS inverters and grounding their inputs*

MOSFETs can be disabled by connecting them as standard CMOS inverters (i.e. gate–gate and source–source) and tying their inputs to ground, as shown in *Figure* 10.8. Individual MOSFETs can be disabled by tying their source to their substrate and leaving the drain open circuit. In use, the IC's input terminals must not be allowed to rise above V_{dd} (the supply voltage) or below V_{ss} zero volts. To use an n-channel MOSFET, the source must be tied to V_{ss} either directly or via a current-limiting resistor. To use a p-channel MOSFET, the source must be tied to V_{dd}, either directly or via a current-limiting resistor.

Linear operation

To fully understand the operation and vagaries of CMOS circuitry, it is necessary to understand the linear characteristics of basic MOSFETs, as shown in the graph of *Figure* 10.5; note that negligible drain current flows until the gate rises to a 'threshold' value of about 1.5–2.5 V, but that the drain current then increases almost linearly with further increases in gate voltage.

Figure 10.9 shows how to use an n-channel 4007UB MOSFET as a linear inverting amplifier. R_1 acts as Q_2's drain load, and R_2–R_x bias the gate so that Q_2 operates in the linear mode. The R_x value is selected to give the desired quiescent drain voltage, and is normally in the 18–100k range. The amplifier can be made to give a very high input impedance by wiring a 10M isolating resistor between the R_2–R_x junction and Q_2 gate, as shown in *Figure* 10.10.

Figure 10.11 shows how to use an n-channel MOSFET as a unity-gain non-inverting common-drain amplifier or source follower. The

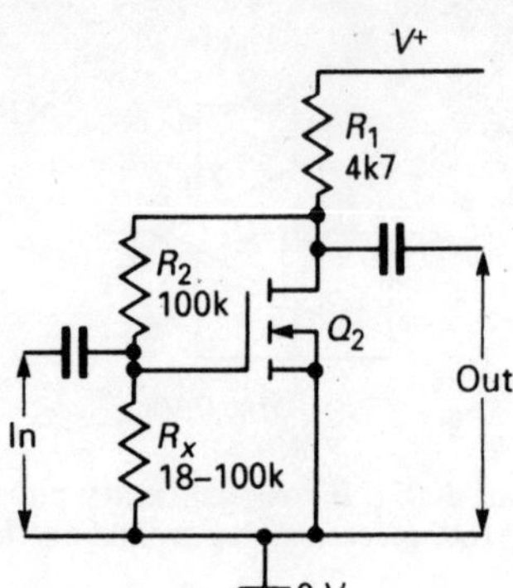

Figure 10.9 *Method of biasing n-channel 4007UB MOSFETs for use as a linear inverting amplifier (with medium input impedance)*

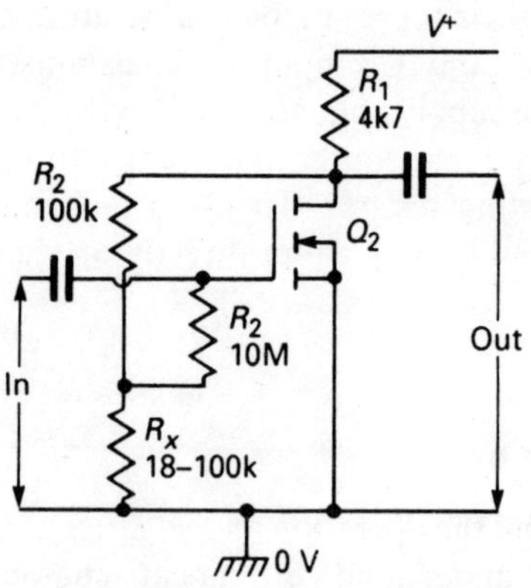

Figure 10.10 *High-input impedance version of the inverting amplifier*

MOSFET gate is biased at half-supply volts by the R_2–R_3 divider, and the source terminal automatically takes up a quiescent value that is slightly more than V_{th} below the gate value.

The basic *Figure* 10.11 circuit has an input impedance equal to the paralleled values of R_2 and R_3 (=50k), but can be increased to greater than 10M by wiring R_4 as shown. Alternatively, the input impedance can be raised to several hundred megohms by using the bootstrapped source follower configuration shown in *Figure* 10.12, in which the Q_2 output signal is coupled back to the R_2–R_3 junction via C_1, so that near-identical 'input' signals appear at each end of R_4, which thus

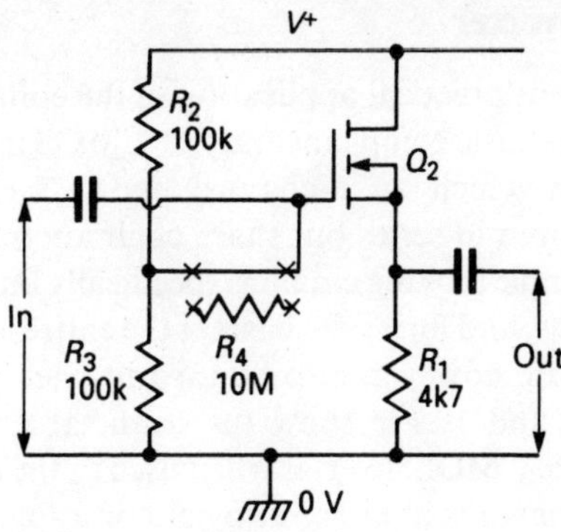

Figure 10.11 *Methods of biasing n-channel 4007UB MOSFET as a unity-gain non-inverting amplifier or source follower*

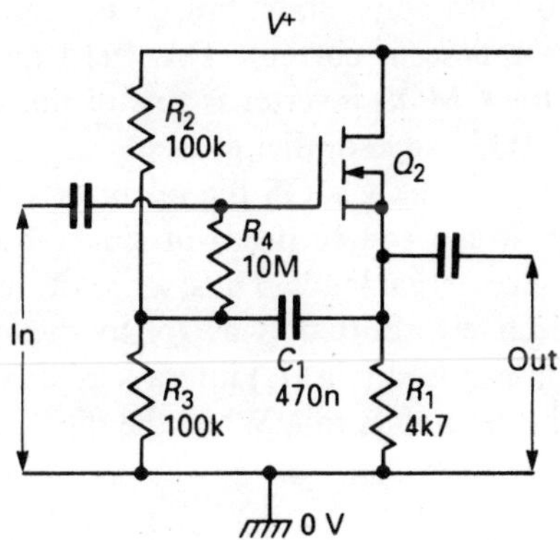

Figure 10.12 *Bootstrapped source follower has ultra-high input impedance*

passes near-zero signal current and appears (to the input signal) as a near-infinite impedance.

Note from the above description that the enhancement-mode MOSFET performs like a conventional bipolar transistor, except that it has an ultra-high input impedance and has a substantially larger input-offset voltage (the base–emitter offset of a bipolar is typically 600 mV, while the gate–source offset of a MOSFET is typically 2 V). Allowing for these differences, the enhancement-mode MOSFET can thus be used as a direct replacement in most small-signal bipolar transistor circuits.

The CMOS inverter

The most important practical application of the enhancement-mode MOSFET is in the basic complementary or CMOS inverting stage of *Figure* 10.13*a*, in which an n-channel and a p-channel pair of MOSFETs are wired in series but share common input and output terminals. This simple looking circuit is specifically intended for use in digital applications, and forms the basis of the entire family of CMOS ICs; the circuit can, however, also be used in linear applications.

Figures 10.13*b* and 10.13*c* show the truth table and the circuit symbol of the basic CMOS inverter when used in the digital mode, in which the input signal is at either a logic-0 or a logic-1 level. Here, with a logic-0 input applied, Q_1 is shorted (fully on), so the output is firmly tied to the logic-1 (positive rail) level, but Q_2 is open (fully off) and the inverter thus passes zero quiescent current via this transistor. With a logic-1 input applied, Q_2 is shorted and the output is firmly tied to the logic-0 (zero volts) state, but Q_1 is open and the circuit again passes zero quiescent current. This 'zero quiescent current' characteristic of the CMOS inverter is one of the most important features of the CMOS range of digital ICs.

Note that, although the CMOS digital inverter consumes zero quiescent current, it can source (feed) or sink (absorb) significant current into or from external loads. Thus, when the input is at logic-0 the output is effectively shorted (via Q_1) to the positive rail, so substantial current can feed (via Q_1) into a load connected between the output and the zero-volts rail. When the input is at logic-1, the

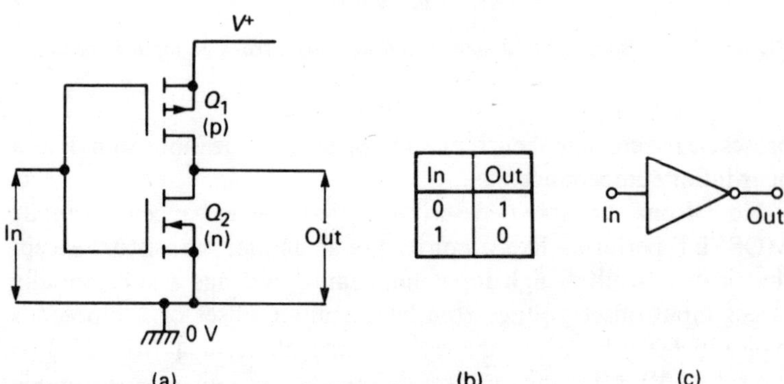

In	Out
0	1
1	0

Figure 10.13 *Circuit* (*a*), *truth table* (*b*) *and symbol* (*c*) *of the basic CMOS digital inverter*

output is effectively shorted (via Q_2) to the zero-volts rail, so substantial currents can be absorbed (via Q_2) from a load connected between the output and the positive supply rail. This is another very important feature of the CMOS digital inverter circuit. Note that Q_5 and Q_6 of the 4007UB IC are fixed-wired in this inverter configuration.

The basic CMOS inverter can be used as a linear amplifier by biasing its input to a value between the logic-0 and logic-1 levels; under this condition Q_1 and Q_2 are both biased partly on, and the inverter thus passes significant quiescent current. *Figure* 10.14 shows the typical drain-current transfer characteristics of the circuit under this condition. Note that the drain current is zero when the input is at zero or full-supply volts, but rises to a maximum value (typically 0.5 mA at 5 V supply, or 10.5 mA at 15 V supply) when the input is at approximately half-supply volts, under which condition both MOSFETs of the inverter are biased on equally.

Figure 10.15 shows the typical input–output voltage-transfer characteristics of the simple CMOS inverter at different supply voltage values. Note (on the 15 V V_{dd} line, for example) that the output voltage changes by only a small amount when the input voltage is shifted around the V_{dd} and 0 V levels, but that when V_{in} is biased at roughly half-supply volts a small change of input voltage

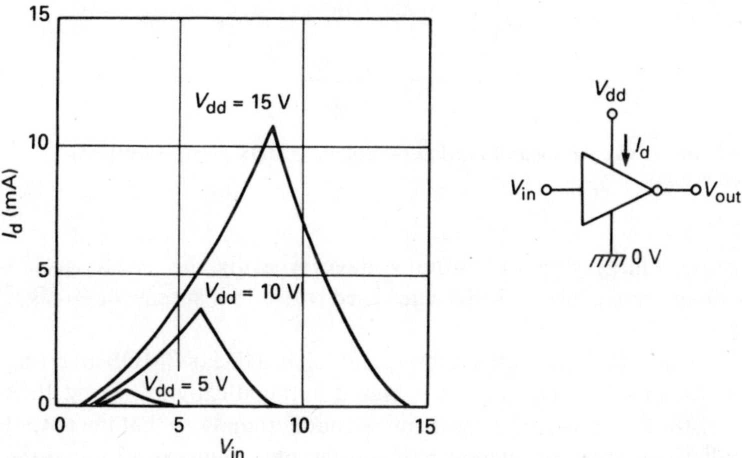

Figure 10.14 *Drain-current transfer characteristics of the simple CMOS inverter*

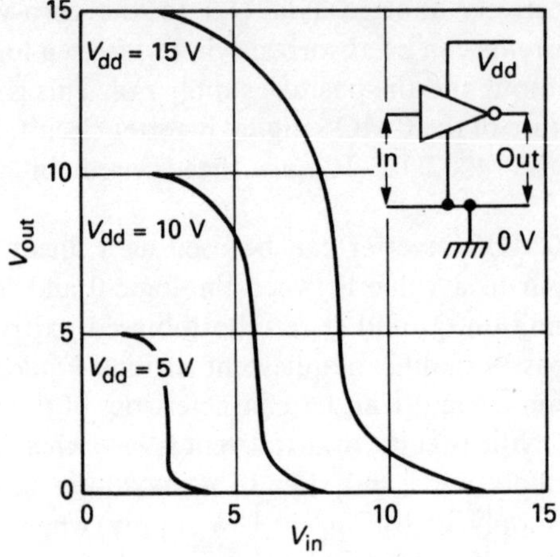

Figure 10.15 *Typical input-to-output voltage transfer characteristics of the 4007UB simple CMOS inverter*

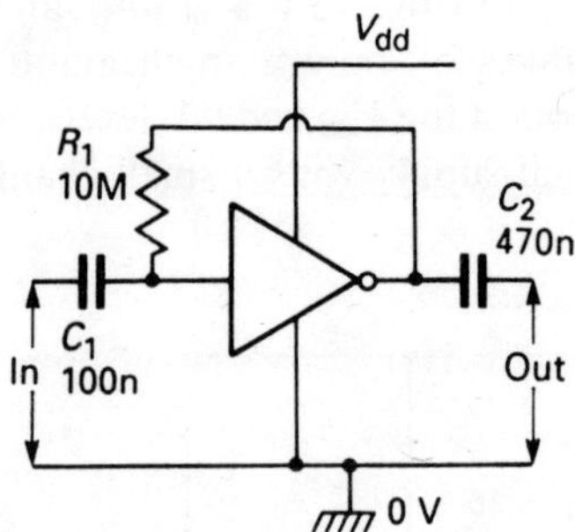

Figure 10.16 *Method of biasing the simple CMOS inverter for linear operation*

causes a large change of output voltage: typically, the inverter gives a voltage gain of about 30 dB when used with a 15 V supply, or 40 dB at 5 V.

Figure 10.16 shows the practical circuit of a linear CMOS inverting amplifier stage. This circuit is biased automatically by wiring 10M resistor R_1 between the input and output terminals, so that the output self-biases at approximately half-supply volts. *Figure* 10.17 shows the typical voltage gain and frequency characteristics of this circuit when operated at three alternative supply-rail values; this graph assumes

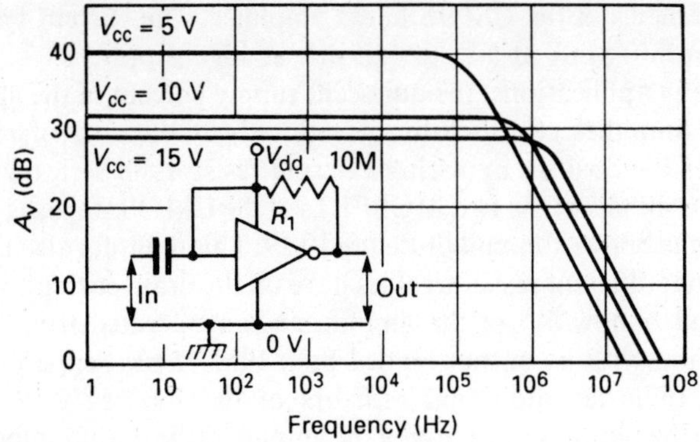

Figure 10.17 *Typical* A_V *and frequency characteristics of the linear-mode basic CMOS amplifier*

that the amplifier output is feeding into the high impedance of a 10M/15 pF 'scope probe, and under this condition the circuit has a bandwidth of 2.5 MHz when operated from a 15 V supply.

As would be expected from the voltage transfer graph of *Figure* 10.15, the distortion characteristics of the CMOS linear amplifier are quite good with small-amplitude signals (output amplitudes up to 3 V peak-to-peak with a 15 V supply), but the distortion then increases progressively as the output approaches the upper and lower supply limits. Unlike a bipolar transistor circuit, the CMOS amplifier does not 'clip' excessive sine-wave signals, but progressively rounds off their peaks.

Figure 10.18 shows the typical drain current versus supply voltage

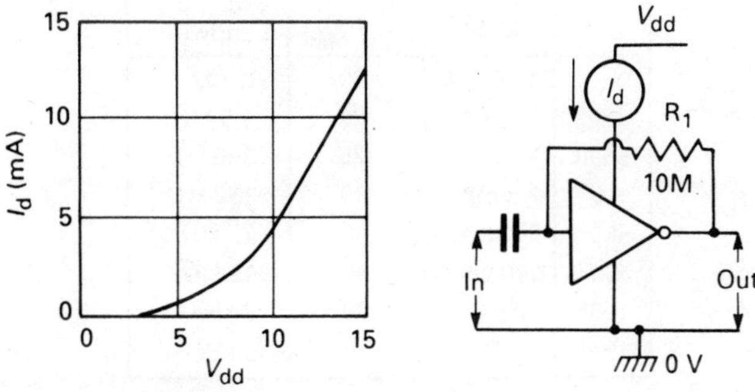

Figure 10.18 *Typical* I_d/V_{dd} *characteristics of the linear-mode CMOS amplifier*

characteristics of the CMOS linear amplifier. The current typically varies from 0.5 mA at 5 V, to 12.5 mA at 15 V supply.

In many applications, the quiescent supply current of the 4007UB CMOS amplifier can usefully be reduced, at the cost of reduced amplifier bandwidth, by wiring external resistors in series with the source terminals of the two MOSFETs of the CMOS stage, as shown in the 'micropower' circuit of *Figure* 10.19. This diagram also lists the effects that different resistor values have on the drain current, voltage gain, and bandwidth of the amplifier when operated from a 15 V supply and with its output loaded by a 10M/15 pF 'scope probe.

Note that the additional resistors of the *Figure* 10.19 circuit increase the output impedance of the amplifier (the output impedance

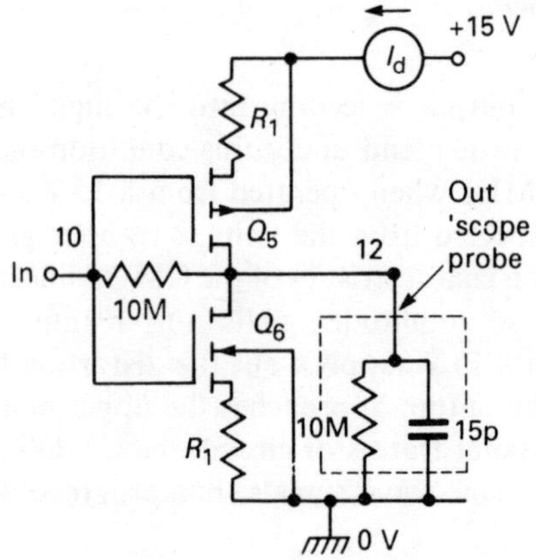

R_1	I_d (mA)	A_v (V_{in}/V_{out})	Upper 3 dB bandwidth
0	12.5 mA	20	2.7 MHz
100R	8.2 mA	20	1.5 MHz
560R	3.9 mA	25	300 kHz
1k0	2.5 mA	30	150 kHz
5k6	600 μA	40	25 kHz
10k	370 μA	40	15 kHz
100k	40 μA	30	2 kHz
1M0	4 μA	10	1 kHz

Figure 10.19 *'Micropower' 4007UB CMOS linear amplifier, showing method of reducing* I_d*, with performance details*

is roughly equal to the R_1–A_v product), and this impedance and the external load resistance/capacitance has a great effect on the overall gain and bandwidth of the circuit. When using 10k values for R_1, for example, if the load capacitance is increased (from 15 pF) to 50 pF the bandwidth falls to about 4 kHz, but if the capacitance is reduced to 5 pF the bandwidth increases to 45 kHz. Similarly, if the resistive load is reduced from 10M to 10k, the voltage gain falls to unity; for significant gain, the load resistance must be large relative to the output impedance of the amplifier.

The basic (unbiased) CMOS inverter stage has an input capacitance of about 5 pF and an input resistance of near-infinity. Thus, if the output of the *Figure* 10.19 circuit is fed directly to such a load, it will show a voltage gain of about 30 and a bandwidth of 3 kHz when R_1 has a value of 1M0; it will even give a useful gain and bandwidth when R_1 has a value of 10M, but will consume a quiescent current of only 0.4 μA.

Practical CMOS

The CMOS linear amplifier can easily be used, in either its standard or micropower forms, to make a variety of fixed-gain amplifiers, mixers, integrators, active filters, and oscillators, etc. A selection of such circuits is shown in *Figure* 10.20 to 10.24.

Figure 10.20 shows the practical circuit of a $\times 10$ inverting amplifier. The CMOS stage is biased by feedback resistor R_2, and the voltage gain is set at $\times 10$ by the R_1/R_2 ratio. The input impedance of the circuit is 1M0, and equals the R_1 value.

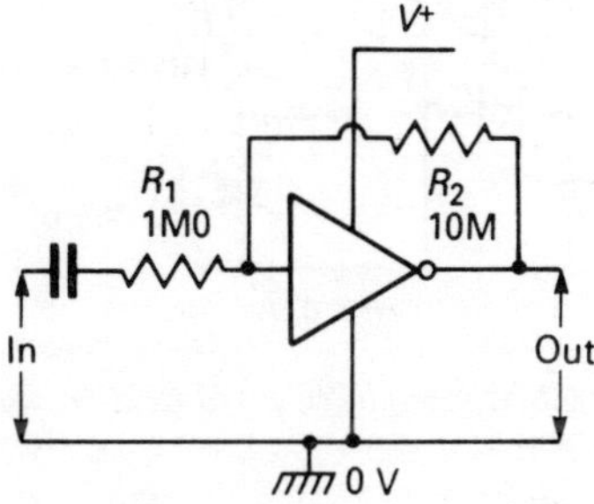

Figure 10.20 *Linear CMOS amplifier wired as $\times 10$ inverting amplifier*

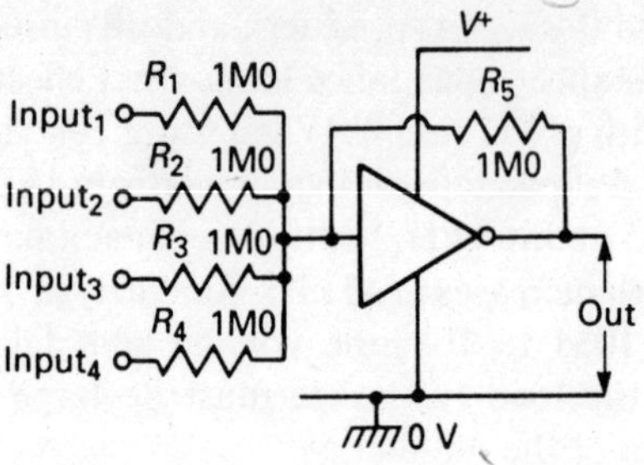

Figure 10.21 *Linear CMOS amplifier wired as unity-gain four-input audio 'mixer'*

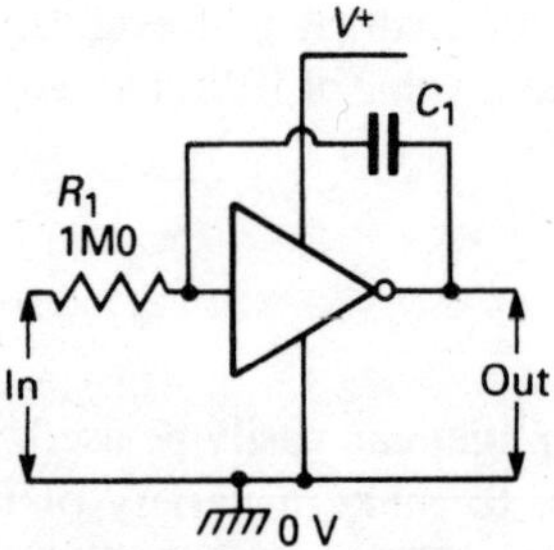

Figure 10.22 *Linear CMOS amplifier wired as an integrator*

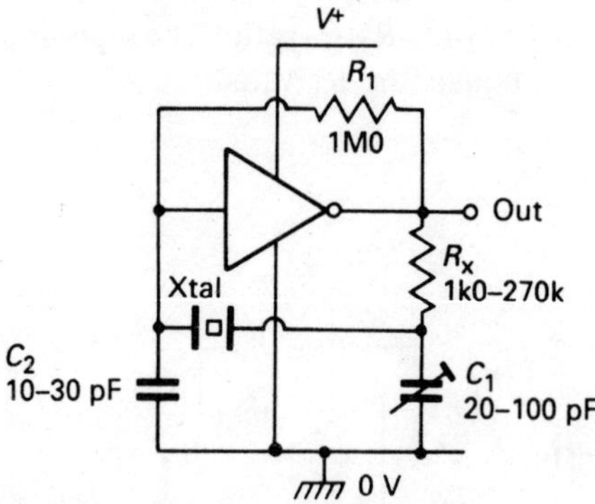

Figure 10.23 *Linear CMOS amplifier wired as a crystal oscillator*

Figure 10.21 shows how the above circuit can be modified for use as an audio 'mixed' or analogue voltage adder. The circuit has four input terminals and the voltage gain between each input and the output terminal is fixed at unity by the relative values of the 1M0 input resistor and the 1M0 feedback resistor. *Figure* 10.22 shows how the basic CMOS amplifier can be used as a simple integrator.

Figure 10.23 shows how the linear CMOS amplifier can be used as a crystal oscillator. Here, the CMOS amplifier is linearly biased via R_1 and provides 180° of phase shift at the crystal resonant frequency, thus causing the circuit to oscillate. If the user wants the crystal to provide a frequency accuracy within 0.1 per cent or so, R_x can be replaced by a short and C_1–C_2 can be omitted. For ultra-high accuracy, the correct values of R_x–C_1–C_2 must be individually determined (the diagram shows the typical range of values).

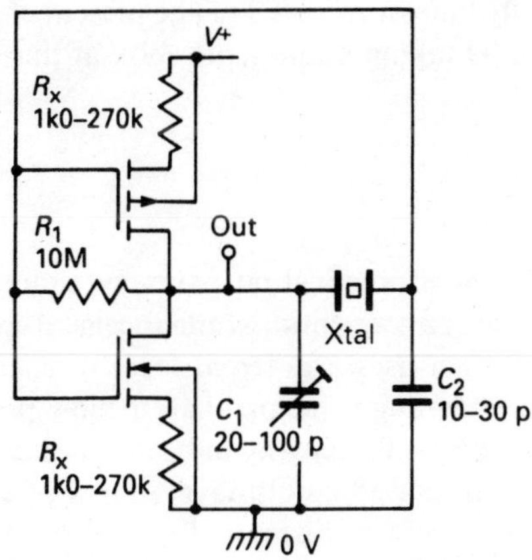

Figure 10.24 *'Micropower' version of the crystal oscillator*

Finally, to complete this chapter, *Figure* 10.24 shows a 'micropower' version of the CMOS crystal oscillator. In this case, R_x is actually incorporated in the amplifier. If desired, the output of this oscillator can be fed directly to the input of an additional CMOS inverter stage, for improved waveform shape/amplitude.

11 VMOS circuits

Chapter 8 explained the basic operating principles of the FET and, amongst other things, gave an introductory explanation of the power-FET family known as VFETs. The present chapter concludes the 'FET' theme by taking an in-depth look at this VFET range of devices.

VFET basics

A VFET can, for most practical purposes, be simply regarded as a high-power version of a conventional enhancement-mode MOSFET, even though it in fact uses a different form of construction and a slightly different operating principle than the low-power MOSFET.

The 'V' in the VFET title actually indicates the fact that the device uses a *vertically* structured (multi-layer) form of construction, in which the main terminal currents flow vertically through the semiconductor materials, rather than being (as in the case of a normal MOSFET) a single-layer device in which the main terminal currents flow horizontally through the surface layer of the semiconductor material. These points are made clear in *Figures* 11.1 and 11.2.

Figure 11.1 shows the basic construction of an n-channel enhancement-mode MOSFET, in which the device comprises a single thin layer of p-type semiconductor material with n-type *source* and *drain* materials infused into the main layer. The gate is electrically insulated from the semiconductor material, but electrostatically controls the width of a drain-to-source conduction channel at the surface of the semiconductor material. The channel is fully closed when zero gate bias is applied, but opens as the gate is positively biased.

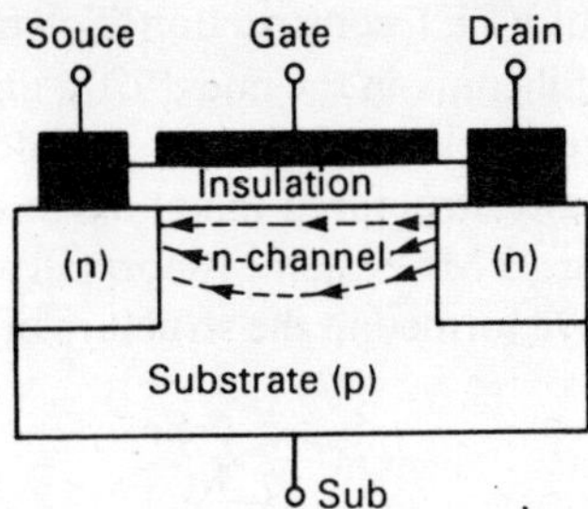

Figure 11.1 *Construction of n-channel enhancement-mode MOSFET; drain–source current flows horizontally*

Note that in *Figure* 11.1 the MOSFET drain-to-source signal current flows horizontally through the conductive channel of the device, and that, because the semiconductor layer is very thin, the maximum allowable drain-to-source currents are very limited (typically to maximum values in the range 2–40 mA).

Figure 11.2 shows the basic construction of an n-channel enhancement-mode VFET device, which uses a vertically structured form of construction comprising several layers of semiconductor material. The gate bias again electrostatically controls the width of a drain-to-source conduction channel, but in this case the drain-to-source current flows vertically through the semiconductor layers: the maximum allowable operating current of the VFET is thus not restricted by the 'thinness' of the individual semiconductor layers, and many practical VFET devices can in fact handle maximum main-terminal currents of several amperes.

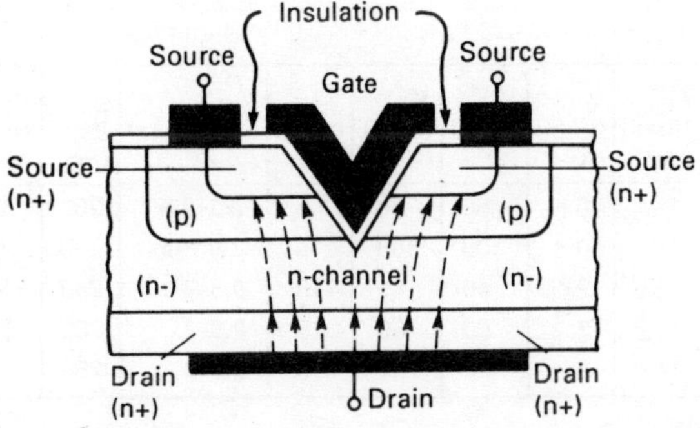

Figure 11.2 *Construction of typical VFET power device; drain–source current flows vertically*

The specific form of VFET construction shown in *Figure* 11.2 was in fact pioneered by Siliconix in the mid-1970s, and the devices using this construction are marketed under the trade name of 'VMOS power FETs' (vertically structured metal-oxide silicon power field-effect transistors). This 'VMOS' name is normally associated with the V-shaped 'gate' groove formed in the structure of the VMOS device.

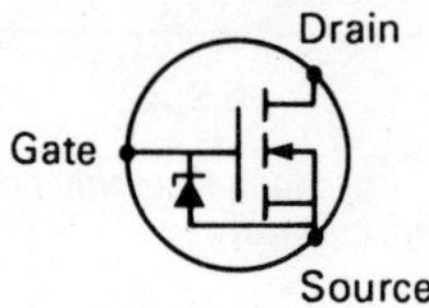

Figure 11.3 *Symbol of Siliconix VMOS power FET with integral zener diode gate protection*

Siliconix VMOS power FETs are probably the best-known type of VFETs. They are presently available as n-channel devices only, and usually incorporate an integral zener diode which gives the gate a high degree of protection against accidental damage; *Figure* 11.3 shows the standard symbol used to represent such a device, and *Figure* 11.4 lists the main characteristics of five of the most popular members of the VMOS family; note in particular the very high maximum operating frequencies of these devices.

Another well-known family of VFET devices is that produced by Hitachi. These use a rather different form of construction than shown in *Figure* 11.2, and are available in both n-channel and p-channel versions. This range of VFETs are well suited to complementary audio power amplifier applications, and *Figure* 11.5 lists the main characteristics of six devices in their 7 A, 100 W range.

Device type no.	P_{tot} (max) (W)	I_d (max) (A)	V_{ds} (max) (V)	V_{dg} (max) (V)	V_{gs} (max) (V)	V_{th} (min–max) (V)	g_m (typ) (m℧)	C_{in} (max) (pF)	f_t (typ) (MHz)
VN10KM	1	0.5	60	60	5	0.3–2.5	200	48	–
VN1010	1	0.5	100	100	15	2 V max	200	48	–
VN46AF	12.5	2	40	40	15	0.8–2	250	50	600
VN66AF	12.5	2	60	60	15	0.8–2	250	50	600
VN88AF	12.5	2	80	80	15	0.8–2	250	50	600

Figure 11.4 *Major parameters of five popular n-channel Siliconix VMOS power FETs*

Device type no.	P_{tot} (max) (W)	I_d (max) (A)	V_{ds} (max) (V)	V_{dg} (max) (V)	V_{gs} (max) (V)	V_{th} (min–max) (V)	g_m (typ) (m℧)	f_t (typ) (MHz)	Channel type
2SJ48	100	7	−120	−120	14	−0.8 to −1.5	1000	900	p
2SJ49	100	7	−140	−140	14	−0.8 to −1.5	1000	900	p
2SJ50	100	7	−160	−160	±14	−0.8 to −1.5	1000	900	p
2SK133	100	7	120	120	14	1 to 1.5	1000	600	n
2SK134	100	7	140	140	14	1 to 1.5	1000	600	n
2SK135	100	7	160	160	±14	1 to 1.5	1000	600	n

Figure 11.5 *Major parameters of six popular high-power Hitachi VFETs*

The VN66AF

The best way to get to know VMOS is to actually 'play' with an example of the device, and for this purpose the Siliconix VN66AF is a very useful and readily available device that is normally housed in a T0-202-style plastic-with-metal-tab package with the outline and pin connections shown in *Figure* 11.6.

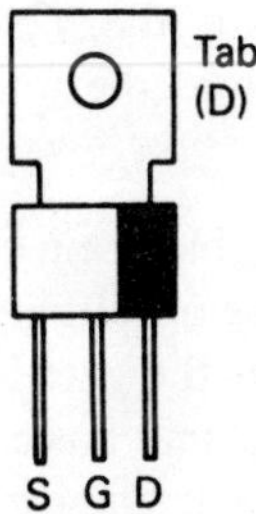

Figure 11.6 *Outline and pin connections of the TO 202-cased VN66AF VMOS power FET*

Figure 11.7 lists the major static and dynamic characteristics of the VN66AF. Points to note here are that the input (gate-to-source) signal must not exceed the unit's 15 V zener rating, and that the device has a typical dynamic input capacitance of 50 pF. This capacitance dictates the dynamic input impedance of the VN66AF; the static input impedance is of the order of a million megohms.

	Characteristic		Value
Static	Max drain-source voltage		60 V
	Max drain-gate voltage		60 V
	Max continuous drain current		2 A
	Max pulsed drain current		3 A
	Max continuous forward gate current		2 mA
	Max pulsed forward gate current		100 mA
	Max continuous reverse gate current		100 mA
	Max forward gate-source (zener) voltage		15 V
	Max reverse gate-source voltage		−0.3 V
	Max dissipation at 25°C case temperature		15 W
	Gate threshold voltage		0.8 V min, 1.2 V typical
	Zero-gate-voltage drain current at 25°C		10 μA max
	On-state drain current at V_{gs} = 10 V		1.0 A min, 2.0 A typical
	Temperature operating and storage range		−40 to + 150°C
Dynamic	Forward transconductance (typical)		250 m℧
	Input capacitance (typical)		50 pF
	Reverse transfer capacitance (typical)		10 pF
	Common-source output capacitance (typical)		50 pF
	Typical switching times, 25 V supply, 23 R load 0–10 V gate drive from A 50R source	Turn-on delay	2 ns
		Rise time	2 ns
		Turn-off delay	2 ns
		Fall time	2 ns

Figure 11.7 *Major static and dynamic characteristics of the VN66AF*

Figures 11.8 and 11.9 show the VN66AF's typical output and saturation characteristics. Note the following specific points from these graphs:

(1) The device passes negligible drain current until the gate voltage reaches a threshold value of roughly 1 V; the drain current then increases non-linearly as the gate is varied up to about 4 V, at which point the drain current has a value of about 400 mA. The device in fact has a square-law transfer characteristic below 400 mA.

(2) The device has a highly linear transfer characteristic above 400 mA (4 V on the gate) and thus offers good results as a low-distortion class-A power amplifier.

(3) The drain current is controlled almost entirely by the gate voltage and is almost independent of the drain voltage so long as the device is not saturated. A point not shown in the diagram is that, for a given value of gate voltage, the drain current has a negative temperature coefficient of about 0.7 per cent per °C, so that the drain current decreases as temperature rises. This

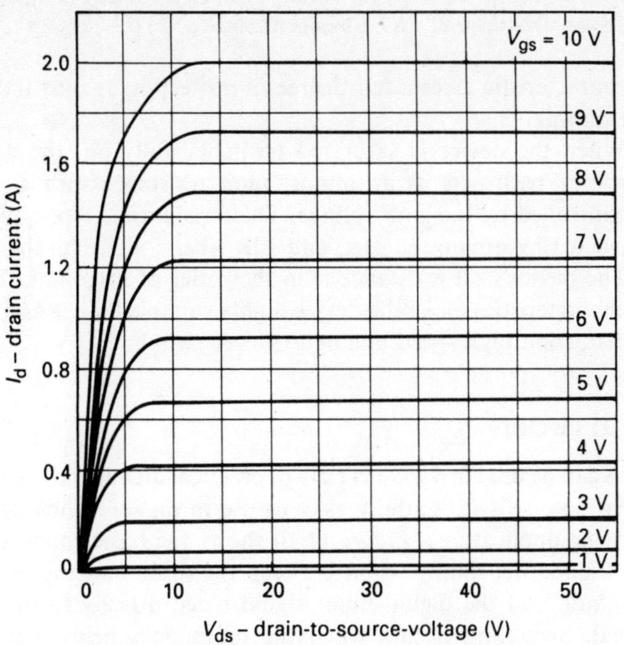

Figure 11.8 *Typical output characteristics of the VN66AF*

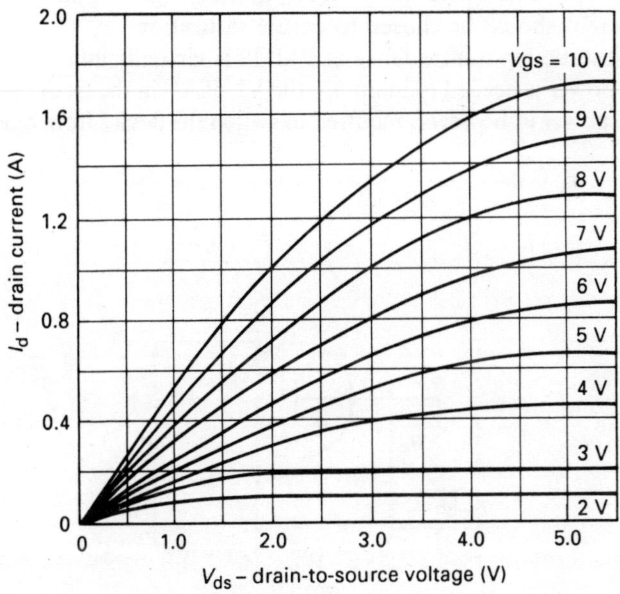

Figure 11.9 *Typical saturation characteristics of the VN66AF*

characteristic gives a fair degree of protection against thermal runaway.

(4) When the device is saturated (switched fully on) the drain–source path acts as an almost pure resistance with a value controlled by the gate voltage. The resistance is typically 2R0 when 10 V are on the gate, and 10R when 2 V are on the gate. The device's off resistance is in the order of megohms. These characteristics make the device highly suitable for use as a low-distortion high-speed analogue power switch.

Digital circuits

VMOS can be used in a wide variety of practical digital and analogue applications. It is delightfully easy to use in digital switching and amplifying applications; *Figure* 11.10 shows the basic connections. Here, the load is simply wired between the drain and the positive supply rail, and the digital input signal is fed directly to the gate terminal. Switch-off occurs when the input goes below the gate threshold value (typically about 1V2). The drain *on* current is determined by the peak amplitude of the gate signal, as shown in *Figure* 11.8, unless saturation occurs. In most digital applications the *on* current should be chosen to ensure saturation.

The static input impedance of VMOS is virtually infinite, so zero drive power is needed to maintain the VN66AF in the *on* or *off* state. Drive power is, however, required to switch the device from one state

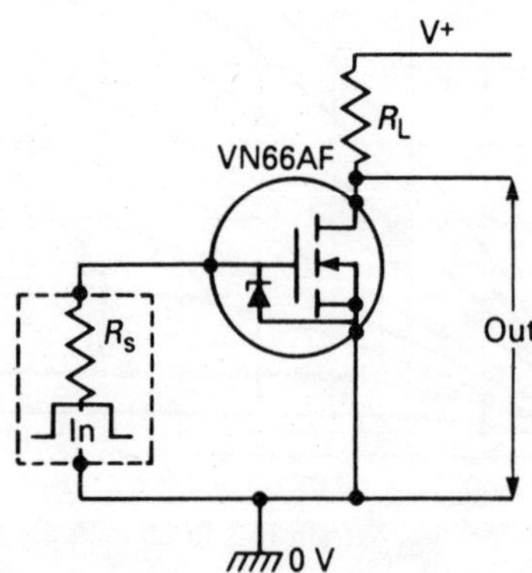

Figure 11.10 *Basic VMOS digital switch or amplifier*

to the other; this power is absorbed in charging or discharging the 50 pF input capacitance of the VN66AF.

The rise and fall times of the output of the *Figure* 11.10 circuit are (assuming zero input rise and fall times) determined by the source impedance of the input signal, by the input capacitance and forward transconductance of the VMOS device, and by the value of R_L. If R_L is large compared to R_s, the VN66AF gives rise and fall times of roughly 0.11 ns per ohm of R_s value. Thus, a 100R source impedance gives a 11 ns rise or fall time. If R_L is not large compared to R_s, these times may be considerably changed.

A point to note when driving the VN66AF in digital applications is that its input zener forward and reverse ratings must never be exceeded. Also, because of the very high-frequency response of VMOS, the device is prone to unwanted oscillations if its circuitry is poorly designed. Gate leads should be kept short, or be protected with a ferrite bead or a small resistor in series with the gate.

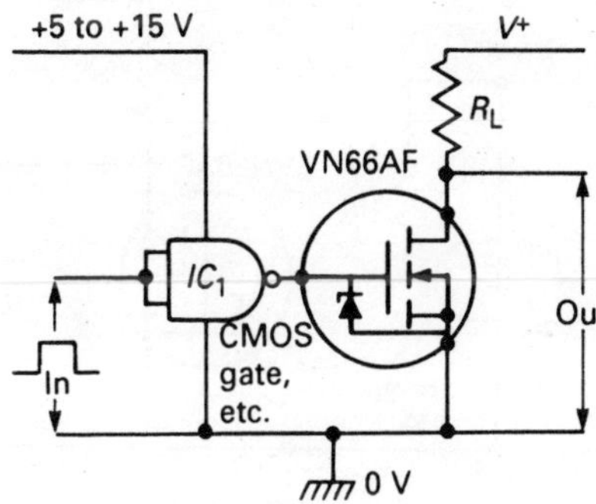

Figure 11.11 *Methods of driving VMOS from CMOS*

VMOS can easily be interfaced directly to the output of a CMOS IC, as shown in *Figure* 11.11. Output rise and fall times of about 60 ns can be expected, due to the limited output currents available from a single CMOS gate, etc. Rise and fall times can be reduced by driving the VMOS from a number of CMOS gates wired in parallel, as shown in *Figure* 11.12, or by using a special high-current driver.

VMOS can be interfaced to the output of TTL (either standard or LS types) by using a pull-up resistor on the TTL output, as shown in *Figure* 11.13. The 5 V TTL output of this circuit is sufficient to drive

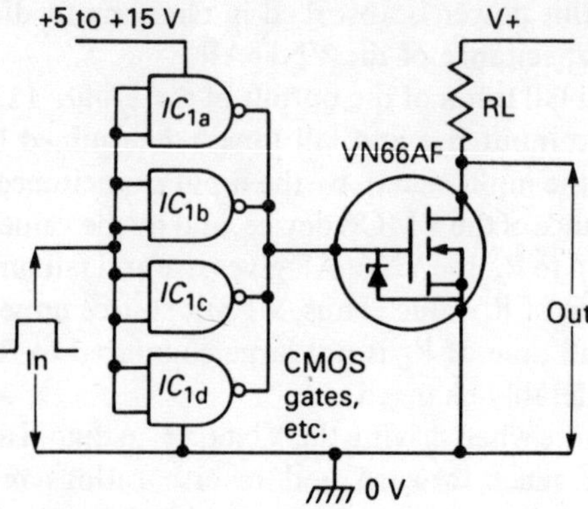

Figure 11.12 *VMOS switching rise and fall times can be reduced by driving it from parallel-connected gates, etc. This circuit gives typical rise and fall times of 25 ns*

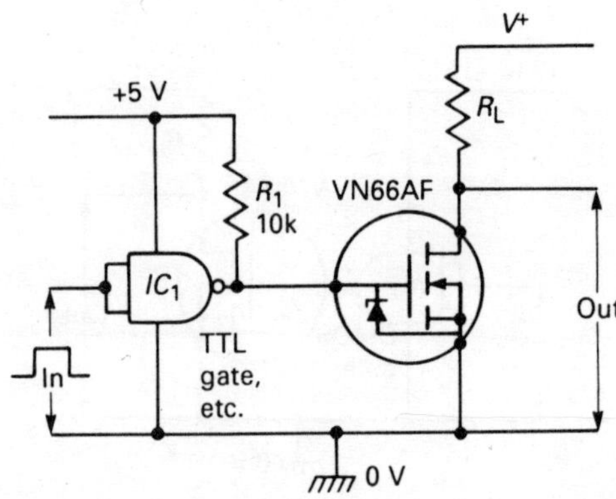

Figure 11.13 *Method of driving VMOS from TTL*

600 mA through a single VN66AF. Higher output currents can be obtained either by wiring a level-shifter stage between the TTL output and the VMOS input, or by wiring a number of VMOS devices in parallel, as shown in *Figure* 11.14.

When using VMOS in digital switching applications, note that if inductive drain loads such as relays, self-interrupting bells or buzzers, or moving-coil speakers are used, clamping diodes must be connected as shown in *Figure* 11.15, to damp inductive back-e.m.f.s and thus protect the VMOS device against damage.

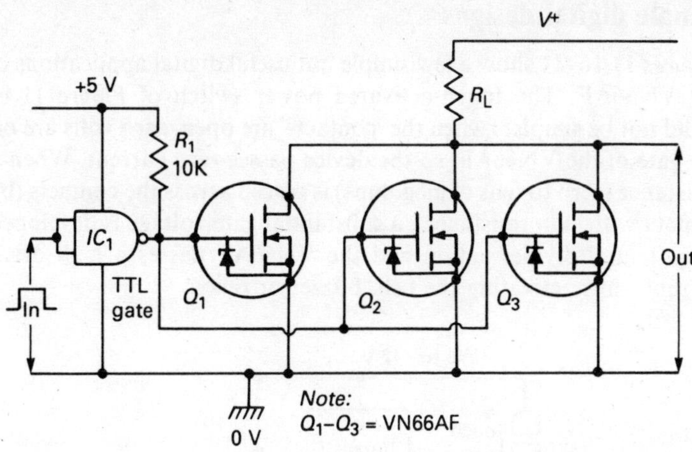

Figure 11.14 *Method of boosting the output of* Figure 11.13 *by driving three VN66AFs in parallel*

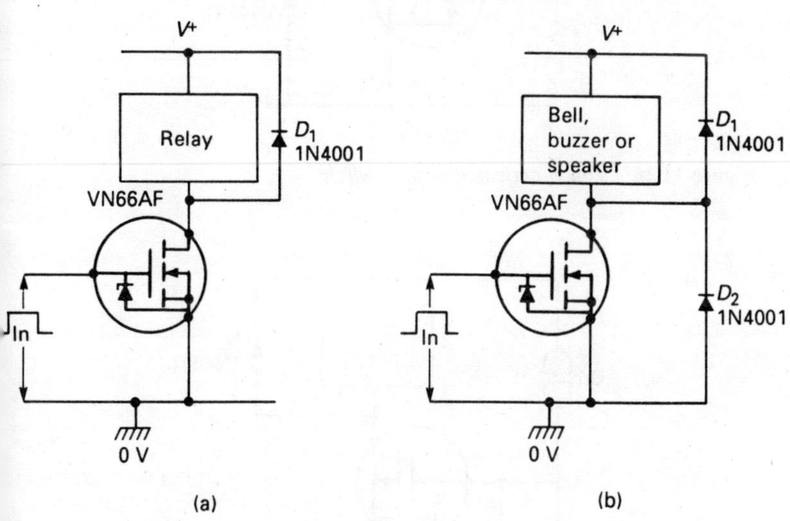

Figure 11.15 *If inductive loads such as relays* (a) *or bells, buzzers or speakers* (b) *are used in digital switching circuits, protection diodes must be wired as shown*

Simple digital designs

Figures 11.16–21 show a few simple but useful digital applications of the VN66AF. The touch-activated power switch of *Figure* 11.16 could not be simpler: when the 'contacts' are open, zero volts are on the gate of the VN66AF, so the device passes zero current. When a resistance (zero to tens of megohms) is placed across the contacts (by contact with skin resistance), a substantial gate voltage is developed by potential divider action and the VN66AF passes a high drain current, thus activating the bell, buzzer or relay.

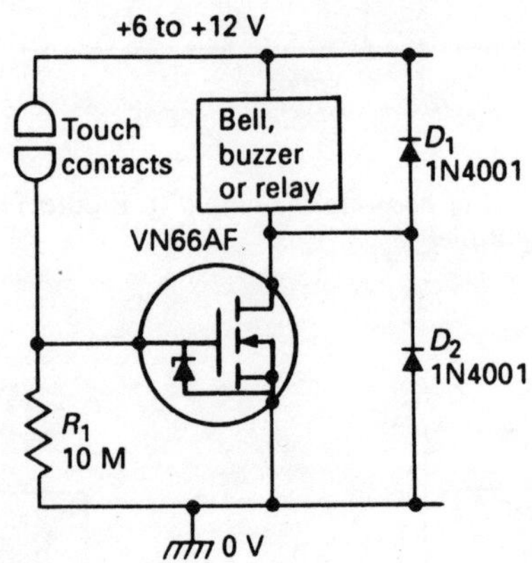

Figure 11.16 *Touch-activated power switch*

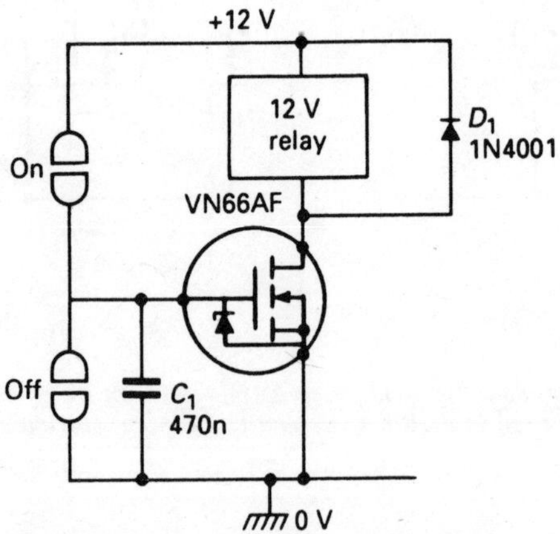

Figure 11.17 *Semi-latching touch-activated relay switch*

The *Figure* 11.17 circuit is similar to the above, but has two sets of touch contacts and gives a semi-latching relay action. When the *on* contacts are touched, C_1 charges via the skin resistance and turns the relay on. The resulting C_1 charge then holds the relay on until the charge either leaks away naturally or is removed by briefly touching the *off* contacts.

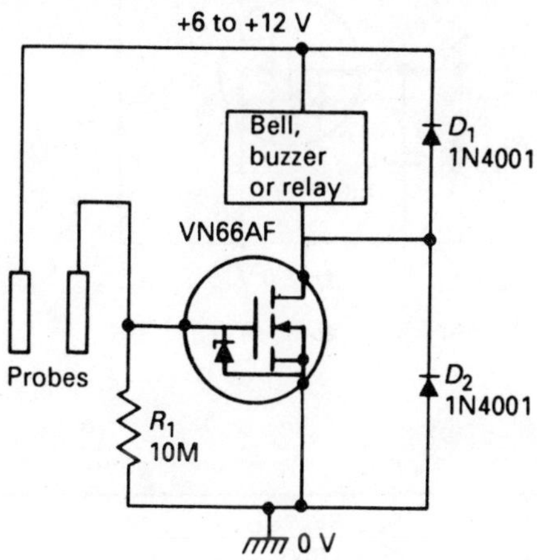

Figure 11.18 *Water-activated power switch*

The water-activated power switch of *Figure* 11.18 is similar to that of *Figure* 11.16, except that it is activated by the relatively low resistance of water coming into contact with the two metal probes, rather than by skin contact.

In the manually activated delayed-turn-off circuit of *Figure* 11.19, C_1 charges rapidly via R_1 when push-button switch PB_1 is closed, and discharges slowly via R_2 when PB_1 is open. The load thus activates as soon as PB_1 is closed, but does not deactivate until some tens of seconds after PB_1 is released.

In the simple relay-output timer circuit of *Figure* 11.20, the VMOS device is driven by the output of a standard manually triggered monostable or one-shot multivibrator designed around two gates of a 4001 CMOS IC; the relay turns on as soon as PB_1 is closed, and then turns off automatically again some pre-set 'delay time' later. The delay is variable from a few seconds to a few minutes via RV_1.

Finally, *Figure* 11.21 shows the practical circuit of an inexpensive but very impressive alarm-call generator that produces a 'dee-dah'

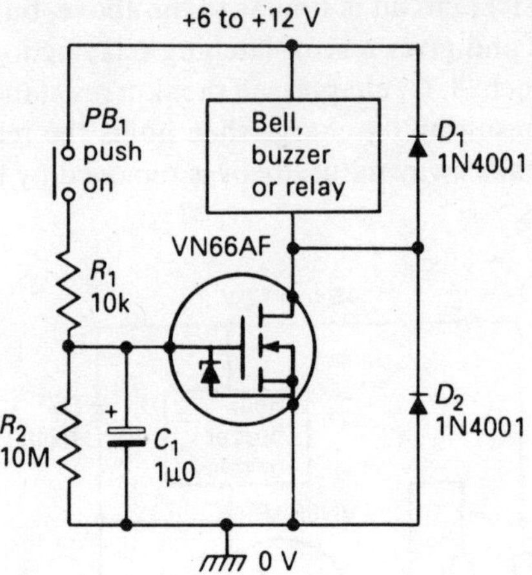

Figure 11.19 *Delayed-turn-off power switch*

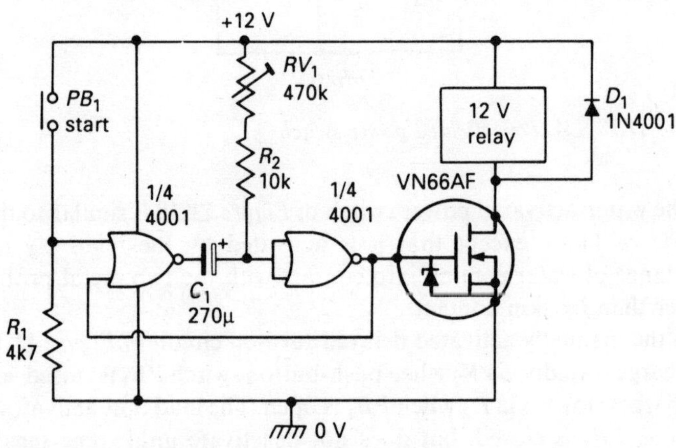

Figure 11.20 *Simple relay-output timer circuit*

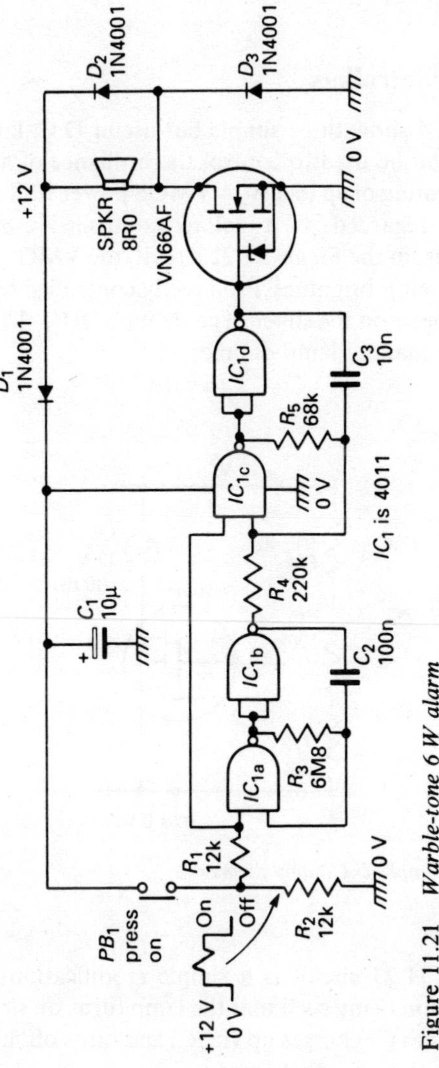

Figure 11.21 *Warble-tone 6 W alarm*

sound like that of a police car siren. The alarm can be turned on by closing PB_1 or by feeding a 'high' voltage to the R_1–R_2 junction. The circuit uses an 8R0 speaker and generates roughly 6 W of output power.

D.C. lamp controllers

Figures 11.22–4 show three simple but useful D.C. lamp controller circuits that can be used to control the brilliance of any 12 V lamp with a power rating of up to 6 W. A VMOS power FET can, for many purposes, be regarded as a voltage-controlled constant-current generator: thus, in the *Figure* 11.22 circuit, the VMOS drain current (and thus the lamp brightness) is directly controlled by the variable voltage developed on the slider of control pot RV_1. This circuit thus functions as a manual lamp dimmer.

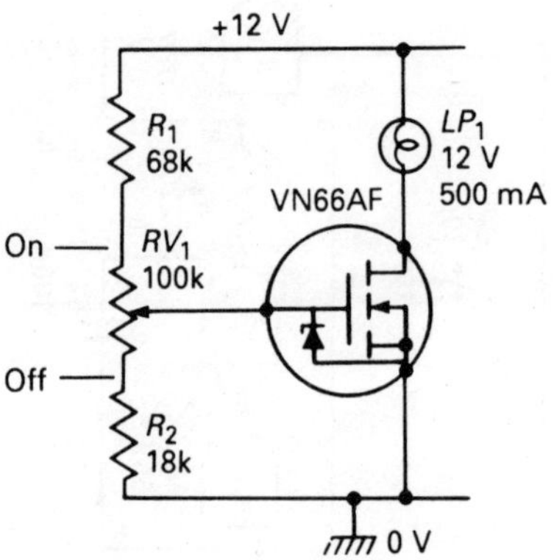

Figure 11.22 *Simple D.C. lamp dimmer*

The *Figure* 11.23 circuit is a simple modification of the above design, the action being such that the lamp turns on slowly when the switch is closed as C_1 charges up via R_3, and turns off slowly when the switch is opened as C_1 discharges via R_3.

The *Figure* 11.24 circuit is an ultra-efficient 'digital' lamp dimmer which controls the lamp brilliance without causing significant power loss across the VMOS device. Here, the two 4011 CMOS gates are

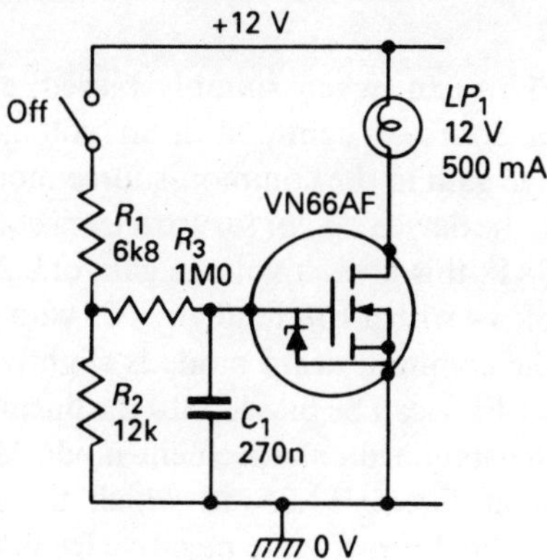

Figure 11.23 *'Soft-start' lamp switch*

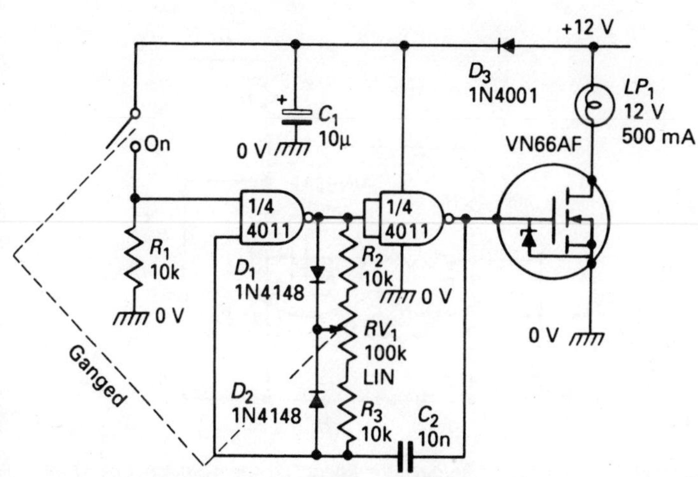

Figure 11.24 *High-efficiency D.C. lamp dimmer*

connected as an astable multivibrator that has a mark/space ratio that is fully variable from 10:1 to 1:10 via RV_1, and has its output fed to the gate of the VN66AF, thereby enabling the *mean* lamp brightness to be varied from virtually fully off to fully on. In this circuit the VMOS device is always switched either fully on or fully off, so power losses are negligible.

Linear circuits

VMOS power FETs can, when suitably biased, easily be used in either the common-source or common-drain (voltage follower) linear modes. The voltage gain in the common-source mode is equal to the product of R_L and the device's g_m or forward transconductance. In the case of the VN66AF, this gives a voltage gain of 0.25 per ohm of R_L value, i.e. a gain of ×4 with a 16R load, or ×25 with a 100R load. The voltage gain in the common drain mode is slightly less than unity.

A VMOS power FET can be biased into the linear common source mode by using the standard enhancement-mode MOSFET biasing technique shown in *Figure* 11.25, in which the R_1–R_2 potential divider is wired in the drain-to-gate negative feedback loop and sets the quiescent drain voltage at roughly half-supply value, so that maximal signal level swings can be accommodated before clipping occurs.

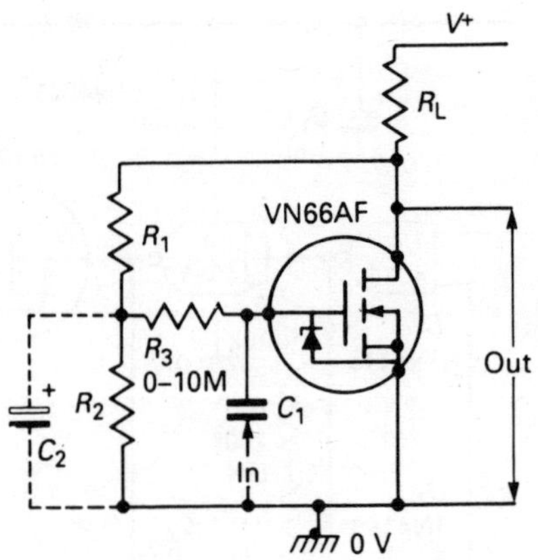

Figure 11.25 *Biasing techniques for linear 'common source' operation*

When, in the *Figure* 11.25 circuit, R_3 has a value of zero ohms, the circuit exhibits an input impedance that, because of the a.c. negative feedback effects, is roughly equal to the parallel values of R_1 and R_2 divided by the voltage gain ($R_L \times g_m$) of the circuit. If R_3 has a finite value, the input impedance is slightly less than the R_3 value, unless a.c. feedback-decoupling capacitor C_2 is fitted in place, in which case the input impedance is slightly greater than the R_3 value.

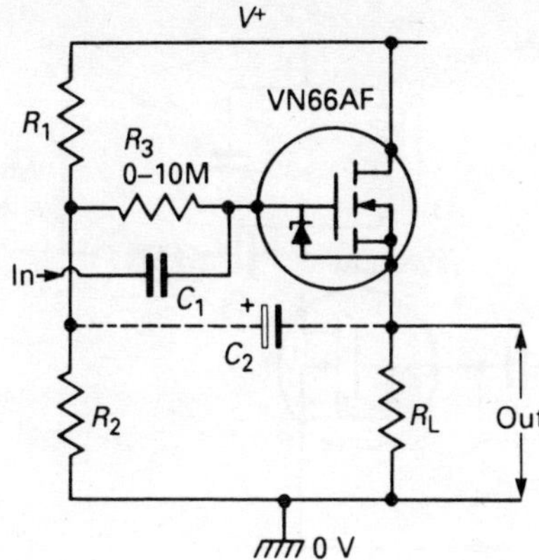

Figure 11.26 *Biasing techniques for linear 'common drain' (voltage follower) operation*

Figure 11.26 shows how to bias the VMOS device for common drain (voltage follower) operation. Potential divider R_1–R_2 sets the VMOS gate at a quiescent value slightly greater than half-supply voltage. When the R_3 value is zero, the circuit input impedance is equal to the parallel values of R_1 and R_2. When the R_3 value is finite, the input impedance equals the R_3 value plus the parallel R_1–R_2 values. The input impedance can be raised to a value many times greater than R_3 by adding the C_2 'bootstrap' capacitor to the circuit.

Figure 11.27 shows a practical example of a VMOS linear

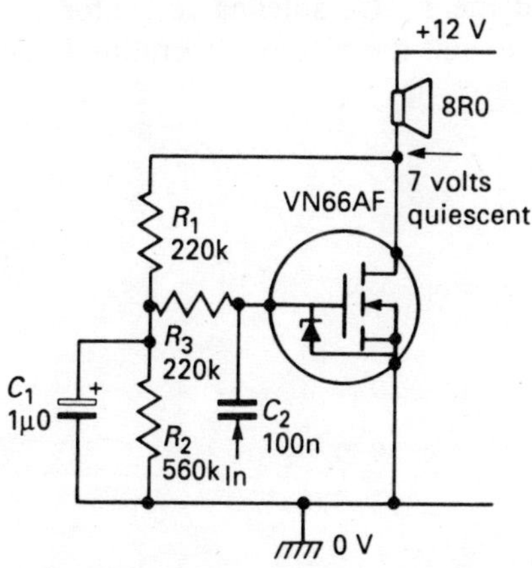

Figure 11.27 *Simple class-A audio amplifier gives 1 per cent THD at 1 W*

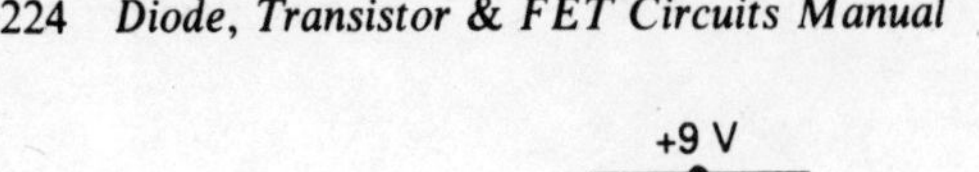

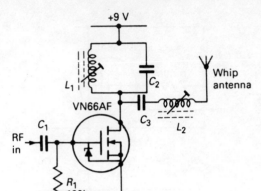

Figure 11.28 *600 mW radio control or CW transmitter*

application. Here, the circuit is wired as a class-A power amplifier which, because of the excellent linearity of the VN66AF, gives remarkably little distortion for so simple a design. The VN66AF must be mounted on a decent heat sink in this application. When the design is used with a purely resistive 8R0 load, the amplifier has a bandwidth that extends up to 10 MHz.

Finally, to complete this look at VMOS power FETs, *Figure* 11.28 shows how such a device can be used to make a simple but excellent 600 mW radio control or CW transmitter output stage. The L_1–C_2 tank circuit and the L_2–C_3 antenna resonator component values must be chosen to suit the required operating frequency.

12 Unijunction transistor circuits

The unijunction transistor (UJT) is one of the oldest and simplest of all active semiconductor devices. It first became commercially available in 1952, and for many years was widely used as a general-purpose timer, oscillator, and high-energy pulse generator. Then, in the early 1970s, many of these tasks were taken over by readily available low-cost ICs such as the 555 timer and the ubiquitous CMOS range of gates, and the UJT slowly fell out of favour, eventually being relegated to only the high-energy pulse generating role. A similar fate also fell on its hopeful replacement, the PUT (programmable unijunction transistor), which is now little used. Both of these devices are still quite versatile, however, and are readily available. This final chapter describes their operating principles, and shows how to use them in practical circuits.

UJT basics

The unijunction transistor is a simple device that consists of a bar of n-type silicon material with a non-rectifying contact at either end (base 1 and base 2), and with a rectifying contact (emitter) alloyed into the bar part way along its length, to form the only junction within the device (hence the name 'unijunction'). *Figure* 12.1 shows the symbol, construction, and equivalent circuit of the UJT.

Base 1 and base 2 form contacts with the ends of the silicon bar, and a simple resistance appears between these two points and measures the same in either direction. This 'inter-base' resistance is given the symbol R_{bb} and has a typical value in the range 4k0 to 12k.

In use, base 2 is connected to a positive voltage and base 1 is taken

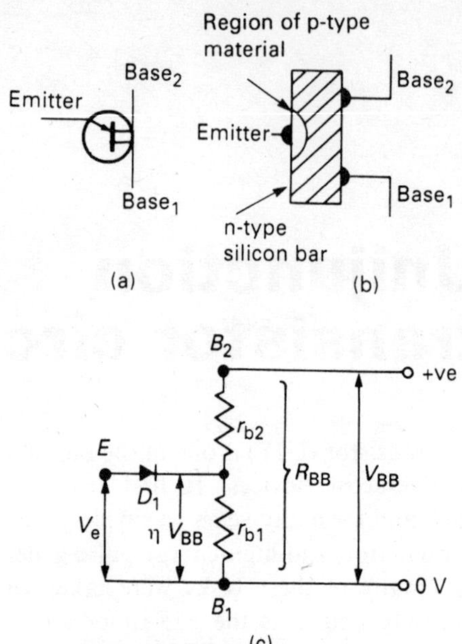

Figure 12.1 *(a) UJT symbol. (b) UJT construction. (c) UJT equivalent circuit*

to zero volts (see *Figure* 12.1*c*), so R_{bb} acts as a voltage divider with a division or 'intrinsic stand-off' ratio (η) that has a typical value between 0.45 and 0.8. A 'stand-off' voltage of $\eta.V_{bb}$ thus appears across the lower (r_{b1}) half of the bar under quiescent conditions. The UJT's emitter terminal is connected to this voltage via junction D_1. Normally the emitter input voltage (V_e) is less than ηV_{bb}, so D_1 is reverse-biased and the emitter appears as the very high impedance of a reverse-biased silicon diode.

If V_e is steadily increased above ηV_{bb} a point is reached where D_1 becomes forward-biased, and current starts to flow from the emitter to base 1. This current consists mainly of minority carriers injected into the silicon bar, and these drift to base$_1$ and decrease the resistance of r_{b1}. This decrease in r_{b1} lowers the ηV_{bb} voltage, so the emitter–base 1 current increases and makes the r_{b1} value fall even more. A regenerative action thus takes place, and the emitter input impedance falls sharply, typically to a value of about 20R.

The UJT thus acts as a voltage-triggered switch that has a very high input impedance (to its emitter) when the UJT is off and a very low one when it is on. The precise point at which triggering occurs is called the 'peak-point' voltage, V_p, and is about 600 mV above the ηV_{bb} value.

The UJT oscillator

The most basic application of the UJT is as a simple relaxation oscillator, as shown in *Figure* 12.2. Here, C_1 is fully discharged when the supply is initially connected, so the emitter is at ground potential and presents a very high impedance. C_1 immediately starts to charge exponentially towards V_{BB} via R_1, but as soon as the emitter reaches V_p the UJT fires and rapidly discharges C_1 into the low impedance of the emitter. Once C_1 is effectively discharged the UJT switches off, and C_1 then starts to charge up again via R_1, and the whole process repeats *ad infinitum* and generates a non-linear sawtooth waveform across C_1.

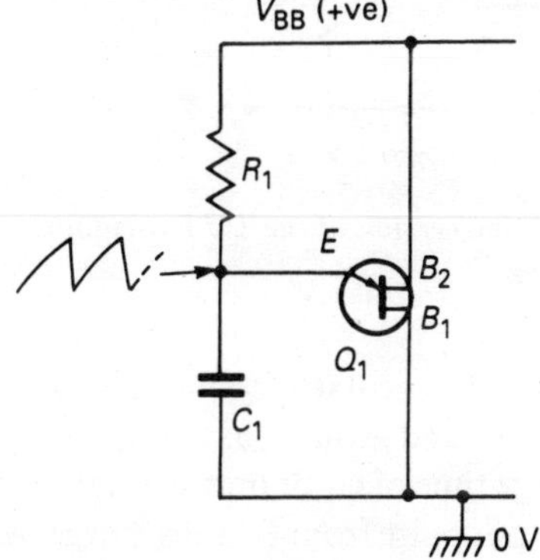

Figure 12.2 *Basic UJT relaxation oscillator*

In this circuit the switch-off action occurs in each cycle when the total emitter current (the C_1 discharge plus the R_1 current) falls to a 'valley-point' value, I_v (typically several microamperes). A minimum 'peak-point emitter current', I_p, is needed to initiate the UJT switch-on action, and typically has a value of several microamperes. Thus, R_1's maximum usable value is limited by the I_p characteristic, and the minimum value is limited by the I_v characteristic.

The oscillation frequency of the *Figure* 12.2 circuit is given approximately by $f=1/(CR)$, and is almost independent of V_{BB} (typically, a 10 per cent change in V_{BB} causes a change of less than 1 per cent in f). The R_1 value can typically be varied from about 3k0 to 500k, enabling the circuit to span a 100:1 frequency range via a single variable resistor. The C_1 value can be varied from a few hundred picofarads to hundreds of microfarads, enabling the circuit to be used over a very wide frequency range (from less than one cycle per minute to hundreds of kilohertz).

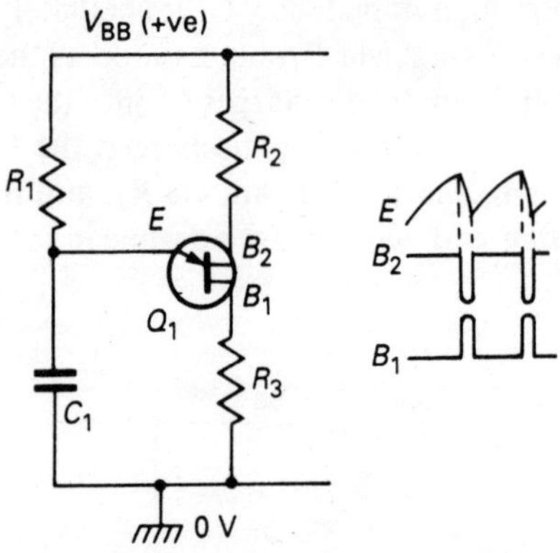

Figure 12.3 *Alternative version of the UJT oscillator*

In most practical UJT oscillator circuits an additional resistor (R_3) is wired between base$_1$ and ground, as shown in *Figure* 12.3, either to control the discharge time of C_1 or (more usually) to give a brief high-energy positive output pulse from C_1's discharge. A resistor (R_2) may also be wired in series with base 2, either to enhance the oscillator's thermal stability or to enable a low-energy negative-going output pulse to be generated via C_1's discharge.

Practical UJTs

The two best-known and most readily available types of UJT are the 2N2646 and the TIS43. The latter device is the more modestly priced of the two, and is used as the basis of all practical UJT circuits presented in these pages. It can be used with supplies up to a

Parameter	2N2646	TIS43
Emitter reverse volts (max)	30 V	30 V
V_{BB} (max)	35 V	35 V
Peak emitter current (max)	2 A	1.5 A
Power dissipation (max)	300 mW	300 mW
Intrinsic stand-off ratio, η	0.56–0.75	0.55–0.82
R_{BB}	4k7–9k1	4k0–9k1
I_p (max)	5 μA	5 μA
I_v (max)	4 mA	4 mA
Outline	B_2, E, B_1 (To-18 case)	B_1, B_2, E (To-92 case)

Figure 12.4 *2N2646 and TIS43 UJT data*

maximum of 30 V, and has maximum I_p and I_v ratings of 5 μA and 4 mA respectively, thus allowing a wide range of timing resistor values to be used. *Figure* 12.4 lists basic details of both types of UJT.

Practical waveform generators

The TIS43 can be used in a variety of pulse, sawtooth, and rectangular waveform generator applications. *Figures* 12.5–9 show a selection of practical circuits of these types.

Figure 12.5 shows a wide-range pulse generator circuit. A high-energy positive pulse is available across R_3, and a low-energy negative-going one is available across R_2. Both pulses are of similar form, but are in anti-phase. With the component values shown the pulse width is constant at about 30 μs over the frequency range 25 Hz to 3 kHz (adjustable via RV_1). The pulse width and frequency range can be altered by changing the C_1 value; reducing it by a decade reduces the pulse width and raises the operating frequency by a factor of 10; C_1 can have any value from 100 pF to 1000 μF.

A non-linear sawtooth is generated across C_1 of the *Figure* 12.5 circuit, but is at a high impedance level and is thus not readily

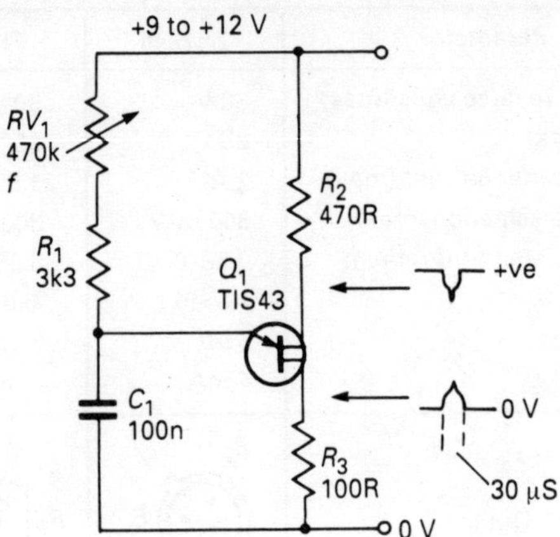

Figure 12.5 *Wide-range pulse generator*

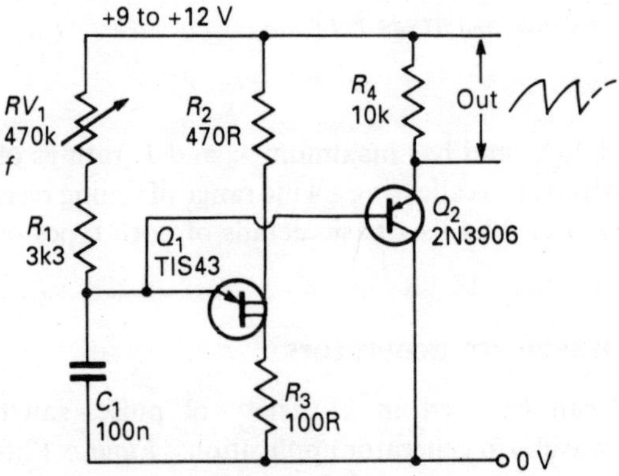

Figure 12.6 *Wide-range non-linear sawtooth generator*

available externally. Access can be gained to this sawtooth either by wiring a simple pnp emitter follower across the timing resistor network, as shown in *Figure* 12.6, or by wiring an npn Darlington emitter follower across C_1, as in *Figure* 12.7. Note that the *Figure* 12.6 circuit gives a fixed-amplitude output that is referenced to the positive supply rail, but that the *Figure* 12.7 design gives a variable-amplitude output that is referenced to the zero volts line.

The UJT oscillator can be made to generate a linear sawtooth waveform by charging its timing capacitor via a constant-current

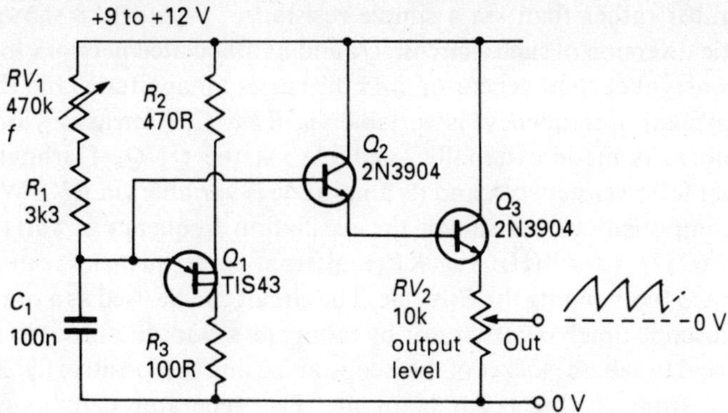

Figure 12.7 *Wide-range non-linear sawtooth generator with variable-amplitude ground referenced output*

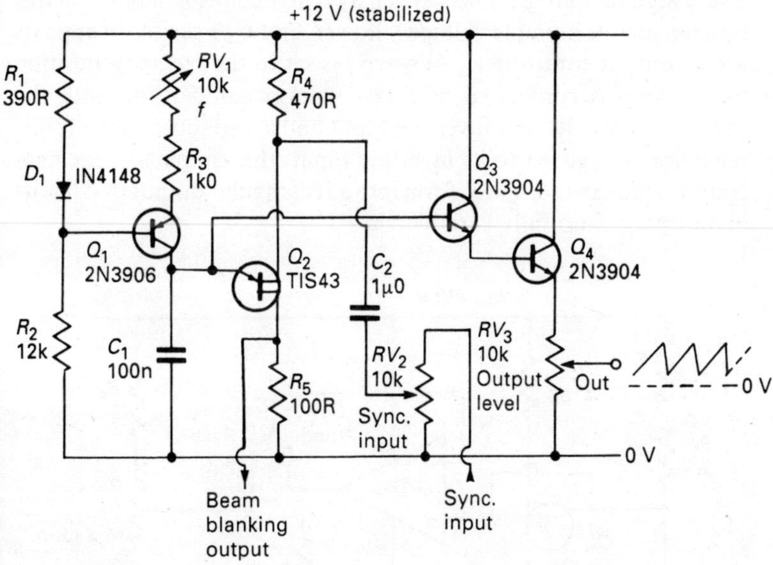

Figure 12.8 *This linear sawtooth generator can be used as a simple oscilloscope timebase generator*

generator rather than via a simple resistance. *Figure* 12.8 shows a practical version of such a circuit. Q_1 and its associated network form the constant current generator, and the current magnitude (and thus the oscillation frequency) is variable via RV_1. C_1's linear sawtooth waveform is made externally available via the Q_3–Q_4 Darlington emitter follower network and its amplitude is variable via RV_3. With the component values shown the oscillation frequency is variable from 60 Hz to 700 Hz via RV_1; alternative frequencies can be obtained by changing the C_1 value. The circuit can be used as a simple oscilloscope timebase generator by taking its sawtooth output to the 'external timebase' socket of the 'scope and using the 'positive flyback pulses' from R_5 for beam blanking. The generator can be synchronized to any external signal that is fed to the *sync input* terminal.

Figure 12.9 shows how a UJT can be used to generate either a non-linear sawtooth or a rectangular waveform with an infinitely variable mark–space ratio. The LF356 op-amp used here is a 'fast' device with a very high input impedance. When S_1 is in the *sawtooth* position this op-amp acts as a simple voltage follower, and C_1's sawtooth appears across output control RV_2. When S_1 is set to the *rectangle* position the op-amp is configured as a fast voltage comparator, with the sawtooth fed to its non-inverting input and a variable (via RV_3) d.c. reference voltage fed to its inverting input; this simple arrangement converts the sawtooth waveform into a rectangular output that has its mark–space ratio fully variable via RV_3.

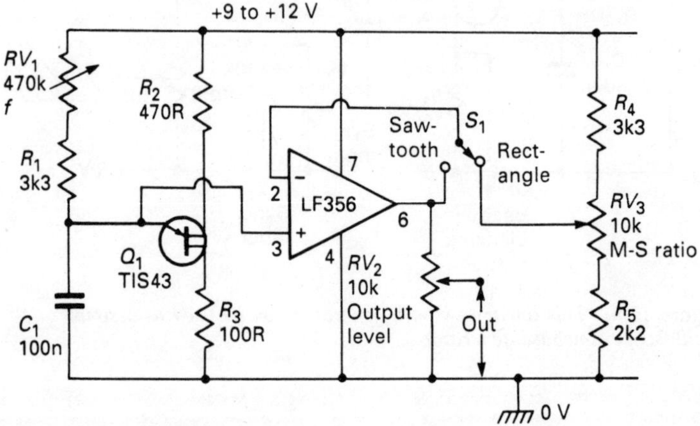

Figure 12.9 *25 Hz to 3 kHz generator produces a non-linear sawtooth or a rectangular waveform with fully variable mark–space ratio*

Gadgets and novelties

Figures 12.10–14 show a variety of ways of using UJTs in handy gadgets and novelty circuits. *Figure* 12.10 is a simple Morse-code practice oscillator; it generates a fixed tone (adjustable from 300 Hz to 3 kHz) directly in a small speaker whenever the Morse key is closed.

Figure 12.11 shows a musician's metronome with a beat rate variable from 20 to 200 per minute via RV_1; the UJT's output pulses are fed to the speaker via Q_2, producing a distinct 'click' each time the UJT completes a timing cycle.

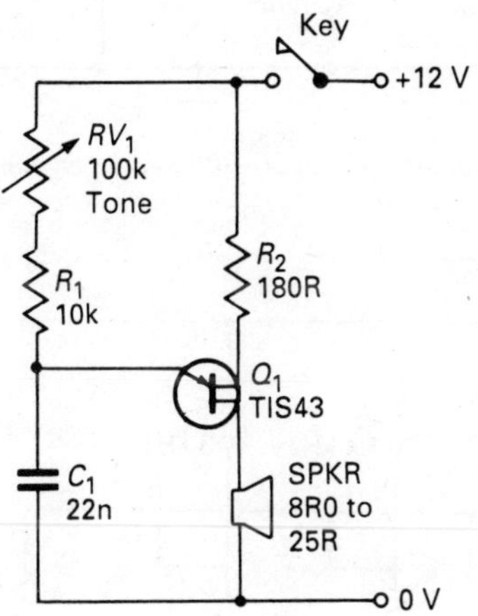

Figure 12.10 *Simple 'code-practice' oscillator; tone is variable from 300 Hz to 3 kHz*

Figure 12.12 shows a multi-tone signalling system that consumes zero quiescent current and generates a tone that is unique to each one of its three push-button operating switches; each switch connects the oscillator's supply via an isolating diode, but selects a unique value of tone-generating timing resistor.

Figure 12.13 shows a simple rising-tone siren, which operates as follows. When power is first applied C_1 is fully discharged, so the UJT operates at a frequency set only by R_3 and C_2. As soon as power is applied, however, C_1 starts to charge exponentially via R_1, and its voltage causes the charge current of C_2 to increase via D_1 and R_2 raising the UJT frequency. Thus, the UJT's oscillation frequency

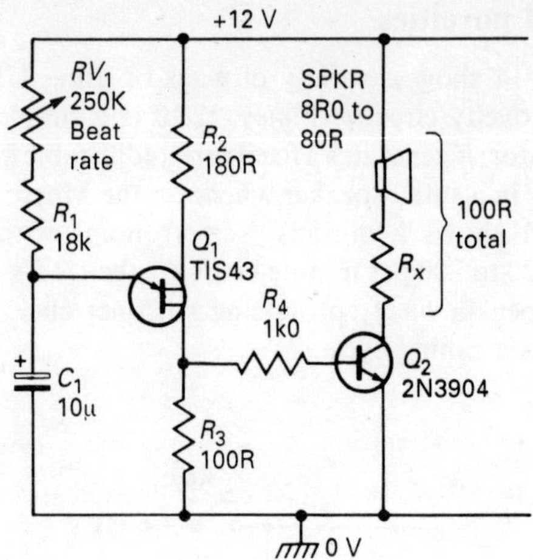

Figure 12.11 *Metronome giving 20–200 beats per minute*

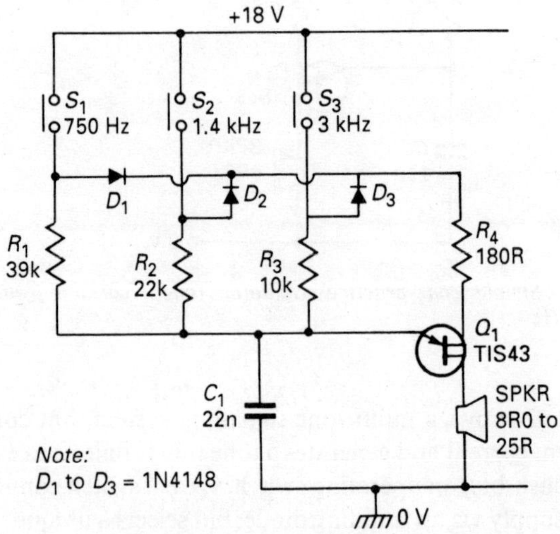

Figure 12.12 *Simple multi-tone signalling system*

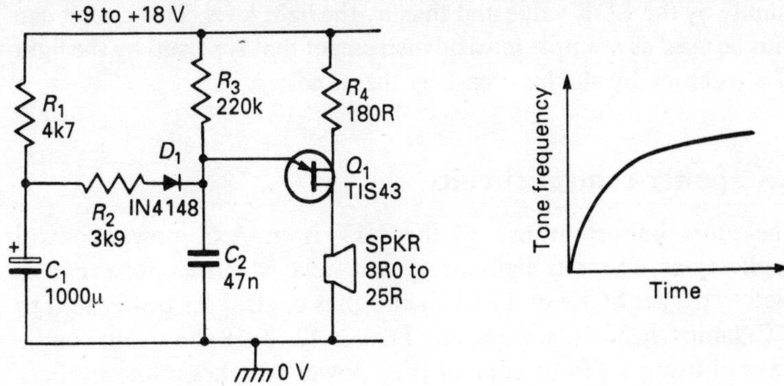

Figure 12.13 *Simple rising-tone siren*

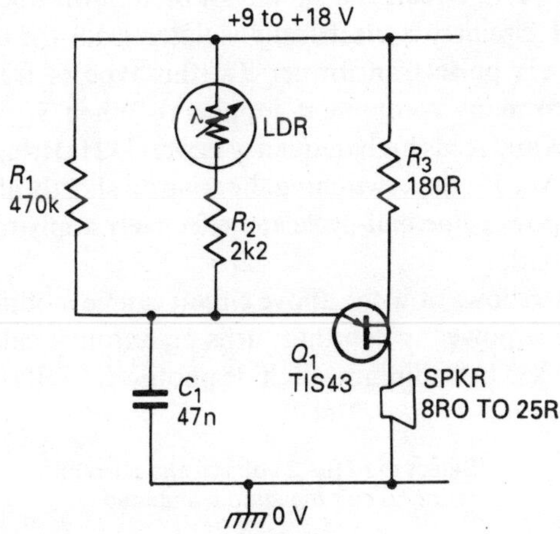

Figure 12.14 *Light-sensitive oscillator*

slowly rises as C_1 charges up, as shown by the diagram's exponential graph, and generates a distinct 'rising' tone.

Finally, *Figure* 12.14 shows the UJT used as a light-sensitive oscillator, with an LDR acting as its main timing resistor. This LDR is a cadmium sulphide photocell; under dark conditions it acts as a very high resistance, so the operating frequency is low and is determined mainly by R_1; under bright condition the LDR resistance is very low, so the operating frequency is high and is determined mainly by R_2. At intermediate light levels the UJT frequency is set mainly by the LDR value and thus by the light level. This circuit can thus be used as a simple musical instrument that is played by the light of a torch or by shadows cast by the hand.

A.C. power-control circuits

The most important use of the UJT is in A.C. power-control applications, where its high-energy time-delayed output pulses can be used to trigger SCRs or TRIACs and thus control the power feed to A.C. lamps, heaters, motors, etc. *Figures* 12.15–18 show four simple ways of using UJTs to control triac power switches. Note in these circuits that the triac's voltage rating must be chosen to suit the A.C. power line that is used (400 V rating on 230 VAC, 200 V rating on 115 VAC), and that its current rating is chosen to suit the load.

The *Figure* 12.15 circuit is a simple on/off unit in which the D.C.-powered UJT circuitry is electrically isolated from the high-voltage triac system via pulse transformer T_1 (this type of transformer is available from many component suppliers). When S_1 is closed the UJT oscillates and feeds high frequency (several kHz) trigger pulses to the triac gate via T_1, thus switching the triac on shortly after the start of each A.C. power-line half-cycle and effectively applying full power to the A.C. load.

Figure 12.16 shows how the above circuit can be modified to act as a light-sensitive power switch that turns on automatically when the light level (sensed by cadmium sulphide photocell LDR) falls below a

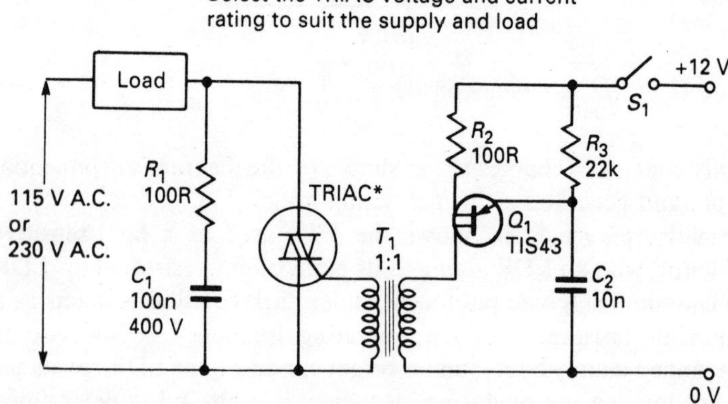

Figure 12.15 *Isolated-input A.C. power switch*

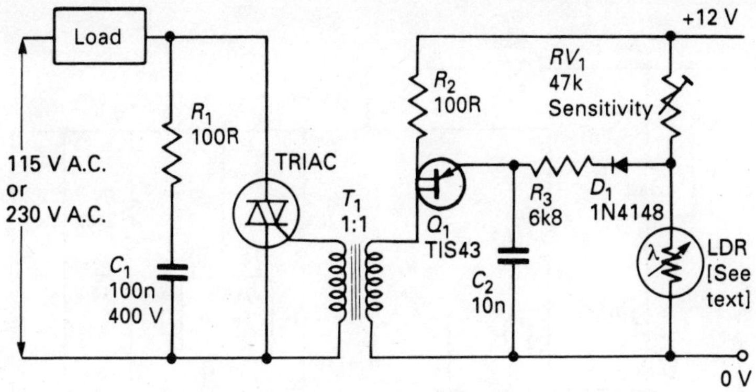

Figure 12.16 *Light-sensitive A.C. power switch*

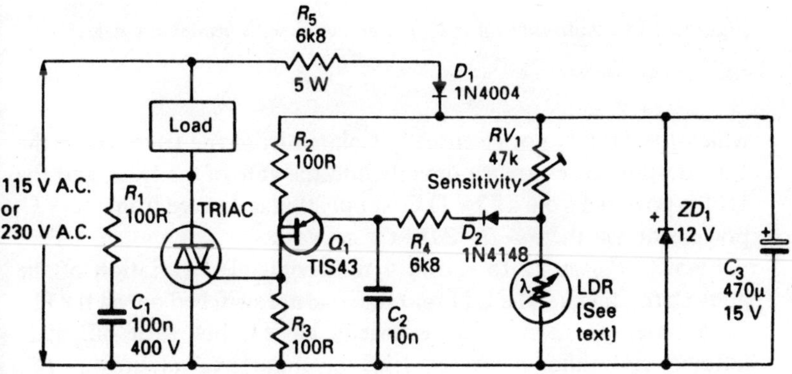

Figure 12.17 *Alternative light-sensitive A.C. power switch*

pre-set level. RV_1 and the LDR form a light-sensitive potential divider which has its output taken to the UJT's timing resistor via D_1. Under bright conditions the LDR resistance is low and the divider's output voltage is too low to enable the UJT to trigger, so the triac is off. Under dark conditions the LDR resistance is high and the divider's output voltage is high and enables the UJT to oscillate, so the triac turns on and applies power to the load. The LDR can be any type that presents a resistance in the range 2k0 to 47k at the desired 'dark' turn-on light level.

Figure 12.17 shows an alternative version of the above circuit in

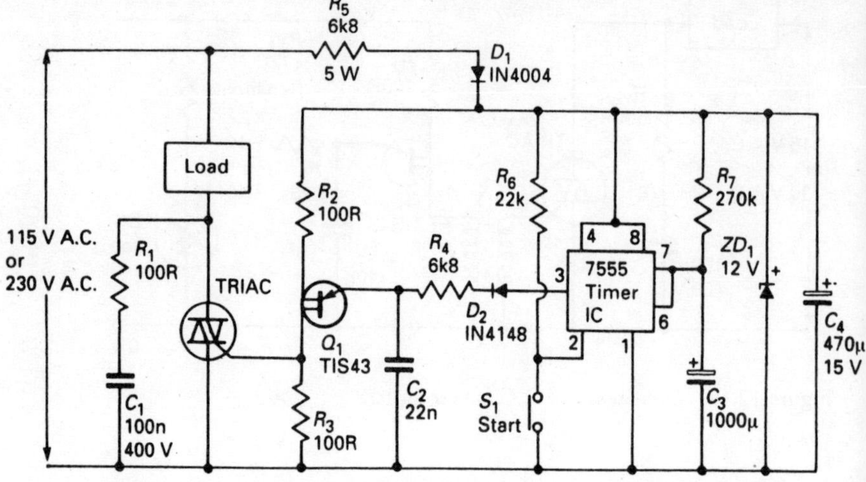

Figure 12.18 *Auto-turn-off A.C. power switch with five-minute delay*

which the UJT is not electrically isolated from the triac. Here, the UJT output pulses are fed directly into the gate of the triac, and the UJT is powered from a 12 V D.C. supply that is derived from the A.C. power line via the R_5–D_1–ZD_1–C_3 network.

Finally, *Figure* 12.18 shows a time-controlled variation of the above circuit. Here, the UJT and the triac are switched on via the IC_1 7555 timer as soon as S_1 is briefly closed, but turn off again automatically after a pre-set delay of about five minutes as IC_1 completes its timing cycle. The circuit's timing period can be made variable by replacing R_7 with a 10k resistor and a 47k variable wired in series.

Note in *Figures* 12.17 and 12.18 that, to generate an adequate 12 V D.C. supply, the R_5 value may have to be reduced when operating from 115 VAC power lines.

PUTs and kindred devices

The action of a UJT oscillator can be simulated by the circuit of *Figure* 12.19, in which pnp transistor Q_1 is in series with npn transistor Q_2; R_1 and C_1 control the circuit's timing action, and R_2–R_3 apply a fixed voltage (the equivalent of a UJT's intrinsic standoff

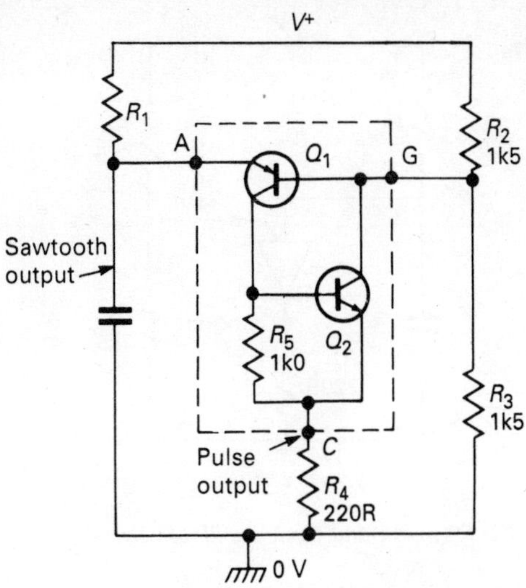

Figure 12.19 *Transistor equivalent of the UJT oscillator*

ratio voltage) to the base of Q_1; R_5 shunts Q_2's base–emitter junction, so that Q_2 is not driven on by Q_1's leakage currents. At the start of each timing cycle the R_1–C_1 junction voltage is low, so Q_1's base–emitter junction is reverse-biased and both transistors are cut off. C_1 then charges via R_1 until Q_1's base–emitter junction becomes forward-biased, at which point both transistors switch on regeneratively and rapidly discharge C_1 via current-limiting resistor R_4, until the discharge current becomes so low that both transistors switch off again, and the timing sequence starts to repeat again.

A practical weakness of this circuit is that its transistors can easily be burnt out, since C_1's discharge current flows through their base–emitter junctions. This defect can be overcome by replacing the three components within the dotted lines with a PUT, which is the direct thyristor equivalent of Q_1–Q_2–R_5 and uses the symbol and basic application circuit of *Figure* 12.20; it is so named because it acts like a 'programmable unijunction transistor', in which the intrinsic stand-off ratio and R_{bb} values can be 'programmed' by selecting the external R_2 and R_3 values.

Note that the PUT symbol of *Figure* 12.10 is similar to that of a silicon-controlled rectifier (SCR), except that the gate is related to the anode rather than the cathode; the PUT is in fact sometimes called an

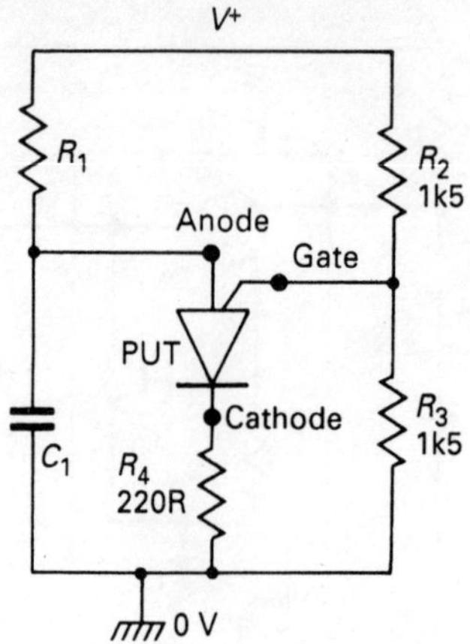

Figure 12.20 *PUT symbol and basic oscillator circuit*

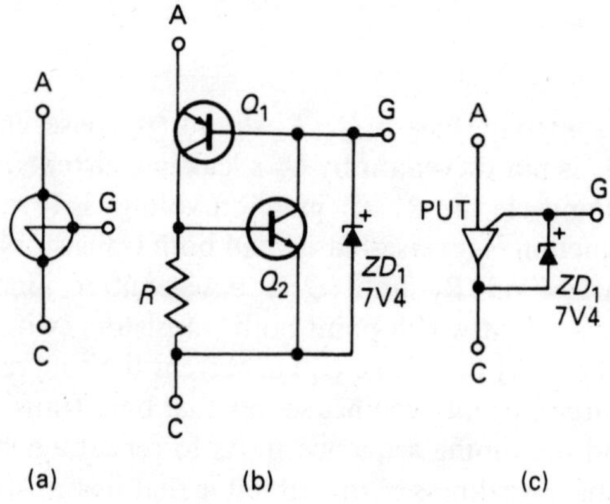

Figure 12.21 (*a*) *SUS symbol and* (*b, c*) *equivalent circuits*

anode-controlled SCR, and is one of four very closely related pnpn thyristor devices. Details of the other three members of the family are shown in *Figures* 12.21–3.

The silicon unilateral switch (SUS) (*Figure* 12.21) acts like a PUT with a built-in zener between its gate and cathode. The gate pin is normally left open, and the device acts as a voltage-triggered self-latching switch that turns on when the anode voltage rises high enough (above 8 V) to make the zener start to break down via Q_1's

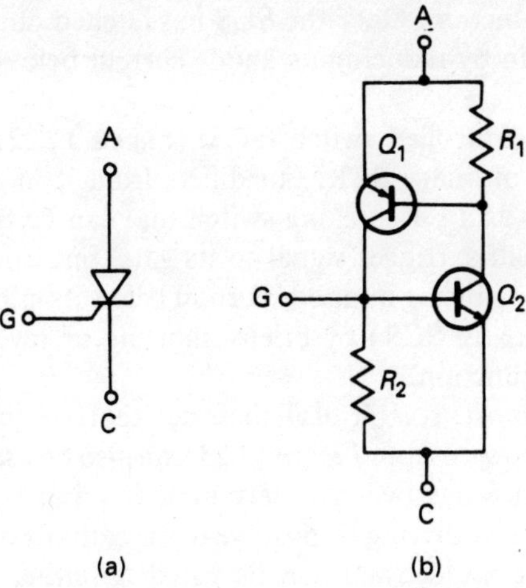

Figure 12.22 *(a) SCS symbol and (b) transistor equivalent circuit*

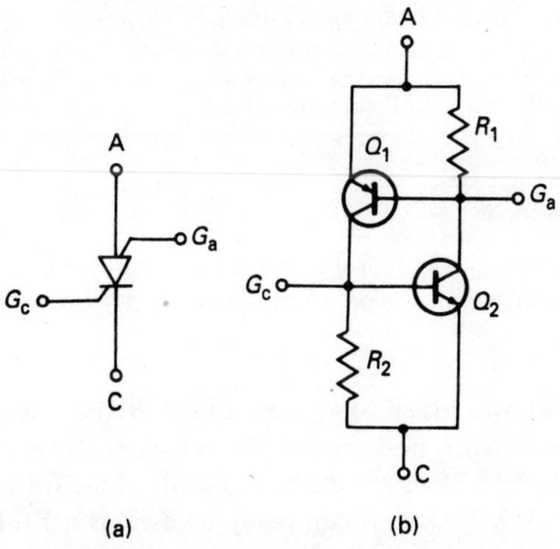

Figure 12.23 (a) Thyristor tetrode symbol and (b) transistor equivalent circuit

base–emitter junction. Once the SUS has latched on, it can only be turned off again by reducing its anode current below the minimum holding value.

The silicon-controlled switch (SCS) (*Figure* 12.22) has the same symbol as an ordinary SCR, but differs from it in one important respect; it acts as a self-latching switch that can be triggered on by applying a positive trigger signal to its gate, but can be turned off again either by reducing its anode current below its minimum holding value or (unlike an SCR) by briefly shorting or reverse-biasing its gate–cathode junction.

Finally, the most versatile of all these devices is the thyristor tetrode which, as can be seen from *Figure* 12.23, can also be used as a PUT or SCS. This device has two gate terminals (G_c and G_a), and can be turned on either by driving G_c positive to the cathode or by driving G_a negative to the anode, and can be gated off either by driving G_c negative to the cathode or by driving G_a positive to the anode.

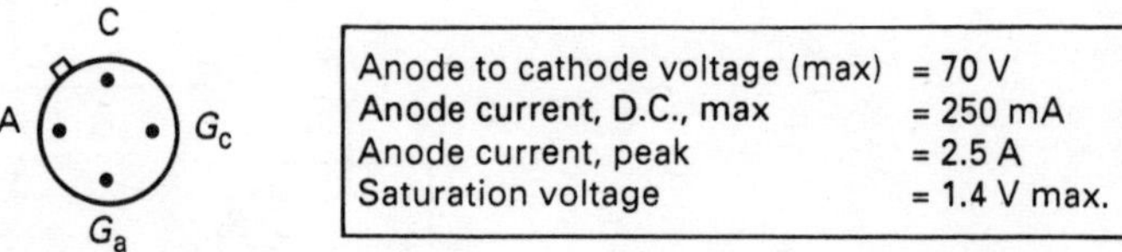

Anode to cathode voltage (max)	= 70 V
Anode current, D.C., max	= 250 mA
Anode current, peak	= 2.5 A
Saturation voltage	= 1.4 V max.

(G_a connected to case)
Pin connections

Figure 12.24 *Basic details of the BRY39 (equivalent to the 2N6027 and D13T1) thyristor tetrode device, which can also be used as a PUT or SCS*

The best-known practical versions of the thyristor tetrode are the BRY39, the 2N6027, and the D13T1, which are virtually identical devices. *Figure* 12.24 shows the basic details of the BRY39, which is housed in a TO-72 case. It can easily be used as a PUT or SCS.

Index

Amplification factor, 76
Amplified diode configuration, 142
Amplifiers:
  analogue, 73–5
  audio, 121–2
  cascode, 92
  common-base, 92–4
  common-collector, 65–79
  common-emitter, 79–92
  differential, 94
  digital, 65–8
  headphone, 183
  high-gain, 183
  linear, 58–60, 85
  micro-power, 202
  power, 146–7, 148–50
    circuit variations, 139–42
    Class-A, 134–5, 224
    Class-AB, 136–9
    Class-B, 136
  voltage-controlled, 187
  see also pre-amplifiers
Amplitude modulation (AM), 103–4
Attenuator, voltage-controlled, 187–8
Audio mirror circuit, 133–4, 205
Avalanche value, *see* zener value

Bar-graph displays, 42
Biasing:
  constant current, 184
  linear, 85–7
  offset, 184
  potential-divider, 86
  variable, 182
Bipolar device, 51
Bootstrapping, 75–6, 143

Cap ratio (capacitance), 50
Chopper *see* converter, d.c.
Clamping-diode circuit, 13–17
Clapp oscillator, 101
Colpitts oscillator, 100–101, 105
Common-base mode, 58–9
Common-collector mode, 58–9
Common-drain mode, 223
Common-emitter mode, 58–9, 88–9
Common-source, 182–4, 222
Complementary metal oxide silicon field-effect transistor:
  (CMOS/COSMOS), 174, 194
  inverter, 198–203
  linear amplifier, 203–5
Control circuits:
  dual relay, 26–7
  LED-, 45

Converter, d.c., 189
C–R oscillators, *see* oscillator circuits, *C–R*
Current constancy, 72
Current mirror circuit, 158–9

Damping diode circuit, 23
Darlington mode, 59, 69–70, 77
Delays, long, 115–16
Digital circuits, 57, 80–83, 212–14
  VMOS, 212–15
Diode circuits:
  gate, 24
  limiter, 17
  miscellaneous, 25–7
  pump, 22–3
  rectifier, 17
  varicap, 50
  see also under specific type names
Diodes:
  basics, 1–6
  junction, 1–3
  light-emitting (LED), 5, 39
  mounting, 42
  multi-colour, 42
  multi-packages, 42
  photo-, 5, 47
  Schottky, 6
  Varactor/varicap, 5
  zener, 3, 30
Divide-by-two (counting) action, 119
DMOS, 173
Driver circuits, 145

Emitter follower, *see* amplifier, common-collector

Field-effect transistors (FET), 161–3, *see also under specific type names*
Filter capacitor, 11
Filters, rumble/scratch, 151–2
Flasher circuit, 45–6, 153
Frequency correction, 108, 115
Frequency modulation (FM), 104
Full wave limiter, 38
Full wave rectifier circuits, 8–9

Generators:
  constant-current, 71–2
  reference voltage, 29
  sound, 154
Gouriet oscillator, 101
Grounded-collector amplifier, *see* amplifier, common-collector
Grounded-emiter amplifier, *see* amplifier, common-emitter

Half-wave limiter, 37
Half-wave rectifier circuits, 6–7
Hartley oscillator, 100, 155, 157
HEXFET, 174

Indicators, use of LED as, 39–41
Insulated gate field-effect transistor (IGFET), *see* MOSFET
Integrated circuits (IC):
  2N2646, 228
  2N3819, 176
  2N3820, 176
  2N3904, 53
  2N3906, 53
  2N6027, 242
  555, 46
  4007UB, 193–4
  7555, 46
  BRY39, 242
  D13T1, 242
  LF356, 232
  LM380, 147
  TIS43, 228, 229

VN66AF, 209–12
digital applications, 216–17
digital circuits, 212–14
Integrator circuit, 205

Junction gate field-effect transistor JFET), 163–7
biasing, 177–9
details, 176–7
source follower modes, 179–81
JUGFET, *see* JFET

Lamp controller 220, 221
L–C oscillator, *see* oscillator circuits, *L–C*
Lie detector, 157
Light detecting resistor (LDR), 47
Light emitting diodes (LED), 5
basic circuits, 39–41
control circuits, 45
flasher, 45–6
multi-colour, 42–3
practical usage, 41–3
Light-sensitive power switch, 237
Long-tailed pair phase splitter, 62, 93

Mark–space ratio generator, 112–13
Metal oxide semiconductor field-effect transistor (MOSFET), 168–71
basics, 190–93
enhancement-mode, 197, 198
linear operation, 195–7
power versions, 173–4
Metal/pipe detector, 156
Meter, suppressed-zero, 39
Metronome, 233
Microphone, 122–4
Morse code practice oscillator, 233

Multi-colour LED, 42–3
Multi-LED circuits, 43–5
Multivibrator circuits, 62–4
astable, 108–14, 153–5
bistable, 118–19
free-running, 186
monostable, 114–17
Schmitt trigger, 119–20
very low frequency (VLF), 186

Noise limiters, 152–3

Optocoupler, 49–50
Oscillator circuits, 95
beat-frequency (BFO), 103–4, 155
Clapp, 101
Colpitts, 100–101, 105
C–R, 96–8
crystal, 105, 205
Gouriet, 101
L–C, 98–9, 155–7
modulation, 103–104
variations, 100–103
light-sensitive, 235
Morse code practice, 233
phase shift, 96–8
Reinartz, 102
UJT, 227–8, 238–9
Oscilloscope trace doubler circuit, 27–8
Overload protection circuit, 25

Peak inverse voltage (PIV), 12
Phase splitter, 61–2, 94, 96–8
Photo-diodes, 5, 47
Phototransistor, 48–9
Pick-up devices, 122, 126–7
Polarity protection circuits, 25
Potential-divider biasing, 86
power amplifiers, *see* amplifiers, power

Power control circuits, a.c., 236–8
Power-supply circuits, 8–9
Pre-amplifiers:
  add-on, 183
  RIAA circuit, 124–7
  simple, 122–3
  universal, 128
Programmable unijunction transistor (PUT), 225, 238–42
Power-supply circuits, 8–9

Rectifiers, 3
  diode circuits, 17
  rating of, 13
  silicon-controlled, 239
Regulation factor, 10
Regulator current boosting, 33–4
Reinartz oscillator, 102
Relay drivers, 68–70, 83–4
RIAA (Record Industry Association of America) standard, 125
Ripple waveform, 8, 12
Rumble filters, 151–2

Schmitt trigger, 64, 119–20
Schottky diode, 6
Scratch filters, 151–2
Signal generator, MW, 155
Signalling system, 233
Silicon-controlled rectifier (SCR), 239–40
Silicon-controlled switch (SCS), 242
Silicon unilateral switch (SUS), 240
Sine-to-square waveform converter, *see* Schmitt trigger
SIPMOS, 174
Siren, rising-tone, 233
Soft-start lamp switch, 220–21
Sound generator, 154
Source follower modes, 179–81, 195
Spikes, 15
Super-Alpha mode, 59, 69, 77
Sure-start circuit, 112
Switch circuit, 57

Thyristor devices, 240, 242
Timing periods, long, 115–16
Tone control:
  active, 132
  passive, 129–32
Touch-activated switch, 216
Tracer, injector, 154–5
Transformer selection, 10–11
Transistors, bipolar, 51–5
  basic applications, 55–64
  characteristics, 54–5
Triggering:
  electronic, 116–17
  manual, 114, 116
  Schmitt, 64, 119–20

Unijunction transistor (UJT):
  basics, 225–6
  oscillator, 277–8, 230–32
  practical forms, 228
  uses, 233–5
  see also PUT
Unity-gain buffer circuit, 67

Variable biasing, 182
Variable voltage circuit, 35–6
Varicap diode circuit, 50
Vertical field-effect transistor (VFET):
  basics, 206–208
  V-groove, 171–2
VMOS, 173, 212–15
  basics, 208
  linear circuits, 222–4

Voltage dropper, 37
Voltage follower, *see* amplifiers, common-collector
Voltage gain circuits, 88–9
Voltage multiplier circuits, 19–22
Voltmeters, d.c., 185–6
Volume control, 129

Waveform generators:
  multivibrators, 108–20
  oscillators, 95–107
  sine-to-square, 119–20
  stop/go, 118
  TIS43, 229
Water-activated switch, 217
White noise sources, 3, 107
Wide-band performance, 89
Wien bridge network, 97–8

Zener diode, 56, 160
  applications, 37–9
  circuits, 29–36
Zener value, 3
Zero quiescent current, 198
Zobel network, 150